BETTER HOMES & GARDENS
Baby Book

BETTER HOMES & GARDENS

Baby Book

A handbook for mothers; from prenatal care

to the child's sixth year

By

The Better Homes & Gardens

Child Care and Training Department

MEREDITH PUBLISHING COMPANY, DES MOINES 3, IOWA

A FAMOUS DOCTOR WRITES ABOUT THIS BOOK

This *Better Homes & Gardens* Baby Book approaches the problem of the birth of the baby and its care from the point of view that the future of our nation depends on a coming generation that will be healthy, vigorous, and intelligent.

When a mother is having her first baby she is disturbed by innumerable fears and doubts; every experience is new. If the baby's eye should seem to turn slightly; if she suddenly discovers the soft spots in the baby's head; if the baby cries and the tone is even slightly different from his usual utterances, the mother may be disturbed. She is like a traveler in an unsurveyed country and she can be helped by guidebooks and maps.

A normal baby will show the following characteristics as it grows: 1. Steady gain in weight. 2. A clear, soft, pink skin. 3. Peaceful sleep, with mouth and eyes closed. 4. A good appetite, without vomiting or spitting up. 5. Bright eyes, and usually a contented expression. 6. Steady improvement in length, weight, and intelligence. 7. Springy muscle movements. 8. Regular bowel movements that are normal in color, frequency, and consistency.

The baby is born without habits. Its habits develop as a result of its care and training, and of the conditions under which it lives. At birth the normal baby can cry, move its arms and legs, and sometimes even lift its head slightly. At birth, the baby can distinguish between light and dark, but he cannot fix his attention on any single object. We form habits from doing the same thing over and over again. Babies begin to acquire their habits on the day they are born. If the child is to have good habits the parents must plan accordingly. Regulation of our lives is what makes good habits. If the baby is fed at a certain time each day, if it is put to bed at a regular time, bathed regularly, and similarly trained as to all its other functions, it will be a baby with good habits.

The first three or four months produce the most remarkable progress in the child's existence. Every day marks some distinct growth or development. Every day, therefore, Mother will see something new about which she will want to know. The answers will be found in this book.

Babies are big industry. The items that they use are small, most of them inexpensive, but there are many babies and there are many people who manufacture and sell the materials and the foods that the babies use. Thru the mass of importunities, advertising, and promotion, the mother must pick her way warily. She must know which baby foods are most suitable for her baby and why. She must know how to get the vitamins and which vitamins to buy and how much of each is necessary. Here again, the authors of this book have had in mind the thousands of questions that have come from mothers all over America and the answers to their questions are embodied in this book.

Keeping records is one of the most important tasks that an intelligent mother can assume. From such records her doctor and her advisers are able to derive information of the utmost importance in planning for the future health of the child. Another advantage of this book is the incorporation of suitable pages for such records, along with the information and the guidance that the book supplies.

Better Homes & Gardens has graciously asked me to go over its pages in the course of their preparation and, with my own advisers, we have done our utmost to make certain that all of the information is authentic and reliable. If it can preserve the health of babies and prevent unnecessary fears in innumerable mothers, we shall be greatly pleased.

Morris Fishbein, M. D.
Editor, Journal American Medical Association,
and Hygeia, the Health Magazine

IN THIS BOOK

Chapter VII

Chapter VIII

Chapter IX

Chapter X

Section III

Your Child From Two to Six Years

Chapter I

Chapter II

Chapter III

Record Section

A Message from
Better Homes & Gardens

Let us congratulate you, first of all, upon the happiness awaiting you in your new baby, and assure you of the interest of *Better Homes & Gardens* in him (or her).

The *Better Homes & Gardens* Baby Health Service started in 1932 in the depths of the depression. Planned to give the greatest possible help to mothers, it went into thousands of homes and had a part in rearing thousands of lovely children, so justly proud parents have told us.

Then in March, 1943, as an improvement in this service, we brought out this beautiful book. Since then it has gone thru many printings.

In developing the Baby Book and continuing to improve it, we have asked a great many mothers what they would like in a book of this type. Above all, they told us, they wanted help with discipline and eating, and a full section for record-keeping. So we've stressed these. We queried the firms upon which parents have long depended for baby food, clothes, and equipment of all kinds. We consulted government officials. We have had the counsel and assistance of eminent pediatricians and physicians.

This book, then, is an extension and elaboration, according to what mothers have said they wanted, of advice which has already proved itself many times over. It is authoritative.

We should like to take this opportunity to thank Dr. Morris Fishbein, editor of the Journal of the American Medical Association, and of Hygeia, the Health Magazine, for his careful reading of the entire manuscript and for his many valuable suggestions. We should like also to express our gratitude to Dr. P. C. Jeans, head of the Department of Pediatrics of the State University of Iowa, College of Medicine, for reading Section II, "Your Child From Birth to Two Years," and for helping us to bring the vitamin section, particularly, into accord with endorsements of eminent doctors, and to Dr. Lawrence E. Kelley, Des Moines, for reading Section I, "Prenatal Care."

We should like to acknowledge our very great debt to Dr. Lee Forrest Hill, chairman of Region III of the American Academy of Pediatrics, and former chairman of the committee on cooperation with nonmedical groups and societies of the same body, who supervised the whole task, and who most generously permitted us to use formulas, diet schedules, immunization forms, and other material which he has developed or has employed in his own practice.

The *Better Homes & Gardens* Baby Book is not intended to take the place of medical care for the sick baby, but it is well for us to remember that the doctors are still carrying double burdens. It is as yet not humanly possible for them to give all the service they gave prior to the war. Fathers and mothers have to be more self-reliant, and we hope this book will help toward that end.

The Editors

Prenatal Care

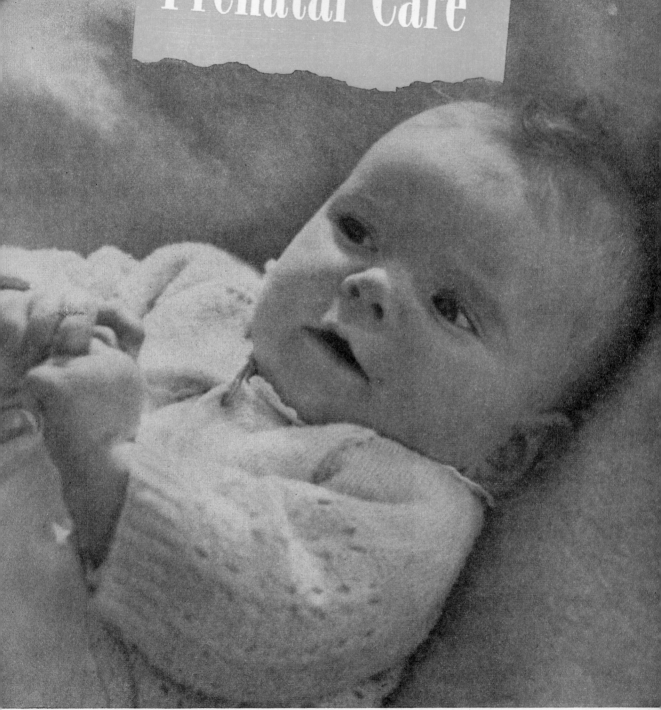

As I Wait and Hope

Thru these long months as I wait for you, my little one, I wonder just what you'll be like.

Will you be my lovely little daughter, or my mischievous small son? Will you have your father's keen blue eyes, or my softer, less-lovely gray ones? Or, by some lucky chance, brown, like your grandmother's? Your feathery new hair—will it be straight and dark like your father's, or curly and brown like mine? Or will you be independent, my darling, and choose to imitate neither of us? I can't help wondering, my little one, as all mothers have done down thru the ages; nor can I help wishing and hoping for you.

I feel you here, and you are with me wherever I go. Tho I talk of other things, you are never out of my thoughts.

If you're a girl, I hope you'll be beautiful, for beauty is a great asset—if it's more than skin deep. I hope you'll have the inner beauty of unselfishness, for no matter what the outward appearance, one who is unselfish, loving, generous, and kind is always lovely. Her eyes and her smile shine thru, and keep her lovely always.

Your father and I hope to teach you all these things. And when you're grown, I hope you'll have courage to meet whatever the days bring. If it be good, thank the Lord who gave it to you. If it be bad, ask Him to help you see it thru. Play fair, darling, in whatever you do. Be a sport, and play the game by its rules. If you lose, be a game loser. Smile and try again.

When you've grown to young womanhood and are thinking about the man with whom you'll spend your life, be sure of your choice. Be certain in your heart and mind that he's essential to your happiness and you to his. And when you've found him, go with him wherever he's called. Love him with all your heart. No matter what happens, stick by him and trust him. If things sometimes go wrong, just smile, and love him all the more; and they will come right again.

My little girl, all these things I want for you. I want you to be happy and to give happiness all your life long. The best way I know for you to be all of these is to be true always to your best self, and to your God.

If you're a boy, I hope you'll have blue eyes like your father, and his ready smile. I hope you'll be straightforward and honest, and kind and gentle, too—for these virtues make friends, and a man without friends isn't a happy man.

Always be fair in your dealings, just as you want others to be honest and fair with you. When you play a game, play it with every ounce of energy and power in you, *but* play fair and square. If you lose, you can always try again.

I hope you'll never know poverty or want, but if you do, I hope you'll have the courage and grit to do the best you can with what you have. Let's pray you'll never be cynical or grumpy, but will ever keep a cheerful grin on your face and hold your chin up until better days come. When they do come, thank HIM, who will look after you always, for helping you thru your trying time.

When you've grown to full manhood and think you've found a life companion, be *sure* she's as fine and splendid as you think. Don't let physical beauty blind you so you miss seeing if she's lovely inside, too. When you're sure beyond any doubt she's the one you want by your side—then win her for your own. Care for her as some precious treasure, for she'll be just that to you.

The greatest hope of my life is that you make as fine a man as your father. I can wish for no more.

As I think these things, little man—or maybe, my little lady—I feel as if you were already here. I can see you here at my knee, looking up with wide, wondering eyes, listening while I tell you these things. You can't understand them yet, but as the years go on I can try to teach you, and help you to be what I dream of your being.

My little one, when you come you may not be beautiful; you may not look as I have dreamed. I won't mind. In my heart you'll always be beautiful and strong and good. I shall love you dearly, no matter what you're like. There's only one thing that really matters, and that I pray for every day—that you come here with a perfect body and a sound mind. Then it's for your father and me to teach and train you to be all of these things I wish and hope for you. With God's help, we will.—*By Mary Fontaine Stamps*

CHAPTER I

Before Baby Arrives

Every manual on the care of the expectant mother begins by saying that pregnancy is a perfectly normal state—which is true, of course, as far as it goes. From my own experience I'd say this is a trifle misleading, however. Few women feel just as well at this time as at any other. With some lucky women this is indeed the case. Many even feel better than at other times. But personally, I believe it would be nearer the truth to say that pregnancy is a normal state, attended for most women by various discomforts which may be greatly diminished by proper care and understanding.

Even if you feel none of these discomforts, or are so well otherwise that you don't mind them, there are certain laws of hygiene that you should observe: first, in order that your baby may have the best chance to be strong and healthy; and second, that your pregnancy may be as comfortable and your confinement as safe and easy as possible.

The first rule is to go to a doctor as soon as you suspect conception has taken place. Even tho you have had children before, have come thru without any difficulty whatever, and have no reason to feel you'll have difficulty this time, you will still be better off for getting as quickly as possible upon the hygienic routine and schedule that your doctor will map out for you.

As we write this, there are more expectant mothers than in recent years, and fewer doctors to take care of them. This situation will call for some patience and forbearance on your part. It may mean longer hours of waiting in your doctor's reception room. You may even hesitate to add to his burdens when things seem to be going all right with you and you are feeling well.

But now more than ever it's desirable that expectant mothers shall have a doctor's supervision from the beginning of pregnancy. Serious complications, which might have been avoided by early diagnosis, are a much greater drain upon your doctor's time and strength, and upon hospital and nursing resources, than routine examinations and a normal delivery.

A great waste of the overtaxed medical resources of the community, and of small human lives as well, can be avoided if every woman will go to a good doctor just as soon as she thinks she's pregnant.

Signs of Pregnancy

That naturally brings up the question, how can you tell whether or not you're pregnant?

Usually the first sign is a missed period. If you're very regular, and go over 10 days or more, you may begin to suspect conception. If you miss two periods, it's fairly certain. If you have gone over your period and start losing your breakfast, or begin to urinate frequently, lady, your doctor wants to see you!

There are other signs by which your doctor judges—for one, the breasts grow larger, and the brown circle around the nipple widens— tho sometimes it's hard for him to be sure before about the third month. In times of stress, especially, women sometimes counterfeit the symptoms of pregnancy. It's not at all uncommon for a bride, tho she isn't pregnant, to skip a period and even to feel morning nausea because the possibility of pregnancy is in her thoughts.

If you can't wait to find out whether you're really pregnant, there's the "rabbit test" which is about 95 percent accurate. You might ask your doctor about it. This test is rather expensive, however, and unless you've a special reason for wanting an early, accurate diagnosis, you can put yourself in your doctor's hands and let Nature take its course.

During the first half or so of pregnancy, if all goes well, you should visit your doctor once a month. In the latter half, he may ask you to come every two or three weeks, and in the last month or so, perhaps every week. When you first go to your doctor, ask him about charges. The usual practice is a lump sum which covers everything in a normal pregnancy. Some doctors charge extra for extra visits. But you needn't worry that your busy doctor will have you come more than is necessary!

If you are pregnant, your doctor's part, as he'll no doubt emphasize, isn't so much to treat a patient as to manage your life so you'll remain comfortable and happy.

When to Expect Your Baby

The doctor will probably give you a date on which your baby may be expected, but don't hold him to it too closely! It has been established that the length of pregnancy may vary as much as 60 days and still be normal, and sometimes there are other factors which make close calculation difficult. The doctors usually figure on 280 days, or 10 lunar months. The method is simple. Count back three calendar months from the first day of your last menstrual period, and add seven days. Let's say that your last period began on December 16. Count back three months to September 16, and add seven days, which makes the expected date of your baby's birth next September 23. Remember, tho, that this is only a stab in the dark, since neither your doctor nor anyone else knows just how long it will take that baby to get ready to be born. With a first baby in particular, two weeks one way or the other is nothing at which to be surprised.

Your frequent trips to the doctor toward the end, and his examination of the baby's heartbeats, will insure you that all's well, and that when your baby gets good and ready, he'll be coming along! Don't urge your doctor to hurry things. If he decides the birth should be hastened, he'll take proper measures.

Activities in Which You May Indulge

What you do at this time depends upon what you have been in the habit of doing previously. The outdoor girl, who is accustomed to tennis, golf, swimming, and driving a car, may continue these sports in moderation, provided her doctor consents and she feels no ill effects.

Be sure to talk these matters over with your doctor. Ask him also about driving a car after the sixth month. He may consider it all right in your case, but under some circumstances he may prefer that you don't.

If you're accustomed to doing your own housework, you'll benefit by continuing to do it, provided you delegate the heavy tasks to others and don't overtire yourself. Take care not to lift heavy objects nor to do things which involve reaching or stretching.

A baby on the way may make drastic changes in your living arrangements. If you're like many expectant parents, you may plan to move. One authority points out that it's all right—provided you let somebody else do all the work! He even suggests that you go clear away until the moving's done, lest you be tempted to lift and carry and generally overdo.

If you're not accustomed to exercise or to housework, it may prove unwise for you to take up a new exercise at this time. On the other hand, some exercise is a necessity, but it should conform, as nearly as possible, to your usual habits.

The best answer to the exercise problem is to take two walks a day, in the morning and evening, beginning with short ones and gradually increasing them to any range which doesn't tire you. The rest of the time, stay in the open air as much as you can. Most doctors advise a healthy woman to walk every day even tho she's doing some housework.

Have Fun!

Above all, don't be a hermit! Nowadays people take pregnancy as the natural thing that it is. Get out and see your friends, have them in. In fact, have as nice a time as you can and don't overtax your strength. Dr. Nicholson J. Eastman, obstetrician-in-chief of Johns Hopkins Hospital, says he likes to get a delivery case straight from a bridge party, so to speak, for it means that the woman is in a relaxed frame of mind, and has been thinking of something outside herself.

Should You Travel?

Your doctor must decide how much traveling you ought to do, and pass upon the means of transportation. Long auto trips prove tiring to many pregnant women, and have brought on miscarriages. Usually they should be taboo. If there's good reason why you should take one, plan to take it by easy stages. Boat trips are all right if the water isn't rough.

Airplane travel seems to do no harm unless you suffer from nausea. But even a short airplane ride can upset an already uneasy stomach.

If you must travel, trains are best—if overcrowded conditions don't make train travel too burdensome. During the last two months of pregnancy, it's wise for you to stay in your own city, or to go to the locality where you are expecting to be confined, and remain there.

You Need Fresh Air

The old theory that the expectant mother must eat twice as much as usual has been exploded. But it's coming to be understood more and more that the expectant mother must breath for two. Hence it's very essential that you have plenty of pure air. You should be outdoors in the daytime all you can—in summer, cooking, eating, and sleeping out if possible; in winter, getting out for walks at least. The rooms in which you spend any time during the day must be well ventilated, as your bedroom must be at night.

Close and crowded places where the air is stagnant are unwholesome for you and your baby. Besides keeping your home well ventilated, stay out of public places where the air is likely to be bad.

Smoking

Moderate smoking seems to do no harm—that is, under eight or 10 cigarettes a day. If you're a heavy smoker, doctors advise that you cut down, but don't try to quit entirely, as this is an added strain.

If you have been accustomed to an occasional cocktail, this too is not expected to injure you or the baby. Naturally an expectant mother will neither smoke nor drink to excess, since this would do definite damage.

Intercourse

Medical authorities usually advise that couples abstain from intercourse during the second and third months of pregnancy at the time when the wife usually has her period, for there's a greater tendency to miscarry then. Intercourse shouldn't be indulged in at all during the last two or three months of pregnancy. At other times it's quite all right in moderation.

Baby Grows on What You Eat

Since your baby, during the period of gestation, grows and develops according to what you eat, your diet is most important.

We know now that an expectant mother doesn't need any more food than at any other time, but the quality is enormously significant.

True, you're eating for your baby as well as yourself, yet you mustn't get too fat. Fat increases the difficulties of delivery, and is mighty hard to get rid of afterwards! The up-to-date doctor therefore "weighs in" his patients when they come for their regular examinations, and in most cases insists that they don't gain more than 25 pounds during the whole time.

This means that without eating any more than you did before, you must include all the food elements your baby needs for the very best development. These are, in fact, all the elements contained in food—proteins, carbohydrates, fats, minerals, and vitamins. In addition, you must have from six to eight glasses of water a day, but part of this may be taken in various beverages.

You Need Milk for Calcium

Milk helps answer the question as to how to get better quality without increasing amounts. It contains the minerals needed for the baby's skeleton, and in a form that makes them easily used by both you and the baby. It's also a rich source of proteins, which build tissues; carbohydrates, for energy; and important vitamins.

Milk, it's true, is fattening. You must allow for that by cutting out other fattening foods, such as sweets and starchy things, which don't begin to give you as much nourishment in proportion to their calories.

You should drink at least two glasses of milk a day, and get two more in milk drinks (cocoa); milk desserts (custards, ice cream, cornstarch, rennet, or tapioca pudding); creamed soups; or creamed vegetables. You may use irradiated evaporated milk as well as, or instead of, fresh milk, for it contains all the elements of fresh pasteurized milk. If you don't 'like to drink milk, try slightly diluted evaporated milk in cooking or on your cereal. Since it is concentrated, it will give you more nutritional value with less bulk. Or mix powdered milk with other foods, thus getting your milk in a highly concentrated form.

Some years ago it was thought that calcium, taken in tablets or wafers, might replace milk in the diet of those who have an antipathy for it, but this substitution hasn't proved wholly satisfactory. Unless you're markedly allergic to milk, you're now advised to get your calcium from milk or cheese, which is very highly concentrated milk. (A one-ounce cube of yellow American cheese, about an inch and a quarter in diameter, has about the same amount of calcium, phosphorus, proteins, and vitamins as a glass of whole milk.) Cheese shouldn't be used, however, to replace more than one glass of milk in your day's diet.

Cottage cheese is rich in protein but not as rich in calcium. (It would take about 10 tablespoons of cottage cheese to get the calcium contained in a glass of milk.) Therefore, while cottage cheese is an excellent food, it should be used in addition to milk rather than in place of it.

If you gain too much weight, cut down on something else—not on milk. If you find milk constipating, try the suggestions made later under the care of the bowels. But don't cut out milk!

Leaf and Stem Vegetables for Iron

Second in the list of needs for you, and especially for your baby, comes iron. This is well supplied, along with calcium, other minerals, and various vitamins, in the leaf and stem vegetables. There's some tendency to anemia on a mother's part during pregnancy. This is counteracted by iron. Also, your baby is storing iron in his liver to last him for some months after he's born. So take plenty of iron-rich foods.

These are:

Artichokes	Broccoli
Celery	Lettuce
Asparagus	Brussels Sprouts
Chard	Spinach
Bean Sprouts	Cabbage
Dandelion Greens	String Beans
Beet Tops	Cauliflower
Kale	Water Cress

In addition to their other excellent qualities, spinach and kale are rich sources of Vitamin K, the element that assists blood to clot. Vitamin K, if given to the mother before delivery, has been found very helpful in preventing hemorrhages of the newborn, which cause many infant deaths.

There is indeed much virtue in the list above. Besides all the body-building elements, they're healthful laxative agents. They'll help to keep the intestines in good working order, which is especially important at this time.

We urge, therefore, that you eat at least two of these every day, one cooked and the other raw (either in a completely natural state or in salads). Canned vegetables can be used as well as fresh ones. When you cook the fresh ones, do it quickly in a small amount of water to save as many vitamins as possible. Use the water, too, since it contains some of the minerals you and your baby need.

You Need Vitamins More Than Ever

In addition to the vitamins in the vegetable list, you'll need those contained in fruit. Vitamin C is found widely in raw fruit— particularly oranges, lemons, grapefruit, pineapple, and tomatoes, which rank with fruits in this respect. (Raw cabbage also has a lot.) Other fruits that are especially good for you are apples, prunes, raisins, figs, and dates. Eat these instead of candy and pastry and you'll keep your weight down and get vitamins and minerals, besides.

Proteins Build the New Life

Milk supplies the framework of your baby's body, but proteins provide the actual building materials. These are found most richly in meat, eggs, milk, and cheese. The last two we've already considered. The first two are practically equal in value.

Eggs, besides being concentrated protein, are rich in iron and vitamins. Remember, you're harboring a little iron-hoarder, and that's one type of hoarding we encourage, so eat at least one egg every day (unless you're allergic to eggs.) Most doctors also advise a serving of lean meat every day, with liver at least once a week. Chicken, ham, lamb, mutton, and any red meat are allowed. Doctors do differ a bit on this, however, and your doctor may have reasons for not wanting you to eat much meat. If he says thumbs down on it, follow his directions. Otherwise, enjoy it.

Liver contains iron, copper, and valuable vitamins in addition to its protein, so it gives extra value. Oysters are only a little behind liver in these respects and may be eaten liberally when you can get them.

Fresh fish is also excellent, and sea food is especially good because it contains iodine. Eat any kind except lobster and crabs. Boil or broil the fish. Or you may fry it, if you take pains to drain off the extra fat.

Whole Wheat—Energy and Vitamins

Carbohydrates, the energy foods, are needed in pregnancy as at other times. These include cereals, bread, potatoes, and the various sweets. While they're fattening foods and need to be taken rather sparingly, they have a definite place in your diet, especially whole-grain breads and cereals.

Recent research has shown that Vitamin B, found in the germ and shell of wheat, is particularly vital to pregnant women, and that you need more Vitamin B now than at other times. Choose the bread and cereals you eat, therefore, from either the whole-wheat or enriched variety, so you'll get these needed vitamins along with the energy. Eat at least three slices of whole-wheat or enriched bread, buttered, every day. Eat a whole grain or enriched cereal every day for breakfast or supper.

And There's Vitamin D

No matter how much milk you drink, Vitamin D is needed to help your body use the bone-building calcium and phosphorus it contains. You may get Vitamin D by sunbaths in summertime, but the rest of the year it's an added precaution to take a teaspoon of fish-liver oil, or some form of concentrate prescribed by your doctor, every day.

Dietary "Musts" in Pregnancy

Here are the foods which you should eat *every day* for your own well-being, and to enable your baby to grow as you would like him to do:

1. Milk. One quart. (Or its equivalent in irradiated evaporated or powdered milk, and cheese.)

2. Leaf and stem vegetables. One cooked and one raw. Other vegetables as desired.

3. Fresh fruits. The equivalent, at least, of two oranges.

4. Meat, fish, or fowl. One serving. (Unless your doctor objects.)

5. One egg. (Unless you're allergic to them.)

6. Whole grain or enriched cereal. One serving.

7. Whole-wheat or enriched bread. Three slices, buttered.

8. Fish-liver oil. One teaspoon. (Unless your doctor objects.)

Be sure you get these every day. Then, if you are still hungry, eat such other foods as you want and can eat without getting too fat.

Foods Not to Eat

Foods which do you no particular good and may distress you are:

Rich foods	*Sausage*
Condiments of all kinds	*Lobster*
Fried foods	*Crabs*
Veal	*Smoked or salt fish*
Kidneys	*Pastries*
Duck	

Use salt sparingly because it encourages retention of water in the tissues, and there's considerable tendency to that anyway during pregnancy. Don't add salt to food already prepared, and in cooking, don't put in quite as much as you'd like.

A Good Diet During Pregnancy

Breakfast:

Egg

Cereal, with sugar or honey, and cream or ir-radiated evaporated milk

Fruit

Slice of buttered toast (whole-wheat or enriched bread)

Glass of milk. You may have one cup of coffee if you like, or cocoa, instead of the milk.

Lunch:

Cottage cheese, or macaroni and cheese

Vegetable

Fruit

Slice of whole-wheat or enriched bread, buttered

Glass of milk, and other beverage as desired

Or if you like, a creamed vegetable soup with fruit and milk or beverage instead of the above, will make an excellent lunch.

Dinner:

Lean meat

Small serving of potato

One leaf or stem vegetable

Salad containing a large portion of lettuce or other leafy vegetable

Dessert made of milk

Whole-wheat or enriched bread, buttered, or a bran muffin

Glass of milk (You may take another glass of milk before you go to bed)

Ideally it's probably better to have your large meal at noon, and a lighter one at night. Most American families, however, have their dinner at night, and the point is not important enough for you to prepare one kind of meal for your family and another for yourself.

If your family's large meal is at noon, eat the "dinner" we've suggested then, and the meal we've called "lunch" at suppertime.

Care of the Bowels

It's easy to understand that you need to keep your bowels functioning regularly, since the waste products of the baby's body as well as of your own must be carried off thru your excretory system. As far as possible, the bowels should be controlled thru diet and regular habits.

If you choose your foods from the list just given and eat large quantities of vegetables and fruits, you should have little trouble. Should you have a tendency to constipation, the following foods will be especially helpful: cream, oatmeal, green vegetables, figs, dates, stewed fruits, prunes, oranges, baked apples, and whole-wheat bread.

The other constipation guard is regularity in going to the toilet. If you haven't already done so, you should form the habit of going to the toilet every morning after breakfast and staying there for some time. Don't strain. Instead, relax as much as possible. This practice, combined with the diet we've described, will in most cases establish a daily movement.

If you need further help, try this regimen:

1. Drink a glass or two of cold water when you get up.
2. Eat a coarse, laxative cereal, such as oatmeal, for breakfast, with one of the laxative fruits just mentioned. Marmalade on your toast is also a stimulus to bowel action.
3. Eat some fruit before going to bed at night.
4. Use mineral oil in dressing your salad.

Don't take any laxative other than mineral oil (it's really a lubricant rather than a laxative), except under your doctor's express directions.

Care of the Kidneys

The importance of the kidneys at this time is recognized in the regular examination of urine which every reliable doctor gives his obstetrical cases. Aside from having this examination, you usually need to do nothing except drink plenty of water (the six to eight glasses a day already mentioned), and observe the other hygienic rules. In early and late pregnancy there's a tendency to urinate frequently because at these times the uterus presses upon the bladder and urethra. There's nothing abnormal about this. If, however, the urine becomes scanty, hard to pass, dark colored, or has a strong odor, have your doctor examine a specimen at once.

Signs of Danger

If any of the following occur between your visits to the doctor, don't delay but let him know AT ONCE!

1. Swelling of the face, hands, or feet

2. Dimness or blurring of vision

3. Pain in the abdomen

4. Fever

5. Any vaginal bleeding

6. Persistent vomiting

7. Continuous headache

8. A rush of water from the vagina

9. A hard fall. If you have one, go to bed, notify your doctor, and be examined for any signs of danger.

These may be of slight importance, but on the other hand, they may indicate a condition that needs immediate attention. Only your doctor can decide.

Take Care of Your Teeth

Science has now cast doubt upon the old theory that the fetus helps himself to the lime in his mother's teeth, if she doesn't provide enough in her diet. Nevertheless, there does seem to be a tendency toward decay in the teeth of pregnant women, and you should be under the watchful eye of your dentist as well as of your doctor.

It won't injure your baby in any way for the dentist to work on your teeth, and it's wise to arrest any decay that shows itself.

Brush your teeth three times a day, using the usual paste or powder.

Care of the Nipples

The condition of your nipples when your baby is born will have a good deal to do with your success or failure in nursing him. Baby's toothless gums bite down mighty hard. If your nipples are tender, he'll soon reduce them to somthing that feels like raw meat, making nursing an almost unbearable ordeal for you. If your nipples are stiff and hard, it will be difficult for the baby to get milk from them. Later, in the section dealing with the feeding of the newborn baby, we'll tell you how to handle the nursing to make it as painless as possible. But now's the time to condition your nipples for the task ahead.

The first requisite is absolute cleanliness. The nipples should be washed every morning with pure soap and water. Then dash cold water over them lightly to toughen them. If the nipples are stiff or hard, you may cover them with abolene, vaseline, lanolin, or warm cocoa butter. Place little squares of clean linen or gauze over them to protect your clothes.

If your nipples are tender, bathe them with witch hazel every day.

Any time from the fourth month on, some fluid may come from the nipples, sometimes enough that your clothes must be protected by pads. If the liquid stays on the nipples, it may make them sore. They should be washed often. If crusts form, wash the nipples gently with boric acid solution, then anoint as we've described.

If you have inverted nipples, spend five minutes a day drawing them out gently

If you have inverted nipples—they collapse into the breast instead of pointing out—spend five minutes each day gently drawing them out between thumb and finger, then relaxing them. You may use cocoa butter for this massage. If you feel the need of a support for your breasts, use the uplift type of bra, which pulls the breasts up and out and doesn't press on the nipples. Never wear a bra which presses the nipples in, as this makes nursing more difficult for your baby.

If cracks appear in your nipples, wash them with boric acid solution and keep them covered with sterile gauze. Report the condition to your doctor.

Streaks on the Abdomen

The streaks or lines which often appear on the abdomen, and even down on the thighs, can be helped by a maternity corset which supports some of the weight. You may also massage your abdomen nightly with cocoa butter, oil, cold cream, or vaseline. The marks do no harm, however.

Baths

It's extremely important that the skin of an expectant mother be thoroly cleansed every day. Great care must be used not to slip in the tub, or in getting in and out of the tub. Place a mat or towel in the bottom of the tub to prevent accidents.

During the last six weeks, take sponge baths entirely, no tub baths at all.

Clothing

From a hygienic standpoint, the rules for dressing at this time are simple:

1. No tight rubber or other bands, either at the waist or around the legs.

2. All clothing to hang from the shoulders as much as possible, so its weight doesn't come at the waist.

3. Nothing tight or confining, especially over the breasts, waist, and abdomen.

A maternity corset will be helpful in most cases. No other kind should be worn during pregnancy. It should be understood that the maternity corset doesn't make the figure ap-

suggest that you ask your doctor to recommend one for you.

The best type of shoe for pregnancy is a low-heeled, broad-toed one. You'll have a tendency to a swaybacked and teetering posture anyway, since you're carrying so much extra weight in front. High heels would throw you even more off balance. However, if you're used to wearing high heels, and feel uncomfortable in any other kind, dependable medical authorities allow you a heel not more than an inch and a half high.

Low-heeled shoes and a loosely fitting coat are helps at this time. A short smock is much used for indoor wear

Some of the loveliest figures you see belong to mothers of one or more tots. Soon yours will be slender again

An uplift type of brassiere should be worn if support is needed. Take care your bra does not press on your nipples tightly

pear smaller. Indeed, it may make you look larger. Its purpose isn't for appearance as much as to give proper support to your abdomen, and back and breasts, too, if they need it. There are several models on the market. We

Very pretty and ingenious maternity dresses may be bought or made which will help your morale greatly. For street wear, a smock-like upper garment is now used. Under it your figure may swell and swell!

Wear your usual kind of underwear as long as it keeps you warm enough and doesn't bind around your waist. It's vital to be warm! Closed panties are also desirable as a sanitary precaution.

You'll be Sylph-like Again

As you get more and more ungainly, you may be haunted by a fear that you're going to stay that way. Not so, my dear. The walking or other mild exercises prescribed for you will help keep good muscle tone. Your abdomen may sag for a time after your baby's birth, but that's a temporary condition, too. Good posture, attention to diet, and possibly some special exercises under your doctor's direction will bring that waistline into bounds again. Many of the lovely figures you see going up and down the street belong to women who have had one or more babies.

Follow instructions about not getting heavier than is necessary at this time, and don't worry!

You Must Rest

Plenty of rest is all-important. You should have at least eight and preferably nine hours' sleep every night, and a rest besides during the day.

Your Day

Let's suppose now that you're one of those lucky women who don't suffer from nausea or any other complaint of pregnancy. You want to stay that way, and provide a quiet environment, too, in which your baby's nerves can flourish as well as his body. Here's a regimen which will do it:

Daily Regimen for Normal Pregnancy

Arise, brush your teeth, care for your breasts, take a short walk.

Eat breakfast, go to the toilet. Relax, take your time.

Do your housework, keeping windows open and going out of doors for as much of it as possible.

Eat lunch.

Rest for two hours. Wear loose clothes and lie in a quiet room. Sleep if possible, and try to arrange so there'll be no interruptions.

Spend the rest of the afternoon out of doors if you can. Visit with friends, or if it's nice weather, sit in the yard or on the porch, sewing or reading. (A foot-powered sewing machine shouldn't be used in later months of pregnancy, but an electric machine is all right.)

Prepare and eat dinner. If tired, rest before washing the dishes.

Spend the evening reading or with friends, but retire by 10:30 p. m. or not later than 11:00 p. m.

If You're a Working Woman

If you have a job, you'll want to know what to do about quitting work.

Your condition will become rather readily apparent by the fifth month. If your appearance is important in your work, you'll want to quit, or arrange to work at home after that.

Perhaps obvious pregnancy doesn't matter (employers are much less squeamish about this than they used to be), but your work keeps you on your feet or is otherwise physically tiring. Then you should quit two months before your baby's birth and spend the time resting and getting things ready for him in leisurely fashion. However, if yours is a "sitting" job and you enjoy it, follow your own wishes about keeping or discontinuing it.

Don't plan to return to work, until your baby is at least 6 weeks old.

Arrange With the Hospital

Your doctor probably has a choice of hospitals to which he wants you to go. Many doctors prefer to make their own arrangements. This is one task, however, which he may wish you to assume for yourself. After your doctor has indicated the hospital he prefers, telephone and make your own inquiries as to price, room, etc. Better yet, visit the hospital and choose your room. Most hospitals make reservations in advance, so you're saved a last minute scramble or word that the hospital is full.

Hospitals tend to be crowded these days, and it may be necessary for you to share a room with another woman, or even with several. Many mothers have found that this helps the time to go more pleasantly. And anyway, if it's necessary in order that everyone who needs hospital care may have it, you won't complain! Hospital rates are quoted according to the kind of room you get, and whether or not you share it with one or more other persons. They include board and nursing service, but there's an extra charge for the delivery room, medicines, drugs, and dressings. In a normal delivery, the hospital nursing service is quite adequate, and it isn't necessary to have specials.

When you arrange for your room, ask what you're to bring for yourself and the baby. Different hospitals have different rules about this. Some furnish everything for the baby, while others want you to bring certain articles of clothing and blankets for him.

Find out just what your hospital expects.

When you enter the last month of your pregnancy, it's time to pack your bag and have it ready. As we've said, it's impossible to tell to the dot when your baby will arrive.

Put in whatever articles the hospital asked you to bring for the baby and the following things for yourself:

Nightgowns or pajamas. For the first few days, you'll wear the hospital gowns, but after that you'll want to have your own pretty ones. Since you'll have to be in bed all day— and in your weakened state, you're likely to perspire a good deal—you'll want a fresh gown every day. If you don't need so extensive a supply, arrange to have them laundered during your stay. Many mothers prefer pajama tops to gowns.

Bed jacket

Dressing gown or bathrobe. If you take a pretty negligee, you should also have a warm robe, for hospital corridors are sometimes drafty.

Slippers

Watch or clock

Fountain pen, stationery, and stamps

Hand mirror

Comb and brush

Manicuring set

Cosmetics

Toilet water

Bath powder. Bath powder is particularly refreshing to dust on your neck, shoulders, and arms when you perspire.

Toothbrush and paste

Sanitary napkins

Take any special books you'd like to have. Your husband or friends can supply you with others, and many hospitals have libraries, for the patients, which deliver books to your bedside.

Signs That the Baby Is Coming

"Lightening," when the uterus sinks down and forward, may occur any time during the last month with a woman having her first baby. With succeeding ones it may be later, perhaps not until labor begins.

The first signs of labor are:

1. Pains at regular intervals. You may have pains during the last month, but they go and come. When they become rhythmical, even tho 15 or 20 minutes apart, and get harder and last longer, they indicate that your baby's birth is at hand.

2. The "show." This is the passage of a small amount of blood from the vagina.

3. Breaking of the bag of waters. This is signaled by a rush of water from the vagina. It doesn't always occur by itself, tho, and may have to be induced by your doctor.

At one or all of these signs, get in touch with your doctor. He'll tell you when to start for the hospital.

Best of luck!

Additional Reading

"Expectant Motherhood" by Nicholas J. Eastman, M. D. (Little, Brown and Company)

"Getting Ready to Be a Mother" by Carolyn Van Blarcom and Hazel Corbin (Macmillan). Gives information about a home confinement.

"Getting Ready to Be a Father" by Hazel Corbin (Macmillan)

CHAPTER II

Complications of Pregnancy

In the first chapter, we talked about the ideal pregancy, which we heartily hope will be yours.

Most of us, however, don't go thru it without a few discomforts and complications. They aren't serious from a medical standpoint, but they are unpleasant for the mother. These used to be looked upon as necessary, and doctors offered little help beyond a paternal smile and an assurance that there was nothing to do but grin and bear it.

Now, however, medical science has relief for practically all the common discomforts of pregnancy, provided you follow directions. If you should get into the office of the paternal kind of doctor who tells you there's nothing to be done, walk right out and go to a doctor who is interested in making you as comfortable as he can.

It is particularly desirable for you to do this as you should have a happy, serene outlook. Your doctor can help you.

Nausea

The commonest ailment is nausea. Some authorities say half of all the expectant mothers are subject to it during the first months of pregnancy, and some place the figure as high as two-thirds. Either figure entitles nausea to first place on our list.

Unless you have pernicious vomiting (which requires constant medical care), considerable if not absolute relief will be given by combining special diet and rest.

The principle of the anti-nausea diet is to keep the stomach full of solids. It calls for six meals a day, each high in carbohydrates and low in fats. For those who must watch weight, the first three months of pregnancy constitute a really marvelous spree in starches and sweets. At the end of the period, tho, you'll be glad to return to normalcy.

When the three months are up, you may cut out the carbohydrates to quite an extent and lose some of your excess weight. In this way, while you may gain a lot at first, you'll be able to keep your weight within bounds when it becomes necessary.

Since butter encourages the tendency to nausea, it should be used sparingly while the condition lasts. If cod-liver oil seems to be upsetting, it should be omitted for the time being.

In addition to the six meals a day prescribed against nausea, have a supply of crackers handy and eat them whenever your stomach gets uneasy. Keep some beside your bed at night, and eat one or two first thing in the morning before you've so much as raised your head from the pillow. Then rest quietly for twenty minutes or so. Follow the same course—lie down and eat a cracker—any time during the day that your stomach begins to act up.

If you're a working woman, keep a small bag of crackers in your desk, and munch one when you feel nauseated. This often helps.

After the first attacks have been conquered, you may have a "regular" dinner at night of lean meat; green vegetable; baked, boiled or mashed potato; lettuce and tomato, or fruit salad; and dessert.

Please remember that this high-calorie diet

Diet for Nausea of Pregnancy

7:30 a. m.

2 soda crackers

8:00 a. m. Breakfast

Stewed prunes (6 large), or baked apple

Cooked cereal with sugar and very small amount of cream

Cup of chocolate with sugar

2 slices of toast, 1 ounce of honey. (The honey takes the place of butter on your toast.)

10:30 a. m.

2 slices of toast, or 2 crackers

1 glass of milk, cocoa, hot malted milk, or cup of tea

12:30 p. m. Lunch

Vegetable, cream of celery, or potato soup, with crackers

2 slices of bread

Lettuce, ½ head

1 cup of custard, 1 cup of cornstarch pudding, 1 cup of apple tapioca, 1 cup of ice cream, or 3 ounces of gelatine dessert

4:00 p. m. Tea

Fruit juice, or tea with sugar

2 slices of toast

1 slice of sponge cake

6:30 p. m. Dinner

1 cup of cream of pea soup, or other soups as at lunch

2 crackers, or 2 slices of toast

Baked sweet or white potato (large), or 3 ounces of rice

3 ounces of stewed carrots, or beets

Desserts as at lunch, 1 ounce of dates, or 1 ounce of raisins

9:30 to 10:00 p. m. Bedtime snack

Toast or crackers

1 glass of milk, cocoa, or hot malted milk

is to be used only while nausea threatens. As soon as you're over it, change gradually to the diet (on page 24) for normal pregnancy.

Rest Lots If Nauseated

Rest is quite as important as diet. Diet does little good unless you go to bed at 8 or 9 o'clock —never later—every night, and you should rest some during the morning and afternoon. Likely you will be able to do regular housework, but outside activities must be curtailed. If guests come in the evening, excuse yourself when you are ready to go to bed, otherwise the morning after may be very painful.

As every nausea victim knows, the unpleasantness leaves as if by magic when the three months are up, altho it may recur temporarily if there's too long an interval between meals, or if you become too tired.

You may start taking fish-liver oil, the amount to be determined by your doctor, when you get over the nausea.

During a period of nausea, intercourse should be omitted.

Other Digestive Discomforts

Gas, "heartburn," indigestion, and the heart palpitation often felt by the pregnant woman are all largely caused by something in the diet. The first step in relieving them is to determine what food is causing the difficulty. Then eliminate it.

"Heartburn" will often be prevented by taking a tablespoon of cream one-half hour before meals. The cream shouldn't be taken at mealtime, however. When the "heartburn" is felt, it's usually relieved by taking a teaspoon of milk of magnesia, or a teaspoon of soda in half a glass of water.

Rapid heart action, often experienced in pregnancy, may be due to indigestion or pressure of the uterus on the stomach or heart. Attention to diet and exercise usually help.

Varicose Veins, Itching, Hemorrhoids

These are all conditions for which you should have your doctor's suggestions. However, varicose veins can be helped by proper bandaging and keeping off your feet as much as possible. If you suffer from hemorrhoids, you should also stay off your feet with your legs raised level with your body. A general itching will be helped by soda in your bath water, but your doctor should prescribe for itching in the vaginal region. Douches shouldn't be taken unless your doctor orders them.

Muscle Cramps

Toward the end of pregnancy, you may have a tendency to cramps in your thigh and leg muscles. This is associated with insufficient circulation of blood, and to the use of muscles not usually called into action. A good maternity corset and low-heeled shoes will help you avoid these cramps. If they occur, you can probably get relief by massaging your muscles with oil or cold cream. Sometimes the baby's head presses on certain nerves and causes shooting pains down the legs. Changing your position may help.

Shortness of Breath

As the baby grows and presses upon your vital organs, shortness of breath is to be expected. This is all in the natural course of events, and constitutes a minor discomfort. If it interferes with sleep, prop up your head and shoulders with pillows. Extreme shortness of breath, however, should be reported to your doctor.

Serious Complications

In addition to the annoying but not usually dangerous symptoms described, there are more serious conditions, such as toxemia, pre-eclampsia and others. These, however, are complications to be left entirely to your doctor.

Early symptoms of one or more of the complications of this type were described on page 25. Briefly, they are a constant headache that doesn't yield to ordinary headache remedies; swelling of face or hands; blurring of the vision; bleeding from the vagina; fever; and pain in the abdominal region. Any of them should be reported at once to your doctor, as should nausea which persists.

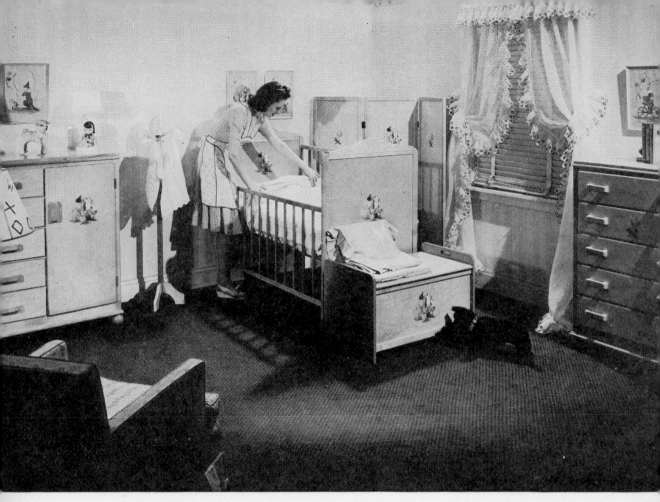

A nursery like this is fun if you can have one. Screen in corner is to set before window when open

← Baby's room, tho warm, should be well ventilated. Use glass or window board

It's handy, tho, to have the → first bed on wheels. This, or oblong type bassinet, is good

A folding bath table, with a → tub attached, is convenient. But an ordinary table will do

← Baby's bassinet can be made from a laundry basket, if you use materials that wash well

If you haven't a folding tub, → one like this, big enough for all-over baths, will do nicely

CHAPTER III

Things to Have Ready for Your Baby

"What clothing and furniture shall I buy for my baby? And how can I tell whether I'm making the right selections and getting full value for my money?" a prospective mother wrote recently. "I'm a new hand at this business. Many questions arise to perplex me, and I get much conflicting advice. If you could see the line-up in the doctor's office, you'd understand why I don't like to bother him with these questions!"

Agreed that busy doctors should be spared questions about furniture and clothing for the perfectly well and normal baby. Fortunately, most items manufactured and advertised nationally for babies have been prepared with an infant's comfort and well-being to the fore. A number have been approved by the American Medical Association. This approval is shown by a little seal which these items carry. The baby section of a good department store, moreover, is a service department where a special effort is made to give "amateur" mothers reliable information. If you'll tell the intelligent and sympathetic saleswoman how much you want to spend, I believe she'll try to to help you get the most value for your money.

A Room of Baby's Own—If Possible

When your baby arrives, he'll not only need a layette, but various pieces of equipment as well. "A room of baby's own" would go at the top of your list. If you are not permanently located at the time, it may not be possible to have everything just as you'd like.

If you can give him a room that's exclusively his, by all means do so. A room of his own will help Baby build better sleeping habits and will also give you more rest. It may be ever so tiny as long as it's well ventilated and quiet so he can have his naps undisturbed. During the first weeks of his life, your baby should be in a room adjoining yours, or that of some other responsible person who will hear him if he cries and give him attention.

Articles that will not be needed in the care of the baby should be taken out of the room. All furnishings should be such that they can be easily cleaned.

If you can't provide a separate room for the baby, then do the next best thing. Give him a corner where his clothes and equipment are kept in orderly array, and he can rest in peace and quiet. (See the picture on page 34.) Should you have just one bedroom, plan to put him in it for his naps. When you go to bed, wheel or carry his bassinet out into the living room, or whatever room you've selected as best fulfilling the qualifications outlined below.

His Room Should Be Warm

A very young baby needs a warmer room than an adult.

The room your baby uses (whether it's his own, or the arrangement suggested of your bedroom by day and the living room by night) should be easy to heat, for during the first few weeks the temperature shouldn't go below 60°F. during the night and 70°F. dur-

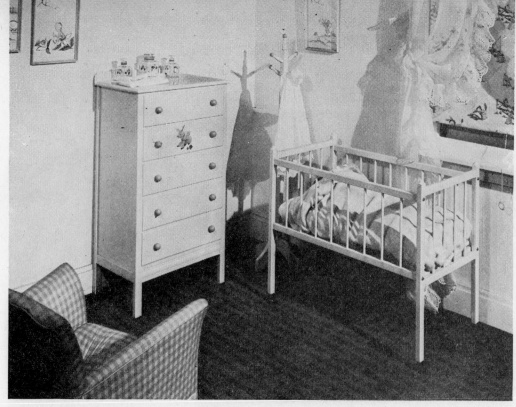

A corner he can call his own, with places for his things, will suit Baby as well as a model nursery

ing the day. When he's awake, or when the covers are off, the temperature should be kept from 72° F. to 74° F. Special care should be taken to maintain plenty of moisture in the atmosphere, so his delicate nose and mouth membranes won't become dry. This can be done either by keeping water in the furnace, or by setting shallow pans of water near the radiators.

Should Be Well Ventilated

At the same time the baby's room should be well ventilated. Ideally it should be cross ventilated, but his bed shouldn't be in a draft. You can prevent drafts by placing window boards or cloth screens in the windows when they're open, or keeping a screen between the baby's bed and the draft. A screen of this type is shown in the model nursery on page 32.

A room in which there's a fireplace is a nice one for a baby, for the open chimney provides a constant stream of fresh air without drafts.

Baby's Furniture

The nursery may be furnished as simply or as elaborately as you wish. Don't have dazzling white for the color scheme, tho, as this is hard on the baby's eyes. Any soft colors will do.

For your baby's first bed, a bassinet on wheels is very convenient, since it can be taken anywhere in the house and wheeled out on the porch for naps. However, a big laundry basket, well padded, does very well.

Whatever kind of bed you use, be sure it's long enough and wide enough to let the baby kick and squirm all he likes.

How to Make Up Baby's Bed

It will make little difference to your baby whether his room is an elaborate nursery, such as the one shown on page 32, or the little corner shown on this page, but the way his bed is made up will matter lots!

Mattress. First of all the mattress must be firm, for a baby's bony structure is soft, and too prone to fit itself into a sag. No pillow is used for the same reason—to keep his spine straight. A number of mattresses today are waterproofed. If the one you buy isn't, you'll want to cover it with a protective sheet that's large enough to tuck well under the mattress.

The sheet may be tied under the mattress with strong tapes, sewed to each corner.

Absorbent pads. The mattress pad for the baby's bed should be both soft and absorbent. Special crib pads are now made of the same extra-absorbent gauze featured in the new types of diapers which we'll discuss later. The sides of these pads tuck well under the mattress and no sheet is needed.

For extra protection, and extra comfort for the baby, place a small waterproof sheet—these are made in several convenient sizes—in the spot where he'll lie, and over this a small absorbent pad. This will soak up excess moisture and cut down the number of times it will be necessary to change the large pad.

Six sheets. If you don't use the type of pad described above, you'll want to get six sheets, long enough to tuck under the mattress.

Four cotton blankets. These should also be long enough to tuck under the mattress. It is better to have several light blankets that launder easily than only one or two heavy ones.

Two comforters.

Wardrobe and Chair

You'll also want a wardrobe or chest of drawers in which to keep the baby's clothes. The picture of the nursery on page 32 shows two types. Or you can repaint an old chest of drawers or contrive one yourself. It will be all the same to the baby!

Bath Articles

Your baby's bath articles may be kept in his room or in the bathroom, whichever's more convenient. As the bathroom is warm in the average house, it's often the best place to bathe the baby. The following articles should be provided:

Bath table. The folding canvas variety, with bath attached, is marvelously convenient. The canvas molds slightly to the baby's body, and will help to keep him from rolling off. When not in use, it can go into a closet or stand behind a door.

If you don't have a folding table, use any table that's a convenient height. An ordinary table, however, will need to be thickly padded in order to keep the hard surface from making the baby uncomfortable. A pillow or folded blankets will do the job.

Tub. If you haven't the bath table and tub combined, you'll want a tub. For the first sponge baths after the baby gets home from the hospital, a wash basin will do. For tub baths, a regular baby tub or container of adequate size will be needed.

Bath tray. A square enameled basket is the most practical for this purpose. It should contain:

Bath thermometer

Castile, or other mild pure soap

Baby cream

Boric acid ointment

Baby or olive oil

Small jar (covered) of boric acid

Safety pins, assorted sizes

Surgical gauze

Sterilized cotton

Washcloths—squares of cheesecloth or other soft material; or regular baby washcloths

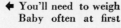

Have ready a bath basket or tray ➡ with things Baby will need for his toilet

⬅ You'll need to weigh Baby often at first

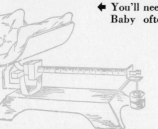

3 bath towels, large enough to wrap clear around the baby. (One of our *Better Homes & Gardens* mothers buys 36-inch-wide, extra-soft bath toweling and cuts it into two-yards lengths, hemming the ends. This makes towels of excellent size.)

The bathroom closet or cabinet should contain these articles, ready for use when needed:

Rectal clinical thermometer. (During the first four years at least, the temperature should be taken in the rectum.) Small hot-water bottle, to warm the baby when necessary.

Baby's Layette

Your baby's clothing needs are few, for his wardrobe has been simplified until it approaches the vanishing point. The basic dress, as our pediatrician calls it, in summer or winter, is shirt and diaper. The old custom of swathing the tiny baby in wool and flannel even in hot weather has fortunately gone out. Some babies have gotten along with no wool at all, except in outside garments, such as sweaters or other light wraps.

The warmth of your baby's clothing should depend upon the climate where you live and the heating arrangements in your home.

Keep in mind that the purpose of clothing him is to make him comfortable, not to prevent colds or other infections. These are contracted thru germs carried to the baby by some other person—not by the weather. If your climate and home heating arrangements are such that warm shirts will be needed to keep the baby comfortable, get them. Preference of fabric is still a matter of opinion. Above all, the child should not be overdressed. Good sense will guide you.

If yours is a warm, evenly heated house, shirts of cotton or similar light materials will be adequate.

If your baby is to be born at home, you'll want to provide three abdominal bands to hold the navel dressing in place till the navel is healed. This band is made of a strip of soft flannel or gauze, 18 to 20 inches long and 4 to 5 inches wide. Most babies born in hospitals, however, no longer need these bands by the time they're taken home. A small dressing of surgical gauze, with vaseline next to the navel, is usually sufficient. (Whether or not a band is needed is a point to be determined by your own doctor.)

The absolute essentials of your baby's wardrobe are:

4 shirts (wool, or other warm material; cotton, linen, or silk, with or without sleeves, depending upon the season and the warmth of your home)

8 kimonos (cotton flannel for winter, cotton crepe for summer)

6 nightgowns (cotton flannel for winter, muslin for summer)

4 dozen diapers 20 or 21 x 40 inches

1 sweater

1 cloak or bunny-bag

1 hood

Quite a variety of materials and styles are available in diapers. The old familiar square of outing flannel or birdseye, folded twice triangularly, has given way quite largely to an oblong shape, 20 or 21 by 40 inches. New, absorbent materials have been perfected that are easy to launder and quick-drying. The oblong shape lends itself to folding in different ways as the baby grows, and the new materials are so soft that the 21- by 40-inch size isn't too large even for a tiny baby. Whatever material you select, you'll need a minimum of four dozen diapers for convenience. There are pads for cribs and Mother's lap in the same soft, absorbent material.

In stores, also, is a very soft and absorbent knitted diaper which is form fitting and needn't be folded. Like the new absorbent one, it's very easy to wash and dry. It's made in several sizes. (See pictures on page 74.)

In addition to these garments, which spell

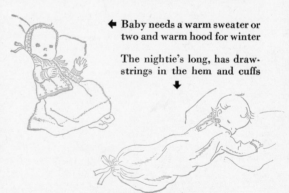

◀ Baby needs a warm sweater or two and warm hood for winter

The nightie's long, has drawstrings in the hem and cuffs
↓

a great advance in an old field, there are several brands of disposable diapers. Whether you want to use these all the time or not, it's smart to have a supply on hand for those periods when, being ill or busy, you'll find it wise to conserve your strength by omitting diaper washing for a time.

There are also paper inserts to place in a cloth diaper and eliminate the worst of the soiling. Fillers made of clean squares of old silk or other soft material may be used for this purpose.

For your baby's outer daytime dress we suggest a kimono, opening down the front so it won't hamper his movements. The wide sleeves make it easy to slip on and off. The kimono should be cotton flannel for winter, while cotton crepe makes an easily laundered garment for summer. Nightgowns, long enough to wrap well around the baby's feet, should be provided for night wear. They should be cotton flannel or other warm material for winter, muslin for summer. A drawstring in the bottom hem keeps the baby from exposing his feet.

Slips, or "gertrudes," and dresses may be worn on state occasions. If a garment must slip over the baby's head, be sure the opening is large enough so it will go on without a struggle.

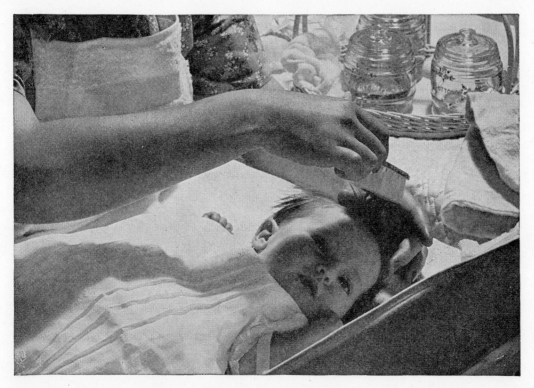

Of course you'll want some things for dress-up occasions—company and the like. Make these as dainty as you wish. But no rough seams or embroidery to cut Baby's flesh. Have openings large, to slip on easily

◄ "Baby Bunting" type bag for Baby's airings is desirable

Gertrude, or petticoat, to ➤ wear under company dresses

Kimonos for every day. Warm ➤ petticoat if house is cold

A Name for Your Baby

Alfred   Brian   Barbara

A family name may be ready and waiting for your baby. If it isn't and you're wondering what to call him, you may find his name among those listed below.

BOYS' NAMES

NAME	MEANING	DERIVATION	NAME	MEANING	DERIVATION
Aaron	A mountain; a tower of strength	Hebrew	Benjamin	A surety	Hebrew
Abner	Paternal	Hebrew	Bernard	Bold as a bear	Teutonic
Abraham	Tall; father of a multitude	Hebrew	Bertram	Fair; illustrious	Teutonic
Absolom	Peace loving	Hebrew	Bob	See Robert	
Achilles	Taciturn, sympathetic	Greek	Brand	A fighter	Uncertain
Adam	Red earth; lover of outdoors	Hebrew	Brian	Strong; sincere	Celtic
Adelbert	Mentally brilliant	Teutonic	Bruce	Positive; daring	Gaelic
Adrian	Pessimistic; hard to please	Latin			
Alan	Cheerful; in harmony	Celtic	Cadwallader	Valiant in war	Saxon
Alban	Pure	Latin	Caesar	Purposeful	Latin
Albert	Firm; responsible	Teutonic	Caleb	A dog lover	Hebrew
Alexander	Leader of men	Greek	Calvin	Bold; bald	Latin
Alexis	Helper	Greek	Carl	Forceful	Teutonic
Alfred	Kingly	Teutonic	Caspar	Gift-bearer	Saxon
Algernon	Prosperous	French	Cecil	Harmony	Saxon
Alison	Musical	Uncertain	Charles	Manly	Teutonic
Allen	See Alan	English	Christopher	Whimsical; humorous	Greek
Alonzo	Ready; willing	Greek	Clarence	Bright; illustrious	Latin
Aloysius	Grace	Latin	Claude	Affectionate	Latin
Alvin	Beloved of all	Teutonic	Clement	Merciful	Latin
Ambrose	Immortal	Greek	Clifford	Valorous	Saxon
Amos	Strong, courageous	Hebrew	Columbus	Curious	Greek
Andrew	Manly	Greek	Conrad	Optimistic; resolute	Teutonic
Anthony	Inestimable; incomparable; praiseworthy	Latin	Cornelius	Studious; noble	Latin
Antonio	See Anthony		Cyril	Lordly	Greek
Antony	See Anthony		Cyrus	Jolly	Persian
Archibald	Holy prince; extremely bold	Teutonic	Dan	A judge	Hebrew
Armand	Public spirited	French	Daniel	See Dan	
Arnold	Strong as an eagle	Teutonic	Darius	Dark; strong	Persian
Arthur	High-minded	Celtic	David	Beloved	Hebrew
August	Venerable	Latin	Dennis	A worshipper	Greek
Augustus	Exalted; imperial	Latin	Dick	See Richard	
Austin	Useful	Latin	Donald	Proud; a chief	Celtic
			Dorian	Golden	Greek
Baldwin	Friendly; bold	Teutonic	Douglass	Thoughtful	Celtic
Barney	Hard headed	Uncertain	Duncan	Brown chief	Celtic
Barry	Straightforward	Celtic	Durand	A lasting friend	Latin
Bartholomew	Warlike son	Hebrew			
Basil	Royal	Greek	Earl	Procrastinating	Uncertain
Benedict	Blessed	Latin	Edgar	Wealthy	Teutonic

NAME	MEANING	DERIVATION	NAME	MEANING	DERIVATION
Edmund	A protector	Teutonic	Jesse	Wealthy	Hebrew
Edward	A guard	Teutonic	Jock	See John	
Edwin	A friend	Tuetonic	Joel	Strong-willed	Hebrew
Egbert	Precocious; bright	Teutonic	John	Given by God	Hebrew
Elbert	Overpowering; illustrious	Teutonic	Jonathan	See John	
Eli	Faithful to God	Hebrew	Joseph	An addition	Hebrew
Elias	See Eli		Julius	Kind	Latin
Elihu	See Eli		Justin	Just	Latin
Elijah	See Eli				
Ellis	Faltering	Hebrew	Karl	See Charles	Swiss
Elmer	Excellent	Saxon	Kay	Strong; determined	English
Emery	Dutiful	Teutonic	Kenneth	Handsome; quick	Gaelic
Emmanuel	God with us	Greek			
Enoch	Teacher	Hebrew	Lambert	His country's brightness	Teutonic
Enos	Mortal man	Hebrew	Lawrence	Victorious	Latin
Ephraim	Very fruitful	Hebrew	Leo	Lion-like	Greek
Erasmus	Amiable	Greek	Leon	See Leo	French
Eric	Princely	Teutonic	Leonard	See Leo	Teutonic
Ernest	Serious; earnest	Greek	Leopold	See Leo	Teutonic
Eugene	Well-born; noble	Greek	Lester	Seeking the truth	Saxon
Eustace	A harvester; healthy	Greek	Levi	A bond; a tie; a promise	Hebrew
Evan	A challenger	English	Lewis	Seeking fame	Teutonic
Ezra	Dawn; the beginning of joy	Hebrew	Lionel	See Leo	Latin
			Llewellyn	Lightning	Welsh
Felix	Happiness	Latin	Lloyd	Indecisive; gray	Celtic
Ferdinand	Adventurous; valiant	Teutonic	Louis	See Lewis	French
Francis	Dutiful son	Teutonic	Lucius	Witty; light	Latin
Frank	See Francis		Luke	Educated; a teacher	Greek
Fred	Peaceful ruler	Teutonic	Luther	Noble warrior	Teutonic
Frederick	See Fred				
			Malcolm	Kingly	Gaelic
Gabriel	Fights for the right	Hebrew	Marcus	Defender	Latin
Geoffrey	Chivalrous; brave	Teutonic	Mark	Hammer	Latin
George	One who amasses a fortune	Greek	Martin	Unyielding	Latin
Gerald	Affectionate; jolly	Teutonic	Matthew	Gift of the Lord	Greek
Gideon	A deliverer	Hebrew	Maurice	Persistent	Latin
Gilbert	Progressive	Danish	Max	Going ahead; a leader	Latin
Giles	Shield-bearer	Greek	Michael	"Who is like to God"	Hebrew
Godfrey	Quiet	Teutonic	Miles	A soldier	Celtic
Gordon	Generous	Gaelic	Milton	Colored red	Greek
Gregory	Watchful	Greek	Mortimer	Ever living	French
Griffith	Having great faith; reddish	Latin	Moses	Drawn out of the water	Hebrew
Guy	A leader; sensible	French			
			Napoleon	Lion from the forest	Greek
Hal	See Henry		Nathan	A gift	Hebrew
Halbert	A gentleman	Gaelic	Nathaniel	See Nathan	
Harold	Unafraid; a warrior	Teutonic	Nelson	A hero	Uncertain
Harrison	Noble; princely	Saxon	Nicholas	Victory of the people	Greek
Harry	See Henry		Noah	Restful	Hebrew
Harvey	Bitter	Celtic	Norbert	Good cheer	Uncertain
Hector	Defender	Greek	Norman	Hopeful	Teutonic
Henry	Home ruler	Teutonic			
Herbert	Gay	Teutonic	Oliver	Dutiful; peaceful	Saxon
Herman	Satisfied	Teutonic	Orlando	Handsome	Italian
Hiram	Nobly born	Hebrew	Orville	Emotional; artistic; serene	Saxon
Homer	Secure	Greek	Oscar	Active	Celtic
Horace	Light of the sun	Latin	Oswald	Power of God	Saxon
Horatio	Worthy to be beheld	Latin	Otto	Rich	Teutonic
Howard	Aggressive	Saxon	Owen	Well descended	Saxon
Hubert	Intellectual	Teutonic			
Hugh	See Hubert		Patrick	Noble; patriotic	Latin
Hugo	See Hubert		Paul	Little; small	Greek
			Percival	A knight; piercing eye	Latin
Isaac	Mirthful; glad	Hebrew	Percy	See Percival	Saxon
Isadore	A good gift	Spanish	Peter	Reliable; dependable; a rock	Greek
Ivan	See John	British	Philip	A lover of horses	Greek
Jack	See John		Quentin	The fifth	Latin
Jacob	The supplanter	Hebrew			
James	See Jacob		Ralph	Home loving; hero	Saxon
Jasper	Master of many treasures	Persian	Randolph	See Ralph	
Jeffrey	See Godfrey	English	Reginald	Kingly	Teutonic
Jeremy	Exalted; placed high above others	Hebrew	Rex	See Reginald	
Jerome	See Jeremy		Richard	Stern, but just	Teutonic
Jerry	See Jeremy		Rob	Winner over all	Teutonic
			Robert	See Rob	

NAME	MEANING	DERIVATION	NAME	MEANING	DERIVATION
Roderick	Famous; rash	Spanish			
Roger	Tall; straight	Teutonic	Ted	Divine gift	Greek
Roland	Adventurous	Teutonic	Theodore	See Ted	
Ronald	Worthy of admiration	Saxon	Thomas	Good company	Hebrew
Roswald	Powerful	Uncertain	Timothy	The fear of God	Greek
Roy	Kingly	Saxon	Tobias	Distinguished of the Lord	Greek
Rudolph	Unconquerable	Teutonic	Tracy	Carrying ears of corn	Greek
Rufus	Red-haired	Latin			
Rupert	Violet	Teutonic	Ulysses	One who adventures far	Greek
			Victor	Conquering	Latin
Samuel	Asked of God	Hebrew	Vincent	Invincible	Latin
Saul	Asked for	Hebrew	Virgil	Growing; flourishing	Uncertain
Sebastian	Reverenced	Greek			
Seth	Deep	Hebrew	Waldo	Self-controlled	French
Sidney	Bruised; troubled	Saxon	Wallace	True	Uncertain
Siegfried	Liberated	Teutonic	Walter	Of great destiny	Teutonic
Silas	See Sylvanus		Warren	Protecting friend	Saxon
Simeon	A servant of the Lord	Hebrew	Washington	Purifying	Saxon
Simon	Obedient	Hebrew	Wilbur	Inventive; constructive	Uncertain
Stephen	Loyal	Greek	William	Resolute	Teutonic
Sylvanus	Woods dweller	Latin	Williard	Protecting	Saxon
Sylvester	See Sylvanus				

GIRLS' NAMES

NAME	MEANING	DERIVATION	NAME	MEANING	DERIVATION
Abigail	Source of delight	Hebrew	Bonnie	Good	Latin
Ada	Happy	Saxon	Bridget	Strong	Celtic
Adah	An ornament	Hebrew			
Adela	Cheerful; shining bright	Saxon	Camilla	Self-sacrificing	Latin
Adelaide	Beautiful princess	Saxon	Camille	See Camilla	
Adele	See Adela		Carlotta	Noble birth	Spanish
Adrienne	Artful	Latin	Carol	A Christmas child	Uncertain
Agatha	Good	Greek	Caroline	Noble-spirited	Teutonic
Agnes	Pure	Greek	Carolyn	Generous; just	Uncertain
Aimee	See Amy		Cassandra	Inspiring love	Greek
Alda	Rich	Teutonic	Catherine	Pure	Greek
Alethea	Picturesque	Greek	Cecile	Lover of harmony	Latin
Alfreda	Queenly	Teutonic	Celeste	Heavenly beauty	French
Alice	Optimistic	Teutonic	Celia	Radiant	Latin
Alicia	See Alice		Charlotte	Noble-spirited	Teutonic
Alma	Fair; good	Latin	Chloe	Blossoming	Greek
Alta	Wholesome	Teutonic	Christine	Christian	French
Althea	Dainty; graceful	Greek	Cicily	Active	English
Amabel	Lovable	Latin	Claire	Illustrious	Latin
Amelia	A worker	Teutonic	Clara	Clear; bright	Latin
Amy	Greatly loved	Latin	Claribel	Brightly fair	Latin
Angela	Angelic	Spanish	Clarice	Making famous	Latin
Angelica	See Angela	Teutonic	Clarinda	See Clarice	
Angeline	Sweet messenger	French	Clarissa	See Clarice	
Anita	Assertive	Spanish	Claudia	Dazzling	Latin
Ann	Gracious	Hebrew	Cleopatra	Triumphant	Greek
Anna	See Ann	Swedish	Clothilde	Maiden of battles; fair-minded	Teutonic
Annabel	A heroine	Hebrew	Clotilda	See Clothilde	
Anne	See Ann		Constance	True; loyal	Latin
Annette	Elfish; exquisite	French	Cora	Cherished maiden	Greek
Antoinette	Incomparable	French	Cordelia	Candid; sincere	Latin
April	"Sun and showers"	Latin	Corinne	See Cora	
Audrey	Golden	English	Cornelia	Quaint	Italian
Augusta	Imperial; exalted	Latin	Cynthia	Belonging to the moon	Greek
Aurelia	Golden; beautiful	Latin			
			Daisy	Gay; cheerful	Saxon
Babetta	Little enchanter	Italian	Daphne	Shy; fleet	Greek
Barbara	Shy	Latin	Deborah	Industrious	Hebrew
Beatrice	Blessing	Latin	Delia	Shining; bright	Celtic
Belinda	Shining; bright	English	Diamond	Priceless	Uncertain
Belle	Beautiful	French	Diana	Goddess; perfect	Latin
Bertha	Bright	Teutonic	Dolly	See Dorothy	
Bessie	See Elizabeth		Dolores	Sorrowful	Spanish
Beth	See Elizabeth		Dora	See Dorothea	
Betty	See Elizabeth		Dorcas	Gazelle	Greek
Blanche	White; fair	French	Doris	The sea	Greek

NAME	MEANING	DERIVATION
Dorothy	*God's gift*	Greek
Dorothea	*See Dorothy*	Teutonic
Edith	*Tall; stately*	Teutonic
Editha	*See Edith*	
Edna	*Capricious*	Teutonic
Elaine	*Bright*	Greek
Elberta	*Responsible; trustworthy*	Teutonic
Eleanor	*Light*	Greek
Eleanore	*See Eleanor*	
Elfrida	*Protector*	Teutonic
Elinor	*See Eleanor*	
Eliza	*Faithful*	French
Elizabeth	*God's promise*	Hebrew
Ella	*Sprightly*	Greek
Ellen	*See Eleanor*	English
Eloise	*Dreamy; romantic*	French
Elsie	*Mirthful*	Saxon
Elvira	*Impartial; fair*	Latin
Emily	*Artistic*	English
Emma	*Energetic*	English
Emmeline	*Intellectual*	English
Enid	*Self-confident; quiet*	Uncertain
Ernestine	*Earnest*	Teutonic
Esmeralda	*Emerald; bright hope*	Spanish
Essie	*A star*	Latin
Estelle	*See Essie*	
Esther	*Good fortune*	Persian
Ethel	*Noble*	Teutonic
Etta	*Home ruler*	Teutonic
Eugenia	*Well-born*	Spanish
Eunice	*Victorious*	English
Euphemia	*Accomplished*	Greek
Eva	*Life, giver of life*	Hebrew
Evadne	*Faithful unto death*	Greek
Evangeline	*Angel-like*	Greek
Eve	*See Eva*	
Eveline	*Pleasant*	Gaelic
Evelyn	*Hazelnut*	Latin
Faith	*Sure reliance*	Teutonic
Fanchon	*See Frances*	
Fanny	*See Frances*	
Felicia	*Happiness*	Latin
Felicite	*See Felicia*	French
Flora	*Flowers*	Latin
Florence	*Flourishing*	Latin
Frances	*Free*	Teutonic
Fredericka	*Rich peace*	English
Gail; sometimes masculine, also	*Abounding joy*	Uncertain
Genevieve	*Humble*	French
Georgia	*Womanly dignity*	English
Georgiana	*See Georgia*	
Geraldine	*Affectionate*	English
Germaine	*Exquisite; lovely*	French
Gertrude	*All truth*	English
Gladys	*Demure; capable*	Welsh
Grace	*God's blessing*	English
Gwen	*Intellectual, with understanding*	Celtic
Gwendolyn	*See Gwen*	
Hannah	*Good*	Hebrew
Harriet	*See Etta*	
Helen	*See Eleanor*	
Henrietta	*Of noble birth*	English
Hesper	*Evening star; inhabitant of the west*	Greek
Hester	*Good fortune*	Persian
Hilda	*Strong; merciful*	Teutonic
Hope	*Hope*	Teutonic
Hortense	*Fragrant; sweet*	French

NAME	MEANING	DERIVATION
Ianthe	*Delightful*	Greek
Ida	*Happy*	Teutonic
Imogen	*Pity for all who need*	English
Imogene	*See Imogen*	
Inez	*Star of the sea*	Spanish
Irene	*Serene; peaceful*	Greek
Isabel	*See Elizabeth*	Teutonic
Isabella	*See Elizabeth*	Italian
Jane	*God's grace*	Hebrew
Janet	*Darling Jane*	Gaelic
Jean	*Loving Jane*	Gaelic
Jeanette	*Little Jane*	French
Jeanne	*See Jean*	
Jenny	*See Jean*	
Jessica	*The Lord's grace*	English
Jessie	*My present*	Gaelic
Jill	*See Julia*	
Jo	*See Josephine*	
Joan	*Gift of the Lord*	English
Josephine	*A reward*	French
Joyce	*Winsomely lovely*	English
Judith	*Praise of the Lord*	Hebrew
Julia	*Volatile; changeable*	Latin
Juliet	*See Julia*	English
June	*With Summer's sunshine*	Latin
Justa	*Just*	Latin
Justina	*See Justa*	
Kate	*See Catherine*	English
Katherine	*See Catherine*	
Kathleen	*Dear to my heart*	Celtic
Kitty	*See Catherine*	
Laura	*A laurel; famous*	Latin
Laurel	*Victorious*	Latin
Leah	*Weary*	Hebrew
Lenore	*See Eleanor*	Teutonic
Letitia	*Glad*	Latin
Letty	*See Letitia*	
Leila	*Dignified*	Uncertain
Lillian	*Pure as a lily*	Latin
Lily	*Pure*	English
Loretta	*Pure*	Spanish
Lorna	*Stately*	Uncertain
Louise	*Beautiful; yielding*	French
Lucette	*A coquette*	Uncertain
Lucia	*Lustrous*	Latin
Lucille	*Shining*	French
Lucinda	*Brilliant*	English
Lucy	*See Lucille*	English
Lydia	*With a good mind*	Greek
Mabel	*Histrionic*	English
Madeline	*Penitent*	English
Margaret	*Child of light; a pearl*	Greek
Marguerite	*See Margaret*	French
Marie	*See Mary*	
Marilyn	*Gay; popular*	Uncertain
Marion	*Entertaining; interesting*	Gaelic
Marjorie	*See Margaret*	Gaelic
Martha	*Resigned*	Hebrew
Mary	*Sympathetic*	Hebrew
Matilda	*Courageous*	English
Maude	*Gift of the Lord*	English
Mavis	*Discontented*	Uncertain
Maxine	*Charming; witty*	Uncertain
May	*See Mary*	Latin
Maizie	*See Mary*	
Melinda	*Grateful*	Saxon
Mildred	*Teasing*	English
Millicent	*Comforter*	English
Millie	*See Millicent*	
Miriam	*Bitter*	Hebrew
Molly	*See Mary*	

NAME	MEANING	DERIVATION
Muriel	*Sad*	Uncertain
Myra	*Weeping*	English
Nan	*See Anna*	French
Nancy	*See Anna*	
Nanette	*See Anna*	
Naomi	*Pleasant*	Hebrew
Nina	*Dissatisfied*	Moorish
Niobe	*Tearful*	Greek
Nona	*The ninth*	Latin
Nora	*Honorable*	Celtic
Octavia	*The eighth*	Latin
Olga	*Gracious queen*	Russian
Olive	*Bringer of peace*	Latin
Olivia	*See Olive*	English
Pansy	*Thoughtful*	English
Patience	*Patience; fortitude*	Latin
Pauline	*Little*	French
Pearl	*Tearful*	English
Peggy	*See Margaret*	
Penelope	*A weaver; industrious*	Greek
Persephone	*A weaver of dreams; author*	Greek
Persis	*See Persephone*	
Philippa	*Lover of horses*	Greek
Phyllis	*Coy*	English
Polly	*See Mary*	
Portia	*Successful pleader*	Latin
Priscilla	*Dutiful; neat; lovely*	Latin
Prudence	*Careful; quaintly pretty*	English
Psyche	*The soul*	Greek
Rachel	*Motherly*	Hebrew
Regina	*Queenly*	Latin
Rena	*Fond of dress*	Uncertain
Rita	*See Marguerite*	
Rosa	*A rose*	Latin
Rosalie	*See Rosa*	French
Rosalind	*See Rosa*	English
Rosamond	*See Rosa*	English
Rose	*See Rosa*	English
Rosemary	*Unspoiled*	Latin

NAME	MEANING	DERIVATION
Roxana	*Dawn of day*	Persian
Roxanne	*See Roxana*	
Ruby	*Red*	English
Ruth	*Friendly*	Hebrew
Sallie	*See Sarah*	
Salome	*Enticing*	Greek
Sarah	*A princess*	Hebrew
Sophia	*Wise*	Greek
Stella	*A star*	Latin
Stephania	*Loyal*	Greek
Stephanie	*See Stephania*	
Sue	*Trusting*	Danish
Susan	*See Sue*	Hebrew
Susie	*See Sue*	Danish
Suzette	*See Sue*	French
Sylvia	*A forest nymph*	Latin
Teresa	*Generous giver*	Italian
Thalia	*See Teresa*	Greek
Theodora	*Divine gift*	Greek
Theodosia	*See Theodora*	
Therese	*See Teresa*	French
Undine	*Daughter of the waves*	Latin
Ursula	*Even-tempered*	Latin
Valeria	*Worthy*	Teutonic
Velma	*Warm-hearted*	Uncertain
Vera	*Faithful*	Slavonic
Victoria	*Conquering*	Latin
Vida	*Life*	Hungarian
Viola	*A violet*	Latin
Violet	*See Viola*	Gaelic
Virginia	*Innocent*	Latin
Vivian	*Lively*	Latin
Wilhelmina	*Practical*	English
Willa	*Watchful*	Uncertain
Wilma	*Reserved*	Uncertain
Winifred	*Idealistic*	English
Winnie	*See Winifred*	

SECTION TWO
Your Baby From Birth to Two Years

Your Baby Is Born

"Thus God has blessed the woman with a baby on her breast!"

This was the refrain of a lullaby my mother used to sing to us when we were little. It had been composed by a neighbor of her own childhood, on the lonely and dangerous Kansas prairie of Civil War days. The neighbor woman had made it up for her own babies, and my grandmother, hearing it, learned and sang it to hers.

"The busy day is over," began the verse, "the night begins to fall. Then comes, for a mother, the sweetest time of all." Simple words, but they must have had a great deal of meaning for these two young wives and mothers.

For their day was busy beyond anything you and I can very well imagine. Their husbands were with the Union armies, help could not be had. By day the women plowed and planted and harvested, else their children would have starved. By candlelight, they did their household chores.

They must have had misgivings. These were bad, bad times. The Union was fighting for its existence. Law and order had broken down, guerilla bands harried the border states. What could lie ahead but chaos and destruction?

There must have been times when they looked at their little sod homes and thought bitterly that this was no life for children. There were no schools, nothing but grueling work in order to survive, and that in a world where hatred and cruelty seemed to be in control. Was it right, they must have asked themselves, to bring children into such a world?

What would be their fate? Brave tho these women were in the face of their own perils and difficulties, they must have known moments of black fear for their little ones.

But at last the long day of toil and worry was done. There came that "sweetest time of all," when the mother could sit in the twilight, or by the light of the candle she herself had made. She could hold and rock her baby, and feel the wonder and blessing of her motherhood. Out of the peace and joy of that moment, my grandmother's neighbor fashioned her little song.

Did she guess that the baby on her breast would live thru the greatest era of progress the world has ever known? Was the future rolled back for her so that she could see her war-torn country united again, and taking its place with the greatest and most powerful nations of the earth?

I doubt it. What was to happen was beyond the imagining of the men and women who lived in that time. If someone had told them, they wouldn't have believed it. Besides, mothers do not need everything blueprinted in order to have faith.

It was the baby on her breast that brought peace and hope and courage to this mother of Civil War days. The peace and hope and faith that babies have brought since the world began, recompense for any hardship and peril and heartache.

That peace and hope, that great flooding wonder, will be yours when your baby is placed upon your breast. There is no other joy to equal it.

And mankind reveres you. For in your arms, you hold the future.

— —*By Gladys Denny Shultz*

CHAPTER I

Your Baby From Birth to One Month

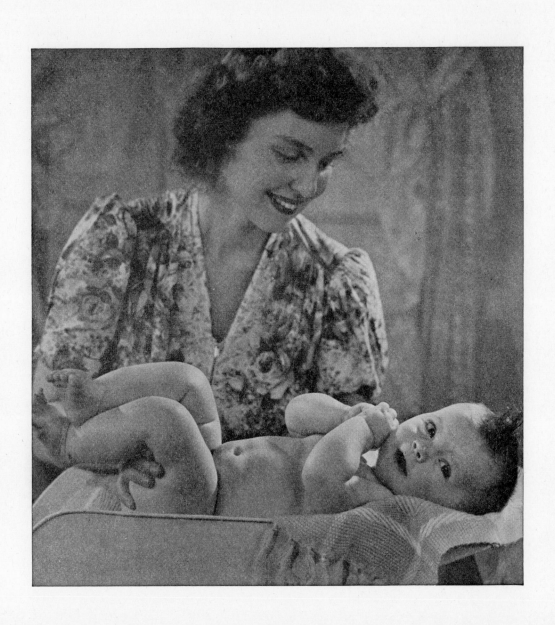

When your baby is born, he may weigh anywhere between 5½ and 11 pounds and still be a healthy, full-term infant. On an average, however, the weight of the newborn baby is 7½ pounds. Boys as a rule are about 3 ounces heavier than girls.

He may be 19 to 21 inches long, with 20 inches the average. Boys tend to be a bit longer than girls, and the first-born child in a family shorter than those who come after him. A baby weighing less than 5½ pounds and shorter than 19 inches is ordinarily considered premature, even tho born at the expected time, and requires special care under a doctor's supervision.

Weight Tells the Story

For the first few weeks, weight will be a very important consideration in your baby's life. His weight may be expected to decrease during the first three days, or until your milk comes in, but the loss is usually made up by the tenth day. After that, whether he's on plentiful breast milk or a formula adapted to his needs, he should gain at least 4 ounces a week. He may gain 6 to 8 ounces a week or even more for the first six months. The gain will probably slow down to from 3 to 6 ounces a week after that.

The legendary "average" baby doubles his birth weight at 5 months and triples it at a year. Remember, tho, that no baby is average. Plenty of variations are possible in your baby's gain, all perfectly proper and normal. If he wieghs 9 pounds at birth, which is more than average, he may not double it at 5 months, and still be all right. A small baby, weighing less than average at birth, will probably more than double his weight at 5 months.

How Much Should He Eat?

Babies differ in their rate of growth and in bodily needs. Their appetites differ from day to day and from meal to meal, even as do adults'. Daily exposure to fresh air and sunshine increases appetite and encourages growth. So does cold weather. Hot weather, however, cuts appetites. Race and sex also play a part in growth.

Don't, therefore, require any particular amount of food at a particular time. The baby's weight tells the story. As long as your baby gains anywhere between 4 and 8 ounces a week, you may be satisfied with his progress.

Consideration for Your Doctor

Never does there seem to be enough good doctors and pediatricians; so try not to take your chosen doctor's time by asking him to perform services you can do yourself.

Before calling a busy doctor, it will help him as well as you to write down whatever you think you should tell him and any questions you wish to ask him so that you will not forget about them and have to make another call. Sometimes just talking over a problem with the doctor will help you to find your own answer. Surely it takes less of his time and costs you less to keep the well baby well than to supply medical care if preventable illnesses occur.

The doctor should look your baby over very thoroly. Chances are that when he gets thru he'll say "Everything perfect!" That will be a great load off your mind. If there are any nursing or feeding difficulties he'll tell you just what to do.

Again when your baby is 6 weeks old go to your own doctor for a checkup of your own recovery, and take the baby to him for another going over period. Until the number of doctors has increased somewhat to fill the shortage in this profession it may be difficult to carry out the full preventive program we've stressed so much in the past. The intervals for examinations of well babies may have to be farther apart. But have a doctor in the offing who knows your baby. Any time anything out of the ordinary comes up, get your doctor on the telephone and tell him about it. He'll want you to do this.

Feeding Your Newborn Baby

Most physicians put the baby to the breast 6 to 8 hours after delivery, 4 times in the next 24 hours, and every 4 hours after that. In special cases, your physician's recommendations should be followed.

The first fluid which comes from the breast is not milk, but the baby should nurse regularly until the breast milk is "in," usually on the third or fourth day. He's expected to lose ½ pound, or slightly more, during this period. As much as a pound may not be cause for alarm, but more than that should be looked into by the doctor. It's important, however, that supplementary feedings should not be started during the first few days unless they're absolutely necessary, for they spoil Baby for working at the breast.

Help Baby to Nurse Well

Your baby should be taught to nurse steadily until he's satisfied. At first there may be difficulty in getting him to take the nipple. Insist that the nurse stay with you until Baby's well started, so that she may be at hand should trouble develop. If it does, the nipple should be pulled out well, then cleansed. Baby's mouth should be placed about the nipple and held there till he takes firm hold. If he stops nursing, tickle him gently on the cheek. This will stimulate him to begin again, and soon he'll have the habit of working steadily until he has enough.

Babies are often too sleepy at first to nurse. Weight should be carefully watched, therefore, during the first week or two, and special efforts made to rouse the baby who is not getting enough.

Care of Your Breasts

The coming of milk into the breasts often makes them tender and sore, and Baby's first nursing efforts quite generally affect the nipples in the same way. The breast binder, which offers support, relieves the first condition. If the breasts are full and extremely painful, hot applications are helpful. Wring out several layers of heavy flannel in hot water (not hot enough to burn) and lay over the breasts, changing cloths as they become cool. Do this for about an hour two or three times a day.

Care of the Nipples

The nipples should be washed with boric acid solution before and after each feeding. In working with the breasts or nipples, the greatest care should be used to keep them sterile, as infected breasts or infections for the baby may result from carelessness. Between nursings, shields may be placed over the nipples to keep the binder from rubbing them. Lead shields should not be used because of the danger of giving the baby lead poisoning. If soreness is severe, zinc oxide or boric acid ointment may be rubbed on the nipples after nursing. This should be carefully removed before the baby is put to the breast again.

Watch His Gains

Baby's expected gain is 6 to 8 ounces a week for the first six to eight weeks. The normal infant should be weighed two or three times a week with diaper on. Failure to gain is usually due to insufficient breast milk. Please remember that it's lack of quantity, not quality that makes the trouble. It's rare for a mother to have unsuitable breast milk. One pediatrician with a large practice says that he has never yet encountered any. Milk varies in women only in fat content and in amount. It's the quantity that's important.

If It's Hard to Nurse Your Baby

In years past, perhaps we haven't paid as much attention as we might to helping mothers nurse their babies. There have been so many satisfactory formulas, it's been easy to provide a bottle when there was some difficulty in getting enough breast milk for the baby!

We'll continue to be thankful for the many excellent substitutes that have been developed for mother's milk, and to which we can always turn in case of need. But we realize now that most mothers can nurse their babies, and we realize, too, that the baby reared on breast milk has a number of advantages over the formula-fed baby. Infant mortality is strikingly lower among the breast fed, and they are much less likely to be sick. Digestion is no problem at all, and constipation is practically unheard of.

Moreover, the baby usually gets more exercise extracting his meals from his mother's breast than from a rubber nipple. Many believe that every baby needs and craves a certain amount of sucking exercise. They claim if he doesn't get it in the course of eating, he'll suck his thumb or fingers or blankets.

Breast feeding is also best for the mother. Many authorities believe that the baby's suckling helps the organs to return to normal more quickly and completely after childbirth.

It's especially desirable that every mother who possibly can should be a source of food for her baby. And most mothers really want to nurse their babies.

Many mothers, however, have to work hard in order to develop a sufficient milk supply. Doctors tell us there have been two main reasons for the modern mother's failure in this respect. One is psychological. She's been sold on the fact that the average modern mother is a poor "milker," and when a mother thinks she can't nurse her baby, she usually can't. That is a fiction which needs to be dispelled. Nervousness and worry also in-

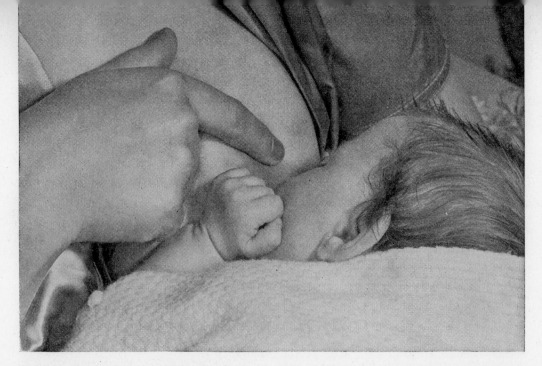

It's important to start nursing off in right way. Be sure Baby takes the whole nipple in his mouth, including brown part behind it. That protects nipple from getting sore. Hold breast so Baby can breathe easily. If he falls asleep before he's thru, tickle his cheek gently to keep him working until he has taken enough

terfere with the milk.

The other reason is physical. The new mother must take things easy, both mentally and physically. Just as you willingly devoted nine months to the proper prenatal growth of your baby, you now must put in another six to nine months in which his proper nourishment is your primary consideration. This doesn't mean that you must lead an entirely vegetable life. You should get out some, you should see your friends, you may knit and sew at home for worthy causes if this doesn't tire you unduly.

But no rushing around, no burdens of committees or organization work! Let others do these things. The best service a young mother can render right now is to follow for nine months the placid, worry-free routine which alone can produce a good supply of mother's milk.

To Avoid Sore Nipples

A factor which often causes feeding trouble at the start is sore nipples. We hope you followed faithfully the suggestions in the prenatal section of this book for getting your nipples in shape for their task. Here are precautions to keep nursing from making them sore:

1. See that Baby takes in his mouth the brown circle behind the nipple as well as the nipple itself.

2. When first put to the breast, he will probably not nurse more than four or five minutes. This is long enough until your nipples become used to it. Let him nurse for gradually longer intervals, but until your nipples become quite hardened, twelve minutes is long enough for one breast at a time. After your nipples are conditioned, fifteen to twenty minutes is the maximum time for one breast at a nursing.

3. Don't let him lie with the nipple in his mouth after he has finished nursing.

4. Protect your nipples from soiling, infection, or injury by always washing your hands before touching them. Wash your nipples with warm, boiled water before nursing. Cover them between nursings with a clean handkerchief or piece of clean linen cloth. Change it at least twice a day.

If Baby doesn't empty the breast in ten

Approach nursing time rested and relaxed. It's a good idea to lie down for this for some weeks after you get home from the hospital. Lie on your side, with Baby's head resting against your arm. Be sure both of you are completely comfortable. An excellent plan till you recover full strength and don't feel like reclining

minutes, empty it yourself with a breast pump or with the hand.

If your nipples are already so sore it's unduly painful for baby to nurse, you should have your doctor examine them. If they're cracked, Baby shouldn't nurse until they're healed. Cover them with an oil or ointment which your doctor will suggest, and either pump out or express the milk, giving it to Baby in a bottle until your nipples are recovered.

Comfortable Position Helps in Nursing

At first, of course, you'll nurse your baby lying down. Arrange yourself comfortably on one side, holding the baby on your arm. It's a good idea to continue this practice for at least six weeks after Baby's birth, and as much longer as you wish. The more rested and relaxed you are, the better your milk supply.

After you feel too peppy to go on reclining, choose a low, comfortable chair for your "nursing" chair. Rest your feet on a footstool, and put a pillow behind your back. Support the baby's head and back with your arm, which in turn rests upon your upraised knee. Hold him close to your breast and lean for-

ward a bit, thus assisting the milk to flow more easily.

While Baby is nursing, hold your breast away from his nose so that he can breathe comfortably. After he has finished nursing, remove the nipple gently by pressing his mouth open with thumb and forefinger. Don't pull the nipple away abruptly, as this may injure it.

Arrange your life so that you approach each nursing period calmly, feeling relaxed and happy. If you can't get adequate household help (which always seems to be a problem when needed most), don't be ashamed to let cleaning and other duties go during these all-important first months. Use your strength only for the essentials.

Why "Bubble" the Baby?

When tiny babies cry, they tend to swallow air. This also occurs frequently when they're eating. The swallowed air makes the baby uncomfortable and fussy, and takes up room in his stomach which should be reserved for food. After he has eaten, it may cause the milk to come up again, or make him wakeful. Proper "bubbling" therefore plays considerable part in your baby's comfort and health.

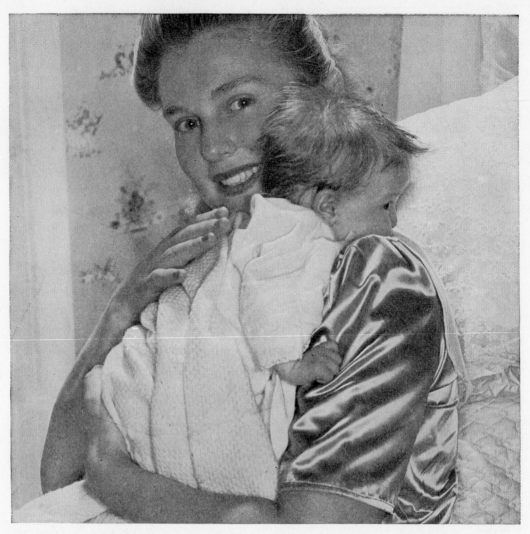

"Bubble" Baby to help him get rid of air he's swallowed. After he's eaten a few minutes, hold him over your shoulder like this, pat his back gently. Repeat at end of feeding, and beforehand if it is needed

How to "Bubble" Him

Place a towel over your shoulder to protect your clothing, for when the air bubble comes up, some milk may come with it. After Baby has nursed as much as he will from breast or bottle, lift and hold him against your shoulder, his face toward your back, and his head over your shoulder. Pat him gently on the back. This helps the air bubble to rise to the top, and lets him belch it out.

Baby may be returned to the other breast or to the bottle for a brief period and then "burped" again. Until he's old enough to burp by himself—5 to 6 months old—pat him gently till he succeeds, even if it should take 15 minutes. This is especially important before he's put to bed. Some babies need to be "bubbled" before the feeding as well as after.

If Baby Hiccoughs

If Baby swallows his food too fast, eats too

much, or gets too much air, he may hiccough. Usually this will last only a few minutes and may be disregarded, save for the routine bubbling process.

If it persists, however, give him a few teaspoons of lukewarm boiled water.

How to Increase Your Breast Milk

If your breast supply is scanty, you may be able to increase it by the following measures:

1. Take extra fluid and foods. Every day you'll need one quart more fluid and one-fourth more solid food than you ordinarily eat, or from 500 to 1000 extra calories. A quart of milk will supply the fluid and 672 calories of food as well, so if you like, one quart of milk a day added to your ordinary diet will give you both the solid and the fluids needed for nursing your baby. Milk is also valuable because of its richness in calcium, which must be furnished the baby to form bones and teeth. Or you may get your extra fluids by drinking a great deal of water, with milk, cocoa, tea, or coffee at each meal.

Eat meat (beef, lamb, chicken, fish, bacon) twice a day and three times if you want it; eggs; cooked cereal with sugar and cream once a day; potatoes and fruit twice a day; and at least two vegetables besides potatoes. Abstain from fried foods; aromatic vegetables such as onions and cabbage; highly spiced or seasoned foods; acid vegetables such as cucumbers; and acid salad dressings. Limit your desserts to fruits, puddings, and gelatins, with a piece of cake now and then.

2. It will help Baby to nurse if a formula is not given the first three days, while your milk is coming in. The doctor, however, should decide whether this course is all right for your baby. Large, strong babies can stand it nicely, but it's usually considered advisable to tide smaller ones over with a bottle. That's for your doctor to decide. During this time he will also prescribe a good deal of lukewarm, boiled water for Baby.

If your baby can wait for food, it's a grand thing, for the demand of a hungry baby upon the mother's breast is the best milk stimulator known at present.

3. Don't skip a nursing period. Some mothers get the idea that if they do this, there will be more milk for the next one. The reverse is true. The more milk your baby gets from your breast—or that you expel with pump or fingers—the more there will be. Never, therefore, skip a period. Wait until your baby is 2 months old to start the "freedom bottle"—the bottle of formula which allows you to attend a luncheon or a dinner and not have to rush home before dessert is served—and then don't give it every day. (The 2 p.m. feeding is usually the poorest of the day. When you do start the "freedom bottle," this is a good time to give it.)

Should Baby fail to make his weight gain, try to increase your milk supply by:

1. Additional stimulation of the breasts thru manual expression of milk or the breast pump. (These operations should be carried out under physician's orders.)

2. Putting the baby on a three-hour schedule. (The extra feeding provides extra breast stimulation, and thus increases the milk supply.)

No drugs, special liquids, or foods are of any value, says our consulting pediatrician, unless the diet is deficient—as it often is.

Is Your Breast Milk Enough?

There's only one way to tell whether or not you have enough milk for your baby—by his weight. If each week he gains anywhere between 4 and 8 ounces or more, it's ample. But if you're doing all the things just listed and he still fails to gain 4 ounces a week, it's your cue to start bottle feedings.

Offer the bottle, however, only after Baby has nursed full time at the breast. Then give the bottle immediately and let him take what he wants.

When to Discontinue Breast Feedings

If your baby gets less than ½ ounce of breast milk from you at a feeding, it's considered that the milk isn't worth the trouble required to get it. The amount of milk Baby is receiving can be determined by weighing him before and after each feeding. Should this be consistently less than ½ ounce after you've made every effort to increase your milk, the breast feedings may be abandoned and the bottle relied upon entirely.

Formulas for Bottle Feedings

Cow's milk in some form or other is usually used for artificial feeding, for properly modified, it has been found to be the most satisfactory substitute for human milk. Cow's milk in the following forms is suitable for infants:

1. *Boiled fresh milk*. A milk not too high in fat content (around 3½ to 4 percent of fat per quart) is best. The milk should be boiled for from three to five minutes before using (whether it has been pasteurized or not), to destroy harmful bacteria and to make it more easily digestible. See method of preparing a formula on page 55.

2. *Irradiated evaporated milk*. This is cow's milk which has been concentrated to one-half its original volume, sterilized, and sealed in airtight containers. The addition of water restores it to the consistency of ordinary milk. This milk, because of the treatment to which it is subjected, is a uniform, easily digested food and has been used with excellent success in infant feeding. For these reasons it has been coming into increasing favor with physicians.

Advantages of Irradiated Evaporated Milk

Irradiated evaporated milk has many things in its favor. Because it's irradiated, babies on this type of milk need less Vitamin D from other sources. It's more easily digested, uniform in quality, clean and germ-free, and, when the can isn't opened, keeps indefinitely. Moreover, many allergic youngsters tolerate it better than fresh milk. Bought by the case, it's less expensive than fresh milk.

Evaporated milk has only one disadvantage, according to some medical authorities. The cream can't be removed. When there's any condition, therefore, such as severe diarrhea or eczema, in which it is desirable to remove cream before preparing the formula, fresh milk is sometimes more desirable.

It's believed, however, that a baby on irradiated evaporated milk is less likely to have eczema. If there is a tendency to eczema it's thought you may reduce it by putting the cans in water and boiling them for two hours. Some physicians, moreover, are reporting that in cases of diarrhea they have put babies on evaporated milk, without adding sweetening, with good results. In any such conditions, your doctor must be the judge of the course to follow.

It can be said categorically that irradiated evaporated milk agrees perfectly with most babies, and has all the advantages we've noted.

These special qualities make evaporated milk particularly valuable for infants and children at such times when deliveries of fresh milk are curtailed by travel or for other reasons that make refrigeration inadequate to keep it pure for the longer periods made necessary.

3. *Dried milk*. This is milk from which practically all the water has been removed. It, also, is used with good results in infant feeding. Restore it to its original form by adding water in the proportion of 2 ounces to 1 level tablespoon of dried milk. Then modify according to the formula. Both whole and skimmed dried milk are obtainable. Use the whole, unless your doctor directs otherwise.

Canned dried milk will keep without refrigeration, but after the can is opened, it must be kept tightly covered and cold.

A Formula If Refrigeration Fails

For certain conditions, doctors prescribe a lactic acid formula in which sweet milk is soured by adding lactic acid. This partially predigests the milk, and makes it possible to use a stronger milk mixture.

A lactic acid formula made with evaporated milk has the advantage, especially valuable in an emergency period, of keeping 24 hours without refrigeration. The formula can be mixed and the bottles kept standing in cold water. If a situation should arise where electric refrigeration is cut off and ice is not obtainable, this formula will be a very useful one. All that is required is U.S.P. Lactic Acid in addition to the milk, boiled water, and sweetening called for by the other formulas described later in this chapter. The lactic acid formula is well tolerated by most babies.

Proprietary Foods

In addition to the formulas using fresh, evaporated, or dried milk, there are many commercial baby foods. These consist of different varieties of carbohydrate (the element added to cow's milk to make it more nearly like mother's milk) and in some instances, of dried or concentrated milk. They're prepared by adding boiled water or milk, and are used widely. Many different formulas may be obtained in this dried, powdered, or concentrated form, including lactic acid formulas, protein milk (for diarrhea), and formulas made without milk for hyper-allergic babies.

Why Add Sweetening?

To make cow's milk suitable for human babies, some form of carbohydrate must be added. This is usually done in the form of a sweetening, tho various kinds of cereal, such as barley, are used for certain conditions. Almost any of the sweetening agencies can be used in formulas—cane sugar, milk sugar, honey, molasses, maple sirup—but the ones most often employed are corn sirup and dextri-maltose.

A Good Basic Formula

A healthy, full-term infant does well on almost any of a great variety of milk mixtures. Here's one which has been used with success in feeding many thousands of babies. If it should fail to agree with your baby, have your doctor give you a formula adapted to your own baby's needs. It's best to consult your doctor, anyway, before using a formula.

First Formula Using Fresh Milk
(one day's supply)

10 ounces whole milk

10 ounces water

1½ tablespoons Karo or

3 level tablespoons Dextri-maltose

How to prepare: Mix the milk, water, and sweetening. Bring to a boil, and boil for from 3 to 5 minutes. Cool rapidly by placing in a pan of cold water. During the boiling and the first part of the cooling, the milk should be stirred constantly to avoid burning and the formation of a scum on the top. (See pictures on page 79.)

Pour into as many sterile bottles as there are feedings during the twenty-four-hour period. Stopper the bottles with sterile cotton or corks, or cover with clean waxed paper. Paper is somewhat troublesome to put on, and the bottle must be kept upright. Store in the refrigerator until time for use.

Baby at first will probably take about three ounces at a feeding, if he relies entirely upon the bottle. He'll take less if he gets some milk from you.

First Formula Using Evaporated Milk
(one day's supply)

5½ ounces (1 small can) irradiated evaporated milk

15 ounces boiled water

1½ tablespoons Karo or

3 level tablespoons Dextri-maltose

How to prepare: Boil water at least five minutes, then cool. Add sweetening and irradiated evaporated milk. Stir well, and pour into as many bottles as there are feedings during the day. Cork each bottle with sterile cotton or a sterile cork and keep in a cool place. (See pictures on page 79.)

The above formula has approximately the same food value as the fresh milk formula.

Lactic Acid Formula

As the addition of latic acid makes cow's milk more easily digested, a considerably stronger solution can be given, and excellent nutritional results are secured. Babies on this formula, incidentally, vomit and spit up less than on sweet milk.

First Formula Using Evaporated Milk-Lactic Acid
(one day's supply)

8 ounces irradiated evaporated milk

10 ounces water

½ teaspoon U. S. P. Lactic Acid

2 tablespoons Karo or

4 tablespoons Dextri-maltose

How to prepare: Boil the water and sweetening together for 5 minutes, then cool. Add the acid, cool and pour slowly into the diluted milk, stirring all the time. Pour into as many bottles as there are feedings, as for the other formulas. Have all materials cold.

A baby relying upon the bottle alone will probably take around 3 ounces at a feeding.

How Much Formula Should Baby Take?

Any of the foregoing formulas may be used to complement insufficient breast milk, or as Baby's sole food at this age. If your baby is getting no breast milk at all, he will probably take around 3 ounces of the bottle at a feeding. If he empties the bottle, you may give him an ounce or so more.

If Baby is on the breast as well as the bottle,

let him nurse first, and then take as much or as little from the bottle as he likes.

Keep Bottles and Nipples Germ-Free

Any type nursing bottle whose every part can be easily reached by a bottle brush is satisfactory, according to the Department of Pediatrics, State University of Iowa. Any nipple that can be turned inside out, scrubbed, and boiled is likewise suitable. The bottles and nipples should be washed thoroly with hot soapsuds and a bottle brush; then rinsed and boiled for five minutes. (See pictures on page 80.) The bottles are then ready for filling. After boiling, the nipples should be kept in sterile covered glass jars. Used nipples should be stored separately from the clean ones. If for any reason there's only one bottle and one nipple available, these should be scrubbed and boiled each time before they're used.

As soon as Baby has taken his feeding, the bottle and nipple should be rinsed and the bottle filled with cold water. When you're ready to prepare the milk for the next twenty-four hours, empty the used bottles, wash, and boil as already described.

A small funnel is a great convenience in filling the bottles. It should be made of material that will stand boiling and cleaning, as it should be boiled each time before it's used. If the saucepan in which you make the formula has a good lip, a funnel may not be necessary. Another convenience is a bottle rack, usually made of wire, to hold as many bottles as there are feedings in 24 hours. This rack should fit inside the large covered kettle which you use for bottle sterilizing. Cotton and waxed paper stoppers should be discarded after each use. If you use corks, or are fortunate enough to have rubber stoppers, boil them each time before they're used. One to two tablespoons of vinegar in the water will dissolve the lime deposit on bottles boiled in hard water.

Make Rubber Nipples Last

Here are some suggestions that will make them last longer and give a mximum of service.

The greatest difficulty for the amateur parent, or the old hand for that matter, lies in making the right-size holes in the nipples. If the hole is too small, the baby will work and work and get nothing for his pains. He may get tired before he gets enough milk. If too large, the milk will come out too fast and make him choke or have indigestion, and he will get all his milk before he has sucked as long as he wants to. Getting the hole just right is, therefore, a matter of considerable importance. The milk should come out in large drops, one at a time, not run out in a stream.

It will take practice, and the waste of several nipples, as a rule, before the right combination is found. Work carefully, therefore, as follows:

To burn hole in rubber nipple, insert blunt end of needle in a cork, heat sharp point over a flame. Stick into nipple. A pencil eraser held inside the nipple may help you

Insert the blunt end of a fine-pointed needle into a cork. Heat the point to a white heat. Insert the eraser end of a pencil into the nipple to hold it out, then quickly burn a hole with the needle point. The longer the hot needle is held against the nipple, the larger the hole will be. It's best, therefore, to enlarge it gradually, trying the nipple each time until the hole is just big enough and not too big.

Immediately after each use, clean the nipple thoroly, for the butterfat in milk deteriorates rubber. Turn the nipple inside out and wash with soapy water which isn't too hot. Rinse.

Sterilize the nipples once a day by boiling for three minutes in salt water (a teaspoon of salt to a quart of water). Don't use a pan made of copper. The salt keeps the nipple from softening thru absorption of water. Don't overboil or the nipples will collapse before their time. And don't let the pan boil dry, for this will scorch the nipples and make them worthless.

As soon as the three minutes are up, remove the nipples from the water and place them in a dry, sterile, covered jar. Then store them in a cool, dark place until needed.

With constant use and daily boiling, nipples eventually will collapse and deteriorate, but it is good economy to make each last just as long as possible.

Please use great care in burning the holes. There's no single item that contributes more to the successful feeding of a bottle baby than nipples with the right-size holes.

How to Give a Bottle Feeding

At feeding time take the formula from the refrigerator and warm it to blood heat by placing the bottle in a pan of warm water. If a sweet milk feeding is overheated, it can be cooled and no harm is done. But take care not to overheat a lactic acid formula, for the curd is likely to crumble and separate from the whey. After warming the formula, place the nipple on the bottle, being careful not to touch the end which goes into the baby's mouth. Test the temperature of the milk by sprinkling a few drops on the inside of your wrist. This is also a test for the size of the hole in the nipple. When the bottle's turned up, the milk should drop out rapidly but shouldn't run in a stream. If the room is cool, wrap the bottle in a piece of flannel to keep the milk warm while the baby is nursing.

Always hold Baby in your arms while feeding him. Assume a comfortable position like the one described for nursing. Hold him close to you so he feels the same security and warmth he'd have in suckling. If for any reason you feed Baby in his bed, hold the bottle thruout the feeding unless he's old enough to hold it himself.

Throw away any milk left in the bottle. Don't feed it later.

Before and after a bottle feeding, Baby should be held upright against your shoulder and gently patted on the back in order to get the air from his stomach. See the illustration on page 52.

What to Do If Baby Vomits

Spitting up, or regurgitation, is common and isn't significant as long as the weekly gain is made. It may be due to overfeeding. Try giving a little less milk. If Baby's head is raised a little by slipping a small pillow under the mattress, he'll probably spit up less in bed.

The condition usually stops when a baby begins taking solid food.

Forceful, or projectile, vomiting of so large a part of the feedings that weight gain is impossible, is significant and may mean there's an obstruction at the outlet of the stomach. The doctor should be notified at once.

Repeated or constant vomiting means that something is wrong. It should be investigated.

Bowel Movements If Baby Is Breast Fed

Constipation, like thumb sucking, is often a source of unnecessary worry to mothers. Much of this worry may be avoided, if you're able to read in a general way the story told by the baby's stools. At the same time you'll be able to understand signals indicating a situation which really needs correcting.

If yours is a breast baby, we can say almost without reservation that his bowels will not require special attention. The breast baby is almost never constipated but ordinarily has frequent stools during the first month or six weeks. When this is the case, the stools may be green and contain curds. (Green, because the bile hasn't had time to change from green to yellow, and curds because they haven't had time to pack together.) From five to six stools a day is within the normal limits during this period.

On the other hand, a baby may have only one stool in two or more days and still be perfectly healthy and all right. There are cases on record of infants who normally have a stool about once every two weeks. Doctors now make longer and longer the period the baby may be allowed to go before artificial aid is given. They assure us that there is seldom cause for alarm about the bowels of the breast-fed baby.

Bowel Movements If Baby Is Bottle Fed

Cow's-milk stools are more pasty than breast-milk stools. Normally there are from one to three daily—dry, pasty, and firm. A concentrated whole-milk mixture, such as the lactic acid formula, will produce a large stool. A diluted mixture will give a small, yellow stool. The color becomes more brown when cereal is added to the diet. As the food range increases, there may be more stools, but the baby will keep his own rhythm.

If Baby's Constipated

As long as the baby's stools are soft and smooth, he isn't constipated no matter how far apart the movements may be. But when the stools are so hard they're passed with straining and difficulty, the baby is constipated. Sometimes stools are so hard to pass that there is blood on the outside.

Such a condition points to a deficiency in the formula. It may not be strong enough, or may not have enough carbohydrate. Check the milk content, and add to the amount of the carbohydrate in the formula. Also, one to two teaspoons of prune juice or prune pulp may be given each day. Be slow to use suppositories or enemas since Baby might learn to rely upon artificial stimulation.

Meaning of His Stools

For your guidance, here are some helpful clues for reading Baby's stools:

Soft and smooth—normal stool of a healthy, properly fed infant.

Dry alkaline stool—excessive protein (too strong a solution of milk for Baby's stage of development), or too little sweetening.

Soft acid stool—excessive carbohydrate (sweetening).

Large, greasy stool—too much fat (cream, fish-liver oil).

Too much fat plus too much carbohydrate make frequent stools.

Too much fat plus too much protein cause constipation and large, firm, soapy stools.

Diarrhea? Call Your Doctor

Diarrhea, or "running off at the bowels," is another condition seldom found in the breast-fed baby. When it occurs in the bottle-fed baby, remove cream and sweetening from the formula; give water; stop other foods; and call your doctor. Diarrhea isn't a matter for home medication.

Sponge Baths Till Navel Heals

Before the navel has healed, sponge baths are given. The process is as follows:

1. Set up in bathroom, bedroom, or kitchen (whichever is warm and most convenient), all the articles needed for the bath—bath table, bath basket, basin of warm water, washcloth, towel, clean clothes. Have room temperature 70° to 75° F. (See page 35 for a description of bath equipment.)

If you can get a folding canvas bath table, with or without the attached tub, you'll find it a great convenience. If you can't, use any ordinary table that's a convenient height for you. Pad it well.

2. Put a soft bath towel on the bath table, and lay Baby on it. Remove his clothes, placing a clean diaper under his buttocks. Then pull a large, soft bath towel over him.

3. Rinse out his eyes with boric acid solution or boiled water on a bit of cotton. If his nose needs attention, clean it with a wisp of cotton that's been rolled in your fingers and dipped in olive oil. Don't do this, tho, unless his nose needs it. The inside of his mouth *SHOULD NOT BE TOUCHED*. Clean his ears with cotton or a blunt finger covered by the washcloth. Use a separate piece of cotton for each eye, each nostril, and each ear.

4. Wash Baby's body with clear water, except around the buttocks and genitals where castile soap should be used to remove urine and stools. Keep all his body covered except the part you're washing. Rinse the soap off thoroly.

5. Shampoo his scalp with soap three times a week, rinsing well. Don't shampoo it every day, for the skin and scalp of some babies can't stand the daily application of soap.

6. Pat him dry with a soft towel, being especially careful to dry the creases.

7. Massage oil gently into his scalp. Rub oil or baby cream into the body creases. It's also a good idea to rub cream over the entire body if there's any inclination to chafing or heat rash.

8. Dress Baby in clean clothes.

Tub Baths Come Next

As soon as the navel is healed, Baby can have his bath in a small tub. If you have a bath thermometer, keep the water at 100° F.

for the first two months. If you haven't a thermometer, use the elbow test, shown in the illustration on page 73. The water should feel lukewarm to your elbow. Place Baby on the bath table as usual for undressing and preliminary steps.

About three times a week, soap Baby's scalp and rinse it, holding his head over the side of the tub. (See pictures on page 73.) Return him to the bath table and apply soap to genitals, buttocks, and other parts of the body as needed.

Then back into the tub for rinsing. Support his head and back on one hand and arm, while you rinse with the other hand.

Finally place him on the bath table again for drying, oiling, and dressing.

When to Change Diapers

Change diapers before and after a feeding, and let Baby be wet between times, unless he's obviously uncomfortable. Otherwise, he may acquire the habit of crying every time he wets. Since this is very frequent in infancy, the result may be an unnecessary amount of disturbance for Baby and extra work for you.

Don't waken Baby at night to change him, but if he wakes and cries, he should be made comfortable. Change him, and make sure he isn't too warm or too cold. If he's perspiring, he's too warm, and some of his covers should be taken off. If his flesh is cold to the touch, he needs more warmth. A hot-water bottle at his feet, filled with warm, not hot, water will help him to get warm and comfortable quickly and go to sleep.

Care of Diapers

Diapers should never be used twice without washing them in soapsuds, rinsing thoroly, and drying. Every second or third washing they should be boiled as well. Don't use water softeners or other chemicals (soda, starch, or bluing) in the washing water. Dry diapers out of doors in the sun whenever possible.

When you take them down from the line, smooth them carefully so there'll be no wrinkles to hurt Baby's tender skin. (Running a hot iron over them will do this nicely.) Fold and put away.

In some convenient place, preferably the bathroom, you'll want a covered diaper pail. Have some water in it. Drop wet diapers into this pail. Every day wring them out of the water, and dry them unless they're to be washed immediately. Put clean water in the pail every day.

Soiled diapers require special treatment. The easiest way is to shake or scrape the contents off into the stool. Flush it, then rinse stained places in the clean water which refills the stool. You can then drop the diaper into the pail.

If the diapers get a strong ammonia smell, they should be boiled after every using. Dry them and then wring them out of a boric acid solution, made by adding 4 tablespoons of boric acid to a gallon of water. Finally, dry them again. Ammoniated diapers can cause a baby much discomfort, so don't allow this condition to continue.

Many communities now have diaper services, which call for diapers, launder, and return them. In some instances the service also furnishes the diapers. This is a tremendous convenience. Better investigate to see whether there's such a service in your locality.

Airings Start at Three Weeks

Baby may be taken outdoors for airings after he's 3 weeks old. Up to this time it's best to let him rest comfortably in a warm room. Wrappings for his airings should depend upon the outside temperature and the weather. In summer, don't expose Baby at this age to the direct rays of the sun.

When Your Baby Cries

One hears of the baby so good that he never cries, but he's rarely met in real life—especially in the early stages. You'll be lucky, indeed, if your baby doesn't prove his lung power the first night or two after he gets home from the hospital, and at other times as well.

The modern mother has had it well ground into her that she shouldn't pick up the baby when he cries. This is good advice, for picking him up teaches Baby to cry in order to be picked up. However, it doesn't mean that you mustn't go near Baby or pay any attention at all to his cries.

As the days go by, you'll become more and more expert at determining the cause and nature of the demonstration. Soon you'll learn to distinguish the hunger cry, which simply means that it's getting toward dinnertime; the fretting of a tired, sleepy baby who needs to be let alone so he can go to sleep; and the cry of pain or discomfort.

In these early days of Baby's life, it's always

proper to make sure he hasn't a good reason to cry. Investigate thoroly and be sure he's as confortable as you can make him. Then (but not till then) it's proper to go away and let him cry. He may be too warm, for it's a common fault to swaddle a tiny infant until he roasts. If he's perspiring, take off some of his covers or clothes. In hot weather, give him a cooling sponge-off.

He may be cold. If he is, his flesh will feel cold to your touch. Put on more clothes or covers, place a small hot-water bottle filled with warm water at his feet.

He may be wet or have a soiled diaper. Investigate and make him comfortable. If he has a skin irritation, bring it to your doctor's attention and get relief for him.

Perhaps his position in the bed is uncomfortable. He may have lain too long on one side, slid down toward the foot, or become tangled in the bedclothes. He may even have a pin sticking him! Correct any such condition.

He may be ill. The symptoms of various baby illnesses are described toward the end of this chapter. Follow the directions according to the behavior displayed.

If Baby isn't picked up or fed off-schedule, or doesn't otherwise gain dividends out of purposeless crying, he'll soon learn it doesn't pay. And then you yourself will have one of those precious gems, a baby who "never cries."

But don't ignore cries. They're Baby's only way of letting you know that something's wrong.

Thumb Sucking

Sooner or later during these early weeks you're going to find your baby with his thumb in his mouth or catch him in the act of putting it there. Time was when a mother would have beamed and said, "A baby that sucks his thumb is a good baby."

But some 20 years ago thumb sucking among babies came into much the same ill repute as drunkenness and similar vices among adults. It was held responsible for crooked teeth and was supposed to lead to sexual perversion later on. Scenes of domestic conflict ensued as the grown folks fell upon this innocent diversion and tried to eliminate it with various mechanical aids. Every once in a while someone would find a device which seemed to work, but if you tried it on your baby it never did! Parents have even resorted to mild torture with the result that their child sucked his thumb harder than ever.

Now we know that 99.9 percent of the worry about thumb sucking is completely unnecessary. Research has established that babies have an instinctive need to do a certain amount of sucking. If they don't get enough in the course of procuring their food, they'll suck something else. During the past 20 years many more babies have been on bottles than formerly and this may account for the fact that more babies seem to suck their thumbs.

It is widely believed by many that if the child stops sucking his thumb before the permanent teeth come in, around the age of 6, no lasting harm is done to the teeth. However, there is still a great deal of disagreement among doctors and dentists about the results of this habit on a child's teeth. It has been proved that there's no connection between thumb sucking and undesirable sex practices.

If your baby's on the bottle, take care not to have the nipple holes so large that he gets the milk without effort. Be sure your baby is well nourished, comfortable, and happy on a good schedule. Then dismiss thumb sucking from your mind. It's probable that he'll stop and you won't realize for some time that the once-feared habit has taken care of itself. The well-nourished, happy, healthy bottle baby will probably stop his thumb sucking, except possibly for times when he's tired or sleepy. Thumb sucking under such circumstances simply means that he needs to go to bed.

If, however, your baby isn't making the weight gain that he should, cries a great deal, usually seems unhappy, and falls upon his thumb as if he would chew it off, ask your doctor to examine him and his diet to see what may be wrong.

If Baby continues to suck his thumb as he gets older, you can keep his hands busy most of his waking time. Don't call attention to the thumb sucking as such. Just remember that if a baby or small child sucks his thumb constantly during his waking hours, he's either hungry, uncomfortable, or lacks something else to do.

Baby Needs His Sleep

When he first comes home from the hospital, Baby will sleep most of the time when he's not being fed or bathed. Gradually he'll sleep less, and perhaps according to a pattern of his own, for babies differ in the amount of sleep they need.

In the section on arrangements for Baby before he arrived, the right sort of sleeping provisions were described. Be sure he has a comfortable bed, and if at all possible, a room to himself even if it's only a well-ventilated cubby-hole. Put him in his bed with the door closed and lights out for the intervals which we'll give you later in the schedules. This way he'll get all the sleep he needs to grow and develop good nerves.

At this age, Baby can't move himself, so you'll have to shift his sleeping position from time to time, from back to one side, and then to the other. To keep him on his side, roll up a blanket and prop him against it.

Don't waken him to show him to people. There's no harm, tho, in letting relatives or dear friends slip in for a look while he's sleeping, providing they don't disturb him.

A Schedule to Fit Your Baby

There seems to be some confusion in the minds of many mothers about the schedule. Some take a schedule given them and try to make the baby conform to it. Perhaps that particular schedule is fine for other babies but doesn't work for theirs, so trouble results. Or a mother may think that if the schedule calls for a feeding at 10 o'clock and she's two minutes late, the baby is ruined.

Difficulties caused by over-tenseness on the mother's part, or schedules that don't fit, have stirred up some rebellion lately against any schedule at all. Don't be led into this trap. Anyone who has reared a baby on a schedule adapted to that particular baby would never go back to the old hit-or-miss methods.

There's an art, however, in finding the schedule on which your own baby will do best. Let him have a hand in it, too. Take things easy for the first week or two after you get Baby home, and get the feel of things. Find out when he seems to want to eat and sleep, and take this into account. At the same time, tho, guard against letting him be disturbed, for this will throw both you and Baby off the track.

A schedule of a sort, of course, has already been established at the hospital. From four to six hours after birth, your baby was put to your breast for five or six minutes, maybe ten. Then after six hours, he was put to the breast again, and so on during that first day. The second day the nursings were probably every four hours.

The regular nursing schedule wasn't begun until the third day, when your milk came in. The rule then is that an infant weighing 7 pounds or more is put to the breast at 4-hour intervals during the 24, while one weighing less is fed at 3-hour intervals.

When you get home, continue whichever schedule your baby was on at the hospital. It's possible, tho, that the change and added responsibilities which land on your shoulders, may interfere with your milk supply. Does Baby cry for some time before every feeding? Don't feed him then, but next time shorten the interval a bit. After you find the time

The mattress for Baby's bed should be firm. If not moistureproof, protect it with a waterproof sheet

when he seems ready to eat with appetite, stick to it. That becomes his feeding schedule, until he's ready to go the full 4 hours.

Baby sleeps from 18 to 20 hours a day during the first two months, and cries from an hour to two hours a day. Follow to some extent his own inclinations as to his times for sleeping and crying.

It's usually convenient to bathe him before the mid-morning feeding, and Baby usually needs a bath after the night's sleep. Hence the bath hour.

By the time he's 3 or 4 weeks old, you'll have found the best time from Baby's standpoint for the various operations of his day. That is his schedule. There's nothing sacred about any particular time for any one operation. His day may begin at 6 a.m., 7 a.m., or 8 a.m., according to his ideas and your convenience.

But when you've established a good working schedule stick to it! Not to the minute necessarily, but within 15 minutes, let's say. Baby will be better and happier, he won't wear himself out with crying, he'll learn that there's a regular time for every necessary act. These are the first steps in discipline.

You need no selling, I'm sure, to follow the schedule yourself. But what about well-meaning relatives, such as grandparents, whose genuine doting on Baby is apt to throw a monkey-wrench into a smoothly functioning schedule?

And when, asks one intelligent mother, may you relax from the rigidity of the schedule? If you may.

With such questions as these, don't hesitate to use your common sense. People who can see Baby any time are simply selfish, even tho they don't realize it, if they ask to have his life disrupted for their pleasure. You certainly can't have the schedule shot to pieces just to please thoughtless people. If an occasion arises, however, which you think is important enough to justify some rearranging, do it.

Let common sense guide you, too, about relaxing the schedule occasionally. We've said that the heavens won't fall if an item on the schedule is a few minutes late or early. Going over very far, tho, usually results in a crying fit on Baby's part that wears out both of you. If it's a matter merely of your own convenience, you'll feel repaid in the long run if you stick pretty closely to your schedule. But there again, events might arise that are important enough to call for a deviation. You alone can be the judge. After you've had a chance to learn how smoothly things go when the schedule's faithfully observed, you'll be in a better position to decide whether or not something is important enough to disrupt it!

Take Dad's convenience into account, tho. One mother, whose husband has alternate night shifts as a pressman, bathed one child at 12:30 and the new baby at 4:30. The first feeding schedule ran 9-1-5-9-1-5. Dad, getting home at 12:30 a. m., gave the baby his night bottle, thus letting Mother have seven hours unbroken sleep. "Caring for a baby takes, above all else, a little imagination," says this mother.

Here's a suggested schedule. Revise it according to your baby's rhythm and your household convenience.

A Beginning Schedule for Your Baby Two Weeks Old

6:00 a.m. Nursing (or bottle feeding) 10 to 12 minutes at first, but increasing as your nipples toughen and Baby gets stronger. After the feeding, make bed and Baby dry and clean, then put him back to bed.

9:30 a.m. Bath.

10:00 a.m. Nursing or bottle feeding, same as above.

10:30 a.m. to 2:00 p.m. Nap in his own room, with door shut and window open. The temperature shouldn't be below 60° F.

2:00 p.m. Nursing or bottle feeding, as above.

3:00 p.m. to 4:00 p.m. Airing, out of doors when the baby is past 3 weeks of age and the weather isn't stormy or too cold. Otherwise, in the bedroom.

5:00 p.m. to 6:00 p.m. Exercise period. Fun for all! Put Baby on your big bed with all his clothing but the diaper removed. (Have a large thick pad over the bed to protect it.) The room temperature should be 75° F. Let Baby kick freely. It's a fine idea to massage his back and hold him during the last half hour of this period. Visit with him, love him, carry him about the house. This will rest him for the night. Don't bounce or throw him around, however. That comes under the head of over-stimulation and interferes with the sleep and digestion of most babies.

6:00 p.m. Nursing or bottle feeding. Put on his nightgown, and return him to bed in a room by himself with the door closed, light out, and window open. Have the temperature not lower than 60° F.

10:00 p.m. Nursing or bottle feeding.

2:00 a.m. Nursing or bottle feeding when Baby wakens. Don't wake him for it. This feeding is usually eliminated when he's 6 to 7 weeks old.

Time for Vitamins C and D

In years past, this section was labeled, "Cod-liver oil and orange juice," but there have been changes. Now we'd have to say, "Fish-liver oils, Vitamin D concentrates, and ascorbic acid, in orange juice or other forms."

For many fish besides the famous cod are yielding up their livers in the cause of better teeth and bony structure for human beings. We have a number of Vitamin D concentrates, besides, and interest has increased in Vitamin C or ascorbic acid, the element which makes orange juice so valuable.

The reason for introducing these new elements into the diet, however, is the same. Milk—mother's or cow's milk properly modified—while containing all other elements needed for best growth, is lacking in Vitamins C and D, and possibly in Vitamin A. It's also lacking in iron and copper, two minerals which Baby has to have for health.

Baby comes into the world with enough copper and iron stored up to last him for some time, but he needs C and D vitamins added almost from the first. This is why they're now introduced in some form as early as the second or third week.

Starting Vitamin D

Fish-Liver Oils. Fish-liver oils contain both Vitamins D and A. A pure, unflavored variety is best. Begin with a very small amount (5 to 10 drops) twice a day, offered in a spoon— a small coffee spoon is excellent but a teaspoon may be used. (See the illustration on page 72.) As Baby lies against your arm, or on the bath table, you may gently press his mouth open with thumb and finger against his cheeks, then slip the oil over his tongue and into the back of the mouth. When cold, the oil has almost no taste. Be very gentle, but insist that it goes down. (Babies usually love the oil after they get used to it, but don't bother whether he likes it or not! He has to have it, for teeth, bones, and general well-being.) Increase the amount by a drop or two each day until he's taking a teaspoonful a day.

Vitamin D Concentrates. Many doctors have been prescribing Vitamin D concentrates, a number of which are on the market. Far less of a concentrate is required to do the job, and babies usually do less spitting up on concentrate than on fish-liver oil.

A handy way to give Vitamin D concentrate at first is a drop or two at a time in a medicine dropper, gently pressing open the baby's mouth. Increase the amount as your doctor advises. When Baby gets big enough to recline against your arm, a cool teaspoon containing the oil or concentrate can be pressed against his lips. He'll probably suck it in—and will have learned to accept food from a spoon. Or insert it thru a corner of his mouth. Even in the summer months doctors now advise a teaspoon of fish-liver oil, or a few drops of concentrate, every day to insure good bone formation.

Irradiated Milk. Irradiated milk (evaporated milk which is subjected to the irradiation process) contains considerable Vitamin D. If this type of milk is given, less fish-liver oil or concentrate is needed.

Know Your Units

Vitamin-rich foods are now assayed in standard units. It's not enough just to give a certain amount of fish oil or concentrate. You also need to know the number of units of Vitamin D in the brand you're using. To insure superior skeletal development, at least 400 I. U. (International Units) of Vitamin D must be provided every day. Weak or debilitated children need more than this. No fish oil or concentrate should be bought unless the potency is stated in units per ounce on the label.

Around 400 units of Vitamin D are contained in 1 teaspoon of U.S.P. cod-liver oil, 3 drops of viosterol, 4 drops of percomorphum, and in 1 quart of some irradiated milks. It's a common failing not to give enough fish-liver oil from a standpoint of unitage, and too much concentrate. Read the unitage on the brand you're using, and govern the dose ac-

cordingly. Start with a small amount, however, and increase gradually until Baby's getting his needed unitage every day.

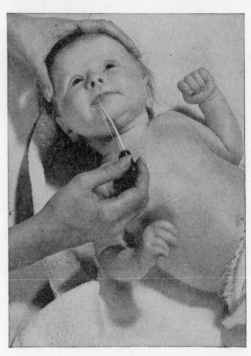

Give Vitamin D concentrate—so necessary for good strong bone and teeth formation—when he's 4 weeks old. Squeeze from medicine dropper into his mouth. Let the doctor prescribe amount

Starting Vitamin C

Next begin Vitamin C. You can use either orange or grapefruit juice at first. Give Baby 1 teaspoonful diluted with 1 teaspoonful of water which has been boiled and cooled to body heat. (Never heat juice or add hot water to it, as this destroys Vitamin C.) The juice may be offered in a 4-ounce bottle, or in a glass or aluminum spoon. (Silver gives the juice a metallic taste.) The method is the same as for the Vitamin D. Increase the amount one teaspoon every few days, omitting the water, until at 3 months Baby's getting 3 ounces or more a day. Pineapple, lime, and sweetened lemon juice may also be used.

Tomato juice is a good source of Vitamin C, and may be used to advantage a little later on. But twice as much is required as of orange juice for the same amount of ascorbic acid, hence it isn't so practical with the tiny baby who may have difficulty taking enough tomato juice to supply his Vitamin C needs.

By the time your baby is 1 month old, he will have a slightly different formula and schedule.

The formula for this age, using fresh milk, is as follows:

Fresh Milk Formula for Baby 1 Month Old

14 ounces whole milk

10 ounces water

2½ tablespoons Karo or

5 tablespoons Dextri-maltose

How to prepare: Method same as for formula on page 55.

Irradiated Evaporated Milk Formula for Baby 1 Month Old

7 ounces evaporated milk

17 ounces boiled water

2 tablespoons Karo or

4 tablespoons Dextri-maltose

How to prepare: Method same as for formula on page 55.

This recipe will make six 4-ounce bottles, an amount which should be ample for your baby at this age.

(Please remember that these formulas are for the perfectly normal and flourishing baby. If your baby is smaller or weaker, isn't making his gains, or in other ways not doing as he should, please see your doctor at once.)

Vitamin B₁

Vitamin B_1 is coming more into the limelight in the feeding of infants because there is a direct connection between energy metabolism and the requirement of thiamin (Vitamin B_1). Your baby is an energetic little fellow and needs his thiamin! In early infancy, the baby on bottle feedings doesn't take enough milk to get his day's requirements of Vitamin B_1, and isn't yet eating whole-grain cereals and other Vitamin B_1 foods. Therefore, many doctors now add Vitamin B_1 in the form of thiamin chloride tablets, dissolved in Baby's milk. Ask your doctor about this.

Vitamin A

Your baby at this age needs from 1000 to 2000 I. U. of Vitamin A every day. Check to see whether the form of Vitamin D you're giving Baby also contains enough Vitamin A. Cod-liver oil and some concentrates supply both Vitamins A and D. Other concentrates supply only Vitamin D in an adequate amount.

If the form you're using doesn't contain enough Vitamin A, make it up as soon as your doctor permits by adding egg yolk to Baby's diet.

Your doctor may suggest that you add egg yolk to the formula. To do this, separate the yolk from the white. Add 2 or 3 tablespoons of cold boiled water to the yolk and mix well. To this add an equal amount of hot feeding and mix well. Then strain the egg mixture into the balance of hot feeding, stirring constantly. Place over the fire and bring just to the boiling point. Don't boil the formula after the egg has been added to it.

Other Vitamins

Baby's vitamin needs, other than those just described, are supplied by his food, except for Vitamin K which must sometimes be given to the newborn baby. Your obstetrician takes care of that whenever it's necessary.

A Word About Worrying

Some mothers worry themselves sick when their babies really are doing beautifully. That's one reason why you should have your baby thoroly examined before you leave the hospital. The other reason is, of course, that you should do it for your baby's sake.

But let's say that the doctor has found your baby perfect in every respect—a fine, healthy fellow. Then what's your role? (If there's anything requiring his attention, naturally your doctor will take charge.)

Given loving care, warmth, and proper food, your healthy baby will continue to be all right. You can always reason that as long as he's happy, eating his food, and making his gains, there can't be anything much the matter with him.

He may skip a meal, have small appetite for it, or even lose it without anything serious being wrong. For such mild upsets, you can afford to wait until the next meal or two before you start worrying. If Baby takes his next meal voraciously (as he probably will) and keeps it down, all's well on the infant front. It isn't necessary to bother your busy doctor. And don't bother a perfectly well baby by taking his temperature every whipstitch.

Infant Illnesses Need Doctor's Care

There are, however, conditions which need your doctor's attention at once. Nine times out of ten, these, too, are really harmless. But there's the tenth possibility which we want to avoid. Listed below are the commoner conditions which could—not necessarily will—lead to something serious unless you take steps in time.

We pay attention to the common cold, for instance, because a number of serious diseases start this way. The great majority of times, tho, it's a cold and nothing more. Get in touch with your doctor, for he knows what's going around and what your baby could have, but in all probability does not have. When you protect Baby as much as you can from infections and when you get in touch with your doctor at the first sign of the various symptoms which could—but probably won't—lead to something, you have done all that a mother can do. Leave further steps to your doctor. And don't worry!

Babies are born with a certain immunity to the so-called children's diseases. This cannot be counted upon, however, and the greatest care should be taken to protect your baby from infection. No one with a cold or runny nose should be permitted in the same room with him. If you have a cold, wear a gauze mask over your nose and mouth when you care for him. Better still, turn his care over to someone else until you're well.

If Baby refuses food several times in succession or vomits it, seems unduly listless, develops a cold, or cries as tho in pain, take his temperature by the rectum. There's a special rectal thermometer for this purpose that has a large, round bulb. You should have one. Shake the thermometer down until it registers not more than 96 degrees, then grease the bulb with vaseline or cold cream. Spreading the baby's buttocks apart with thumb and finger, insert the thermometer one-third its length into the anus. (See the picture on page 67.) Leave for two minutes, holding it all the while. Then clean the thermometer with a piece of toilet paper and read what it says.

If you like, you may lay Baby on his bath table, or other firm surface, to take his temperature. Place him on his face, press the buttocks apart, and proceed as just directed.

Rectal temperatures are normally about one degree higher than those taken by mouth, so if the reading is one degree above the line for normal on your thermometer, Baby's temperature is as it should be.

When you're thru, wash the thermometer thoroly with soap and warm water—hot water would break it. When you describe Baby's symptoms to your doctor over the telephone, it will be helpful to him to have this temperature reading.

If Baby shows any sign of indisposition, keep him quiet in his own bed and away from family or visitors until your doctor can see him or advise you what to do.

The Common Cold

This commonest of diseases may also be the forerunner of a variety of other illnesses. So let your doctor know. Isolate Baby in a room that's well ventilated, but with a temperature of 70° or 72° F. Let him have all the boiled, lukewarm water he wants. A cold sometimes interferes with appetite, so Baby may take less food. Don't press it on him.

Keep a supply of tissue for cleaning his nose. If crusts form, you may try to work them loose with cotton swabs, rolled to a point and dipped in oil.

Don't give a laxative unless your doctor advises it.

Croup

Croup often comes on suddenly in the night when the baby seemed perfectly well on going to bed. Its symptoms are a barking cough, hoarseness, and rapid breathing. Telephone your doctor and while you're waiting for him, get moisture into the air of Baby's room. The most satisfactory device for doing this is an electric vaporizer. If you haven't one, an electric bottle-warmer will serve the purpose. Fill it with boiling water and keep the water hot by turning on the electricity.

If you've neither, a kettle boiling on an electric plate will make steam, but you must be extremely careful that Baby doesn't burn or scald himself. Set the kettle so far from his bed that he can't possibly hit or pull it over,

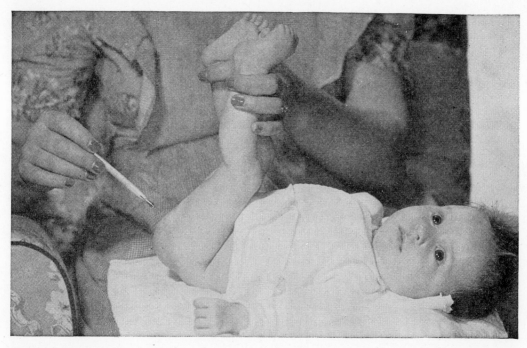

If your baby seems ill, it helps the doctor, when you phone him, to know what Baby's temperature is

and the bedclothes can't come in contact with it. All these things have caused serious accidents. It's a good rule, indeed, not to leave Baby alone in the room when you're steaming him.

Never put a vessel of hot water in Baby's crib!

If you haven't a way of keeping water at the boil in Baby's room, take his bed into the bathroom or kitchen and turn on the hot water there. Or warm his room to about 80° F. and hang up several big bath towels, wrung out of hot water. Several such towels placed over a warm radiator will provide steam.

When Baby's coughing and heavy breathing stop, take all the damp cloths away. Give him dry garments and bedclothes, and let him sleep.

Keep his room warm and the air moist for several days.

Colic

This is usually gas on Baby's stomach. It may be caused by taking too much food too fast, or from air not dispelled from the stomach. Baby will cry hard, clench his fists, get red in the face, draw up his legs and then straighten them out. His stomach may be hard, his hands cold.

Lift him gently, put his head over your shoulder, and pat him a few times on the back to release the gas. Then put him to bed and place a hot flannel cloth or a hot-water bottle over his abdomen. If he doesn't seem to get relief, telephone your doctor and describe the condition.

Convulsions

The baby's eyes become fixed or roll upward, and his whole body twitches convulsively. Attacks are usually of short duration, but sometimes are prolonged. The commonest cause in infants and young children is the high fever associated with the onset of an infection, such as a cold or a sore throat. Convulsions which occur in the absence of a fever are likely to be of a more serious nature and call for immediate medical care. Call your doctor at once. Then prepare a warm bath (105° F) and put Baby in it for from five to ten minutes. Dry him well, put him in his crib, and give him an enema. Then darken his room and keep him quiet until the doctor comes. A convulsion is terrifying to parents, but a baby rarely, if ever, dies in one.

Diarrhea

The bowel movements become loose, watery, frequent, and green in color. The baby may seem perfectly well, or may be obviously ill. His buttocks are sore, and frequently he vomits. All this is evidence of an upset gastro-intestinal tract. Withhold feedings and orange juice from the small baby and give him plenty of water to drink until you get the advice of your doctor. Call him at once.

With the older baby, you may give skimmed milk, boiled for five minutes and with no sweetening added. Let him have all the boiled, lukewarm water he will drink, or lukewarm, weak tea. Withhold all other food. As the diarrhea lessens, you may gradually add solid foods to his diet, beginning with a non-laxative cereal (Cream-of-wheat, farina).

The danger of diarrhea lies in its rapid draining of the water from the tissues. If the water isn't replaced, dehydration and acidosis may result. Hence the necessity for stopping the draining of fluid, and for replacing what has been lost.

Bath to Reduce Fever

If your doctor advises a sponge-off to reduce fever, follow the general plan given for the first sponge baths on page 70. The temperature of the room should be from 78° to 80° with drafts carefully excluded. Lay Baby on one large bath towel and have a second at hand. On his forehead place a cloth, wrung out of cool water. Sponge each part of his body several times. Dry him with the second towel. If the room is cool, keep Baby covered with the second towel.

After you've sponged the front of his body, take the cloth from his forehead, turn him over, and sponge his back, using a fresh washcloth. Dry him well, put on fresh garments and get him back to bed quickly.

Schedule for Baby One Month Old

6:00 a.m. Nurse 20 minutes on one breast, or 15 minutes on one and 5 on the other. Or give as much of the bottle feeding as Baby will take in 20 minutes. If he wants more, give an additional ounce or two. Baby then sleeps.

9:15 a.m. Undress him for his bath. Give fish-liver oil (10 drops increasing to 1 teaspoonful), or Vitamin D concentrate according to doctor's orders. (Giving fish-liver oil while Baby's undressed saves stained clothing.) Follow this with orange juice (1 teaspoonful increasing to 8).

9:30 a.m. Bath.

10:00 a.m. Nursing or bottle feeding, same as above.

10:30 a.m. to 2:00 p.m. Nap in a room by himself, with the door shut and window open. The temperature should not be below 60° F.

2:00 p.m. Nursing or bottle feeding.

3:00 p.m. to 4:00 p.m. Airing outdoors when Baby is past 3 weeks of age, if weather is suitable. If not, in bedroom.

5:00 p.m. to 6:00 p.m. Exercise period.

6:00 p.m. Nursing or bottle. Into his nightgown and to bed. Temperature not lower than 60° F.

10:00 p.m. Nursing or bottle.

2:00 a.m. Feed only if Baby awakens. This feeding is usually eliminated by the time he's 6 to 7 weeks old.

Let Baby take what he wants of the bottle feeding, just as of the breast.

Picture Story of Your Small Baby's Care

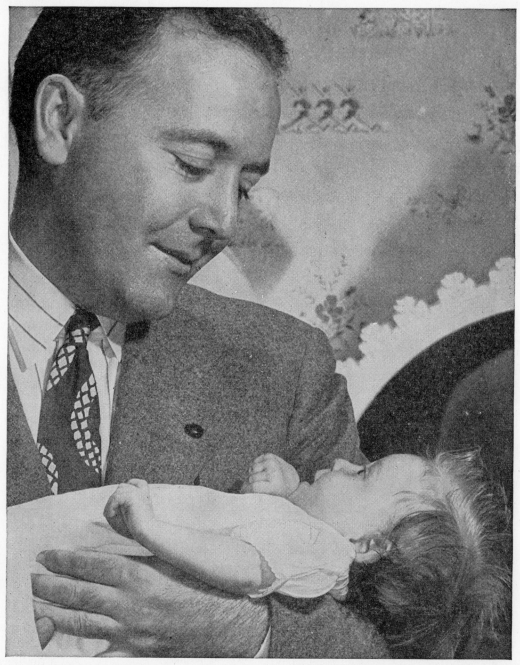

When you hold a tiny baby, be sure to support the wobbly little head and back with your arm and hand. Even the tiniest tot quickly recognizes Dad's firm grasp of the situation and votes him a favorite

How to Give a Sponge Bath

The kind Baby takes until his navel is healed; and the kind to give him if he's ill or if the rooms are coldish

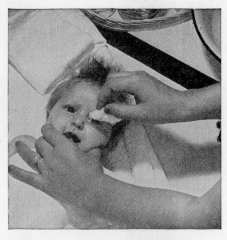

1 Eyes first. Use sterile cotton swab and boiled water. Wash inner corner first, working out

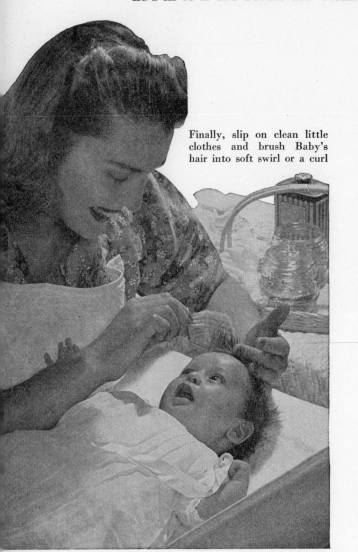

Finally, slip on clean little clothes and brush Baby's hair into soft swirl or a curl

Set the stage carefully for Baby's daily bath. It's important to know just what you're going to do and how you're going to do it, before you plunge in.

Very likely Baby's naval won't be quite healed and will have a small dressing, so you'll start with a sponge bath. It's also the kind to give an ill baby or youngster, so it's an excellent technique to master.

Many mothers find it simplest to bathe their babies before the 10 o'clock feeding, so 9:30 has become the traditional baby bath hour. But there's no reason why it shouldn't fall before the 6 p.m. feeding, if that's easier for you.

Choose a warm room, from 75° to 80° F., depending upon how husky your baby is. Any room will do, but probably the most convenient will be the bathroom or kitchen, with the warm-water supply handy.

First assemble the necessary equipment. You'll find it listed on page 35. Add to it a bath apron for you, and either a bottle of boiled water or orange juice (if he's started taking it) for Baby. Let him have the bottle for a moment if he starts fussing.

Now wash your hands and clean your nails. (Your nails should be fairly short and round for Baby's sake.) Fill the tub or basin with water that registers between 100° and 105° F. on the bath thermometer, or that feels pleasantly warm, not hot, to your elbow. Next lift Baby to the bath table, or to your lap, and undress him, dropping his clothes on a news-

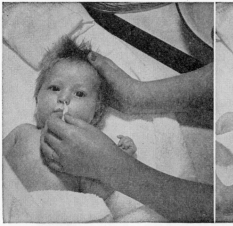 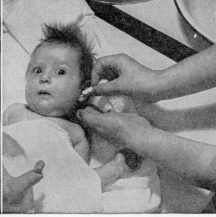 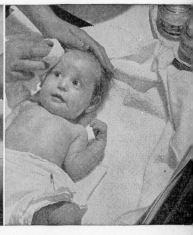

2 For nostrils, roll cotton to a point, dip in oil and gently work out crust. Never use same swab more than once

3 In Baby's ear, nothing sharper than cotton, dipped in oil. Clean inside, tip, and tender place behind his ear

4 Comes a face wash next, with clear water and a soft little washcloth or linen square kept for this alone

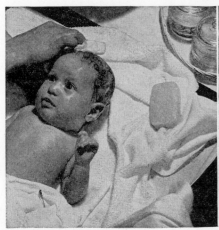 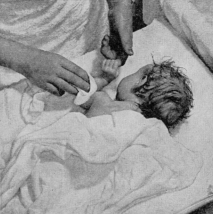 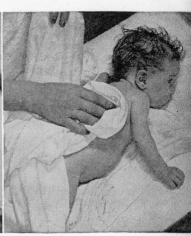

5 Soap his scalp about three days a week, use clear water other times. A pure, mild soap is kept for Baby

6 In giving a sponge bath keep your tiny baby covered, except for arm, leg, or other part that you are washing

7 Always pat Baby dry—don't rub. Get all moisture out of creases with small, very absorbent towel

paper. If his diaper needs changing, put it in the diaper pail. Place a folded, clean diaper under his buttocks and up over his tummy. Cover Baby with a large bath towel, right up to his chin. Now follow the directions in the photographs.

Dry with a small absorbent towel, patting, not rubbing.

Three times a week soap Baby's scalp and rinse well. But if there's any crust or scale, oil his scalp, then soap and rinse. Do this daily till the scale is gone and his scalp is clean.

Now use the second washcloth to wash his body piecemeal fashion, keeping the parts you're not washing covered with the big towel. After the buttocks and genitals have been soaped, rinsed, and dried, give finishing touches by cleaning carefully with an oiled swab. With a little girl separate the folds, and clean all carefully with oiled cotton.

And there you are! Dust powder on evenly, and Baby's sweet as a rose from top to toe.

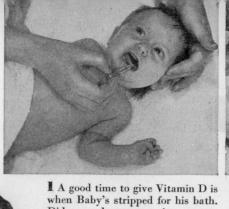

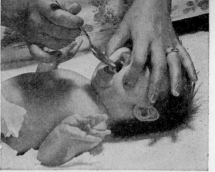

1 A good time to give Vitamin D is when Baby's stripped for his bath. Did your doctor say give concentrate? It's easy with an eye dropper

2 If he said fish-liver oil, use a spoon. Gently press mouth open with thumb and finger. Put the oil well back on Baby's tongue. Begin orange juice the same way

How to Give a Tub Bath

Biggest event of Baby's day —when he goes in all over. These tricks will keep it a joyous one for both of you

6 Here it comes! Support Baby's head and back with one hand; hold his feet with the other, your forefinger between his ankles. Lower him gently into the tub

7 Rinse off all the soap. Baby may howl when you hold him over the tub, but he'll love the water if you're careful. He can stay and enjoy it for a little while

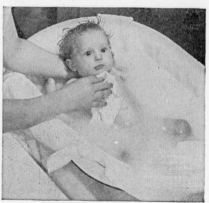

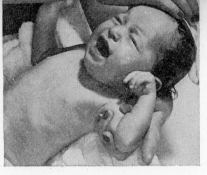

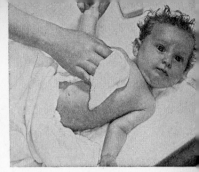

3 Test the bath water before Baby goes in. It should feel comfortably warm to your elbow. If you've a bath thermometer, it should read 98° to 100° for a tiny baby

4 Soap his scalp first, then rinse, holding his head over the side of the tub. Note how Mother's hand supports both his head and shoulders thruout the process

5 Now, with Baby back on the table, soap his body wherever he needs it. Use a pure, mild soap. Extra-soft washcloths are sold for Baby's use

By the time Baby's navel has healed nicely, he's ready to graduate from a sponge to a tub bath. Use the same arrangements as for the sponge bath, except that you substitute a small tub for the basin. A real baby's tub is a joy, but a large pan or tub that can be kept scoured and clean will do. You'll also need three large bath towels besides a smaller, absorbent one.

Set up your bath table in a warm room—it should be at least 75° when Baby's to go in all over—and have a lower table or bench next it to hold the tub. Spread one bath towel over the table, and over that a protective pad or folded diaper where Baby will lie. Place the bath tray (equipped as described for the sponge bath) within easy reach.

Now wash your hands, clean your nails, and put on your bath apron. Place the second

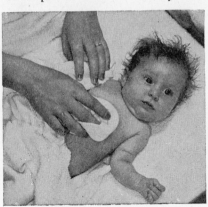

8 Put him back on the bath table, cover up with a big bath towel and pat him dry. A smaller, very absorbent one does this well. Oil and powder him as we've already shown

big bath towel in the tub, fill the tub with about four to six inches of water, and set it on the table or bench. The water should be 98° to 100° by your bath thermometer, or nicely warm by the elbow test. Next undress Baby and proceed, just as you did for the sponge bath, to clean his eyes, ears, and nose, using separate cotton swabs for each operation and dipping them in baby oil to get crusts or wax out of ears or nostrils. Never use the same swab twice. After your young one's 2 months old, you may wash his eyes and ears with the face washcloth.

Three times a week soap his scalp, rinsing it over the side of the tub, while you support his neck and head carefully with one hand.

Lay Baby back on the bath table and soap his body all over, using the second washcloth. Then pick him up ever so carefully and lower him into the tub. With one hand support his head and neck; with the other grasp his legs, slipping one finger between them to keep from squeezing knee or ankle joints together.

If you've a bath hammock, let him rest on it while you rinse him. Otherwise, continue to support his head and back with one hand and rinse him with the body cloth held in the other. Never, *never* leave him alone in the tub, even for a minute.

Lift him out of the tub, cover him with the third big bath towel, and gently pat him dry with the small absorbent towel, giving special care to folds and creases. Anoint the genitals well with a cotton swab dipped in baby oil. Then dust him with powder.

These baths in Baby's tub will continue (unless he's ill, in which case you'll return to sponge baths) until he's sitting up strongly by himself around the sixth month. Then he's ready for the big family tub.

How to Diaper Your Baby

1 To five-fold a diaper for your tiny baby, first turn the left end of the oblong over about eight inches to get the correct width for the complete fold

2 Next step in the five-fold diaper job is to bring the right end over to the left fold. Some diapers have folding lines woven in for your convenience

6 When Baby gets too big for a panel, simply fold over one-third of your oblong, the other one-third over that. The last step before training-panties

7 On the market are fitted diapers like the above, which tie at sides with tapes. Your choice of sizes. Disposable diapers are a help when you travel

No longer does your modern baby wear the time-honored triangle. New materials, the new oblong shape, and ways of folding make it possible to have just one size of diaper for the entire time he'll need them. Moreover this can be made to fit him at every stage of his development, as you will see from the photographs.

One of the brightest new diapering ideas is the panel fold, shown just above. To get this effect, you begin by bringing the right end of the oblong diaper (20 or 21 by 40 inches) to about 12 inches from the left end. Fold the right end back upon itself about 6 inches, making a panel of three thicknesses of cloth. Now bring the left end over to the fold on the extreme right. This puts the extra thickness in the middle, where it is needed, while the sides fit Baby's dimensions quite comfortably.

As Baby expands, you make the center panel narrower and narrower, until the point is reached where the triple fold, shown in Picture 6, must be employed.

Besides the oblong diapers and the kidney-shaped one shown on page 75, there are several types of disposable diapers on the market.

To change, unpin the soiled diaper and wash and clean Baby, carrying away the wet and soil in the discarded diaper. Slip a clean one, folded to fit Baby's measure, as we've shown above, underneath him.

Apply baby oil or cream, and dust him with powder also, if you wish. Bring up the free end of diaper between Baby's legs—see the photograph on the next page—and pin it on either side, securing his shirt as well between the two diaper edges. Now bring the shirt down outside the diaper in front, and pin it.

3 Now you double the diaper over as in the picture above. If you'll count you'll see this gives you five thicknesses, tailored to Baby's own width

4 Width fine, but still too long. So turn up the end as far as needed to fit your baby. Extra thickness goes beneath for a girl, goes in front of a boy

5 A clever fold is the panel, which is described below. Its three thicknesses of cloth give extra protection where it's needed; it fits well, isn't bulky

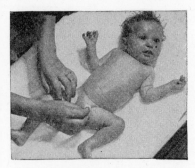
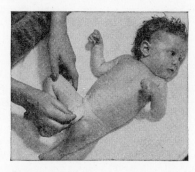
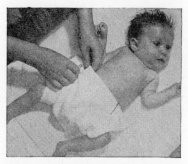

8 Now to get diaper on Baby. Slip it under him, and oil section affected, especially the creases, with a sterile cotton swab, to prevent any soreness

9 After you've oiled your baby thoroly and dried the creases well, you may dust him with a coat of some refreshing talcum powder to prevent chafing

10 Bring the diaper up between Baby's legs and pin it on both sides. When pinning, always keep finger next to Baby to avoid sticking him

That baby of yours is fussy about the fit of his britches. Here are the tricks for tailoring them to his measure

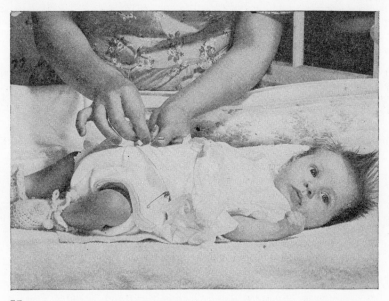

11 And here's the way the diaper fits in with Baby's costume. Shirt caught at sides between the folds of the diaper, so it won't develop holes, but pinned down over the diaper in front. It keeps Baby's tummy warm, yet shirt stays dry

Dress Your Baby the Easy Way

His clothes should be simple but carefully chosen for his comfort and your convenience

The whole idea in getting his clothes on Baby is to do the job as quickly and happily as you can. By the time his bath is over, both you and your small infant may be pretty weary, and the young ingrate will probably be yelling for his 10 o'clock feeding besides. So preparedness and good strategy on your part are called for.

When you get out the bath articles, lay Baby's fresh garments on a handy chair or table, arranged in the order in which you'll put them on him. If the shirt's sleeveless, pull it on over his feet. You can put on a long-sleeved shirt and kimono in one operation. (See Picture No. 3.) If Baby's very tiny, or not feeling well, this eases matters a bit for him. Otherwise, you may put on the shirt and fasten it, then the diaper, then the kimono. The shirt sleeves will be too long at first, so fold them back to leave the baby's hands free play.

Be very gentle in the dressing process. Support Baby's back and head when you lift or turn him, roll sleeves and stockings down so his hands or feet go right thru.

Soon you'll become deft and quick, and Baby will pass from a raw state to one of full dress without a single ruffle in his disposition!

The purpose of putting clothes on a baby is to keep him warm. Do it in the easiest way possible both for you and for him. Use materials that are easy to wash, and garments most of which needn't be ironed. They should slip on and off freely and quickly, and should never interfere with his exercising.

If you like to keep your house at a low temperature during wintertime, you'll naturally have to put more clothes on Baby. But make them short and simple, not hampering to his activity or comfort in any way.

You'll want at least three shirts with long sleeves if yours is a winter baby. Whether you buy cotton or warmer materials will depend upon the climate and season, and the room temperature of your house. For summer and mild climates you'll want elbow-sleeved and some sleeveless shirts. (These last are sometimes called bands. Don't confuse them with navel bands.)

In warm weather and hot climates Baby can appear in just his shirt and diaper, or, if it's sizzling, in his diaper only. Ordinarily, however, Baby wears something over his shirt and diaper. We suggest a kimono (shown in pictures No. 3 and No. 4). It has wide sleeves and is open down the front, allowing complete freedom for Baby's arms and legs.

At night Baby wears a nightie, for the first six months or more, over his basic dress of shirt and diaper. The nightie is the one garment in his wardrobe that's still extra long. It opens in the back and has drawstrings in the bottom hem and cuffs, so his toes and fingers stay warm.

You'll most certainly want Baby to have a few dainty dresses and petticoats for dress-up occasions. Make or buy them as sheer, and as lovely with lace, ribbons, and embroideries, as you wish. But don't have them so long they hamper Baby's kicking, and don't starch them.

1 If your doctor advises a navel band, put it on this way so it will hold the navel dressing firmly, but not tightly. These are worn only until navel is healed

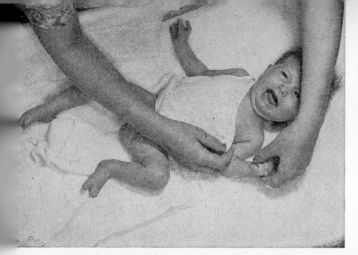

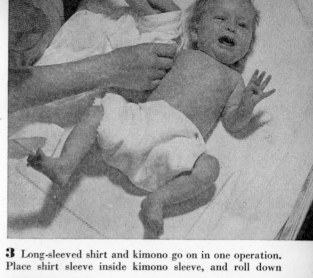

2 This sleeveless cotton shirt, sometimes called a band, was pulled on over Baby's feet. (Still there were protests!)

3 Long-sleeved shirt and kimono go on in one operation. Place shirt sleeve inside kimono sleeve, and roll down

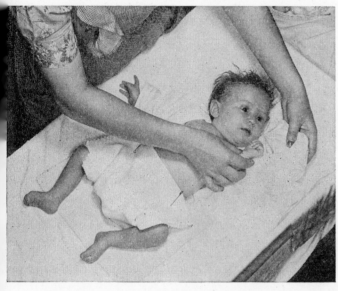

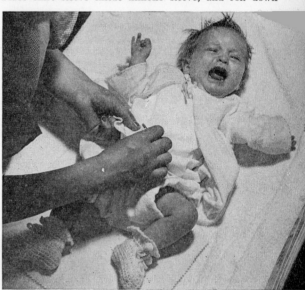

4 One hand goes thru at a time. Tie the shirt, and fasten kimono at top. Fold the back up so Baby won't wet it

5 Next, pin Baby's shirt down outside the diaper. Take care to hold a finger next to Baby to catch the pin prick

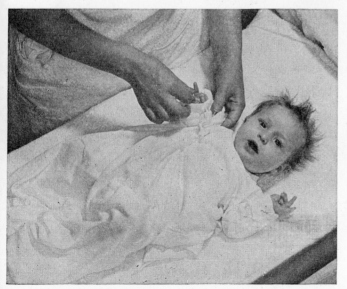

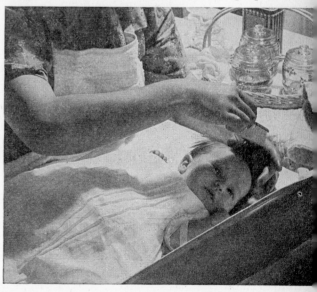

6 Baby's long nightgown goes on feet first, too. Roll back sleeve till Baby's hand is thru. Then pull down and tie

7 Baby's "company dress" alone goes on head first. The petticoat goes on over his feet and buttons at shoulders

It's Easy to Fix a Formula

There's no mystery about this important item. Whether you use fresh, dried, or evaporated milk, preparing Baby's main meal at this stage is simple as can be

1 The irradiated evaporated milk formula is easiest of all to prepare. Here are the things you'll need: can of milk; Karo, or whatever sweetening your doctor advises; as much boiled water as your formula calls for; glass measuring pitcher; mixing pitcher; measuring spoon; sieve; funnel; sterilized nursing bottles; sterile cotton for bottle stoppers

2 Pour into mixing pitcher amount of boiled water called for. (If formula is for fresh milk, take one-half as much canned, add that much water)

3 Now measure in the Karo by pouring from the bottle (or can) into the spoon. If your formula calls for Dextri-maltose or sugar, level tablespoons off with knife

4 Pour evaporated milk into measuring pitcher. (Canned milk is double strength, remember. Add equal part water to make it like whole milk)

5 Now pour into mixing pitcher, and strain thru sieve and funnel into the nursing bottle. That's all you do. No cooking. Isn't it easy?

6 Prepare as many bottles as your baby has feedings in 24 hours. Stopper with sterile cotton or corks or tie waxed paper over top. Store in cold place until mealtime

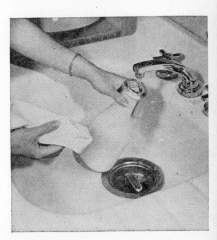

7 The first step in preparing fresh milk formula is to wash off the top of the bottle (under the faucet's the best way) and then wipe it dry

8 Put milk, water, sweetening in a pan. Boil 3 to 5 minutes, stirring all the while. Set in pan of water to cool, and stir while it cools

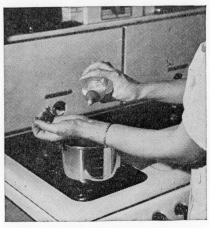

9 When it's time for feeding, heat bottle to blood heat by setting in pan of warm water. (Fire off, tho, when bottle's in pan.) Try by dropping some on the inside of your wrist

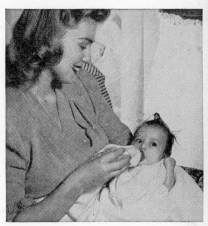

10 When you give Baby the bottle, let him rest comfortably on your arm. Tip up bottle to let milk fill the nipple, so Baby won't suck in air

Right Care of Baby's Bottles and Nipples

For his small Majesty's sake, for protection, and economy

When Baby finishes a feeding, throw away any formula that's left and rinse out the bottle well under the cold water tap. Fill with water and set it aside until next dishwashing time, for a proper washing. Never use formula Baby leaves in a bottle

Once a day, boil for five minutes all utensils used in fixing Baby's formula. A sterilizer or your pressure cooker does the job well. Bottle racks are a great convenience, especially for lifting

You can sterilize just as well, however, in an open pan like this. Put a cloth in the bottom. Water must cover the utensils while they're boiling. Remove by means of tweezers or a long-handled spoon. Set upside down on clean towel to dry, sans wiping

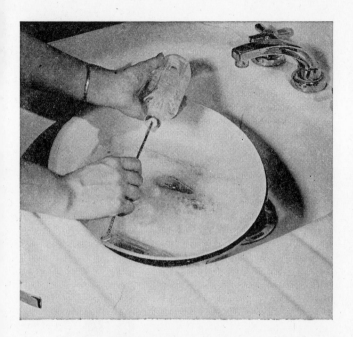

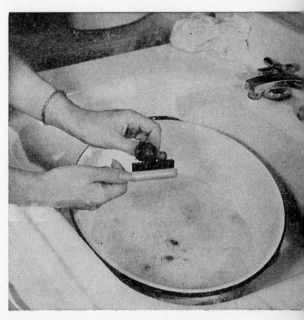

"Proper washing" for Baby's bottles means lots of soap-suds and scrubbing with a bottle brush, which reaches every part—don't buy a bottle with inaccessible corners. Rinse thru several waters, till there's no trace of soap left

Scrub the nipple well immediately after use, turning it inside out, as milk caked on it will make the rubber deteriorate. Use warm water, soap, and rinse well. Store in dry jar until sterilizing time

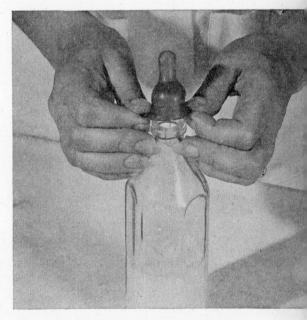

Boil nipples in a separate pan (but not a copper one) with a teaspoonful of salt in the water to keep them from getting soft. Lift out into dry, sterile jar and store in a dark place. Cover until time to use on Baby's bottle

Last part of the task is to get the nipple on without touching the end that goes into Baby's mouth. Quite a feat with a new stiff nipple. But immaculate cleanliness helps keep Baby healthy

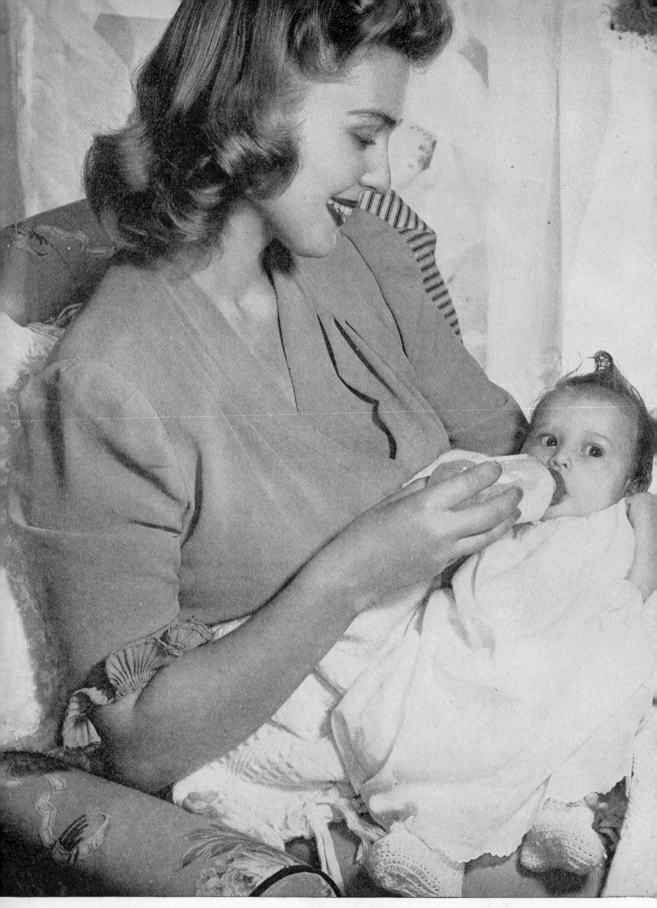

To give Baby the bottle, hold him reclining on your arm. Keep bottle tipped up so milk fills the nipple, lest Baby swallow air

CHAPTER II

Your Baby at Two Months

Development

Around the age of 2 months your baby may:

. . .notice light.

. . .follow a bright object with his eyes.

. . .hold his head up jerkily when placed on his abdomen.

. . .have longer periods of being awake.

. . .hear more acutely and try to turn his head in the direction of a sound.

Physical Development

The expected gain is at least 2 pounds over the birth weight, if your baby's weight was average at birth. Thus a boy weighing 7½ pounds at birth should weigh 9½ pounds at 2 months, and may weigh 10.

Feedings

There should be only five milk feedings daily by this time. If your baby still requires the 2:00 a.m. feeding, he probably isn't receiving enough during the day. (Some very well-nourished babies even show a tendency to sleep thru the 10 p.m. feeding at about this age. If your baby sleeps thru the night and makes his gain, it's proper to drop out this feeding. This leaves only four feedings a day, the last one at 6 p.m.) The baby this age will take around 4 to 5 ounces at a feeding and may take more.

Formula Using Fresh Milk

(one day's supply)

20 ounces whole milk

12 ounces water

3 tablespoons Karo or

6 tablespoons Dextri-maltose

How to prepare: Method same as for formula on page 55.

This formula may be increased by adding an ounce of milk each week.

Formula Using Irradiated Evaporated Milk

(one day's supply)

10 ounces evaporated milk

22 ounces boiled water

3 tablespoons Karo or

6 tablespoons Dextri-maltose

How to prepare: Method same as for formula on page 55.

Tub Bath's the Thing

By this time your baby should be ready for a tub bath. In fact, it's all right at any time after the navel is completely healed. The temperature of the room should be 75° F., that of the bath water 98° to 100° F. If you haven't a bath thermometer, dip your elbow in the water as the mother is doing on page 73. This part of your body is about as sensitive as Baby to temperature. The water should feel comfortably warm, not cold; and not at all hot.

The bath table should still be used for convenience in undressing and dressing Baby. Get everything ready in advance. Place Baby on the bath table and undress him. Wash out his eyes as described for the sponge bath. Clean his nostrils if they need it with wisps of cotton dipped in mineral oil. Wash his face with a soft cloth. Three times a week soap his scalp, then rinse it over the side of the tub, as shown on page 73.

Return him to the bath table. Soap the region of genitals and buttocks, cleaning the genitals thoroly. Then place Baby in the tub, supporting him on your left hand and arm, and rinse off the soap. Return him to the bath table once more and pat him dry with a soft towel. Baby oil or cream rubbed into the creases and over his body generally will keep his skin in splendid condition.

Shall You Start Bowel Training?

In the well-regulated nursery, bowel training used to begin at 2 months, but there has been some shift of opinion about this. We ourselves used to say that the mother should understand it isn't always successful at this age, and advise her not to be disturbed if it didn't "take" for some time.

Now many doctors suggest that bowel training wait until the baby can sit up strongly. The little toilet seat may then be put over the bathroon stool, and much fuss and trouble is saved. There are even some authorities who pooh-pooh any early efforts to train Baby at all. He'll learn in time, they say, so why bother?

At present the question lies in the public domain. You may start bowel training almost anywhere from 2 months on and find excellent backing for your action.

The case for early training is that it accustoms Baby to having a movement at a regular time, and he learns early to respond to the stimulus of the chamber against his buttocks. However, you must realize this is a purely reflex-response, and may be lost later on after your child is old enough to sit up.

If you're a hardy soul who wants to follow in the footsteps of the child-training pioneers and start bowel training now, remember that what you're after is not to avoid washing soiled diapers, but to train Baby in a healthful rhythm. He'll go right on having accidents, in all probability, for months to come. The main thing is not to worry Baby about it. If you try for some time, with no results whatever, or if Baby is thrown all out of kilter, postpone the training. You have months yet before it's really necessary to think about it if you don't want to.

Breast-fed babies are harder to train than bottle babies because they have more stools. The baby who has only one or two stools daily will be easier to train than the one having three or four. Remember that the real purpose is to get Baby into the habit of having a movement in response to putting the chamber against his buttocks. You can consider yourself successful when you have accomplished this, even tho you don't catch all the movements.

According to Gesell, one of the leading authorities, "In the early months, bowel movements occur with some irregularity and vary with diet and general health. But sometime after three months, the mother may take note of the times when the infant is most likely to soil the diaper. She anticipates these times by placing him on a chamber. He makes an association as a result of this oft-repeated experience. In this way a rhythm becomes regularized and if the training has been conducted in a calm, matter-of-fact way the regularity may have a beneficial effect on the growing organism. This regularity, however, must not be construed as voluntary control."

Training to the Chamber

We do not, therefore, advocate bowel training before your baby is old enough to sit up. But there is no harm in beginning, any time after the movements have become regularized, to try to catch them in a chamber. Begin by making a record of the time of the morning movement. You'll find it occurs at a fairly regular time after the morning nursing or bath. When you've found the approximate one, proceed as follows:

Prepare the smallest size chamber by dip-

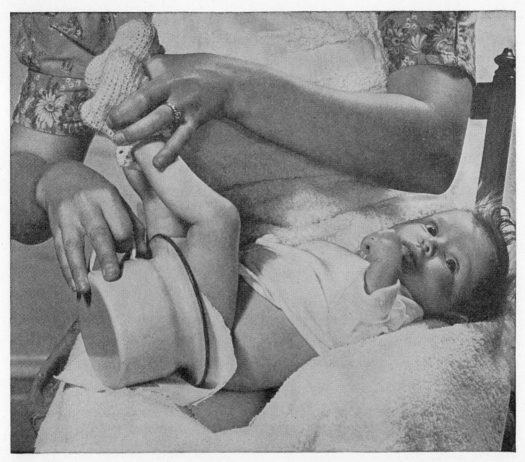

If you wish to start bowel training before your Baby's big enough to sit up, place him on his back on your lap or on bath table and apply chamber as above, after taking chill from it with warm water

ping it in warm water to take off the chill. Place him on your lap as shown above, or lay Baby on the bath table on his back. Next put the vessel against his buttocks.

Should the bowel movement occur before you're ready for it, let the procedure go until the next morning.

After a time Baby will begin to strain and attempt to have the movement when the vessel's applied.

After Baby learns what you want, you may advance the time gradually until you get the movement just when you want it after the first morning feeding. (See the schedule on page 89.)

In future months, as new foods are added to his diet, your baby's rhythm may become changed, and he may soil himself again.

Sun Baths

When the weather's suitable, Baby may be exposed to the direct rays of the sun from the time he's 1 month old. His sun baths may be given outdoors or by a window opened to allow the ultraviolet rays to reach him. Begin with two minutes front and back and increase one minute a day up to 20 minutes front and back. When Baby's on his back in the sun, shield his eyes.

"Suitable weather" will have to be interpreted by your own good judgment. We find that in inclement Iowa, a baby can be uncovered to the sun on a south porch, protected from the wind, around the last of March. He can get his first sunburn around April 1, and be well tanned by late April, with no ill effects from the exposure. The warmth of Baby's flesh can be your criterion as to his comfort. If he feels warm to the touch, he's all right, even tho the day may seem chilly to you.

Baby shouldn't be exposed to the direct

For sunbath, place Baby on porch, by open window or door, exposing bare flesh for short time

rays of a hot midsummer sun. The ultraviolet rays permeate the outdoor atmosphere, and he'll get the benefit of them on a porch or in the shade. Never expose him directly to sun which feels unduly warm to you.

Sleeping on His Face

At 2 or 2½ months, or as soon as he's able to lift his head when on his abdomen, Baby may be taught to sleep on his face. There are several advantages to this position: 1. You avoid flattening the back of his head and wearing the hair off. (Neither of these conditions is serious and both later correct themselves, but Baby's more pleasing to look upon if the back of his head is round rather than

flat and bald.) 2. The covers stay in place better. 3. Baby can lift himself on his hands and arms and exercise his arms and back just as soon as he feels the inclination. (This strengthens his muscles and gives him better command of himself.)

Sleeping on his face must begin within the first months of his life because as soon as he's able to turn himself, he'll roll onto his back. Don't begin, however, until Baby's strong enough to lift his head and turn it in order to breathe easily. Choose a time when he's very sleepy. Put him on his face, speak soothingly to him, and leave him. He'll probably cry the first time or two, but will quickly become accustomed to the new way and will like it.

Sleeping Bags Are a Help

Many mothers have found some kind of sleeping bag very helpful. If Baby's in a sleeping bag, he can't get uncovered and after a time going into the bag becomes his signal to go to sleep. The familiarity of his bag is a help, too, when he's in a strange place or situation. There are several varieties of these bags in stores.

Or you may make your own. One of our *Better Homes & Gardens* mothers buys a double blanket for the purpose. It may be part wool or all cotton, depending on the amount of warmth needed. From this she makes five sleeping bags (like the sketch on next page). She uses the blanket binding to bind the neck, opening, and sleeves. Each is closed with a zipper, but buttons will do as well. She makes the bags plenty long so feet won't get cramped, and uses the material cut out from under the sleeves for the bottom part of the bag, cutting it into an oval shape and fitting it to the top. This gives plenty of kick room.

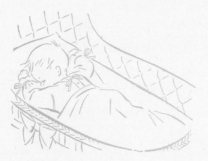

Sleeping on his face is good for Baby. Start when he lifts his head up strongly. Soon he'll like it

Mothers find a sleeping bag a great help. You may begin this practice any time after second month

Baby should mainly be a stay-at-home, but there are times when you'll take him along. A basket is the handiest way to do this, and can serve for Baby's bed if he must nap or sleep away from home occasionally

If you like, flaps may be made to button over Baby's hands. Or you may use draw strings.

When Baby's ready for the night, just slide him into his bag, fasten it, and tuck bag and Baby under the covers.

A homemade sleeping bag, made from a blanket. Extra kick room at bottom from pieces cut out under sleeves

Summer sleeping bags may be made from unbleached muslin.

Either before or after Baby's become accustomed to sleeping on his face—let's not try more than one new experience at a time—put him in the sleeping bag for his long nap. He may resent it at first, but will soon get used to it.

Discipline Begins at Birth

When this revision of the Baby Book was being prepared, we asked a great many mothers what they considered their chief child problem. The majority answered "Discipline."

What is discipline? To the Romans, who gave us the word, it meant first of all training, or learning. Just when and how the idea of punishment got mixed up with it is uncertain, but let's forget that for the time being and center upon the learning angle.

When does discipline begin? When your baby's born, and starts learning things about this world he has come into. When he learns, for instance, that his food and bath come at a certain time each day. Discipline continues when he learns that he must take fish-liver oil and orange juice, whether he likes them or not, because he needs them to grow and develop properly.

YOUR BABY'S SCHEDULE AND YOUR CAREFUL ADHERENCE TO IT ARE THE FOUNDATIONS OF DISCIPLINE. Right now, that's all the thought you need give the matter. Baby can't move yet from the spot where you place him, but he's big enough to know that crying won't get him attention he shouldn't have, or showing his displeasure won't keep you from insisting upon something he should have.

He has learned, also, that all his needs and legitimate wants receive attention. When his stomach contractions begin to get really interesting, his dinner always appears. When he requires attention, he receives it. He feels the love in your voice and hands.

What a lot he knows already, this baby only 2 months old! Your job is to continue to train and teach him in the future as you've done these past 2 months.

It isn't necessary that you follow the training directions in this book to the letter. No baby so far born into the world was quite like your baby. Some of our suggestions—many of them, we hope—will work perfectly, but others will have to be altered a bit to fit you, your home conditions, and your baby's individuality. Don't hesitate to do that.

But be consistent in following the ways you adopt. Don't let Baby get away with something today, then land on him like a ton of bricks for doing the same thing tomorrow. Don't fall into the error of "just this once." You'd be surprised how quickly babies size up their parents and learn whether they mean business, or can be worked.

Much latitude is allowed as to when you should begin some new phase of training. But when you decide the time has come, lay everything else aside and devote yourself to it.

Try to look at things thru your baby's eyes. What a strange, perplexing world this is into which he has come! How much he has to learn! How much we ask of him in changing his ways, throttling natural impulses!

So be gentle and patient. The tense way in which some parents go at training often defeats their purpose. A punishing attitude on your part will bring out all the power of resistance your baby possesses. On the other hand, he'll enter happily into a learning situation which you've made as pleasant as possible.

On the following pages you'll find the training methods which many parents have used successfully. Training is going to take time and effort on your part. When you're thru, you'll find that you have disciplined, or taught, yourself quite as much as you have your child.

But we'll wager this. If you're faithful to your program, discipline will never be your problem.

Your Baby and His Doctor

We hope you had that six-weeks' checkup for both yourself and Baby that was mentioned earlier. Good doctors are always busy men, but keep in mind that if your baby gets sick, or things don't go as they should, HE WANTS TO KNOW IT.

What are the signs of trouble? As long as Baby's happy, makes his regular gains, eats well, and sleeps well, there's nothing to worry about. But if he becomes fretful, refuses several meals in a row or loses them, or develops fever—by all means telephone your doctor and describe the symptoms. He'll tell you whether he thinks he should call, see Baby at the office, or what should be done. But do get in touch with him. Your doctor wants you to do so.

The Schedule Will Change

In forming the 2-months-old baby's schedule, remember that regularity of hours and the right number of feedings each day are the principal points. If five feedings and no more are given the 2-months-old baby, if his bath, naps, and bedtime come at the same hour each day, it doesn't matter a great deal what that hour is. Thus, Baby's day may begin at 6 a.m. and end at 6 p.m., if you like, with a last feeding at 10 p.m.—which is the conventional schedule. Or it may begin at 7 a.m. and end at 7 p.m., or begin at 5 a.m. and end at 5 p.m. The convenience of both parents can and should be consulted in the matter. A number of families prefer the 7 a.m. to 7 p.m. schedule, as it permits the father more time with Baby than the others do.

We have found it convenient to give Baby's supper feeding at 5 p.m., and just as soon as the baby could be adjusted to it, had the morning feeding at 7 a.m., giving the next one after the bath at 10 a.m., and the next at 1:30 p.m.

A normal 2-months-old baby can be trained to any schedule which calls for four feedings within the 12 hours of the day. Decide upon your schedule and then stick to it, performing each operation at the same hour each day. But consult common sense and convenience in mapping out Baby's day.

Baby will now have his airings and his social contacts, for he'll be sleeping less. We suggest, however, that you don't take him away from home, except to the doctor, before the third month. After that, an occasional social visit within the waking time on the schedule will be a good thing. But give him three months of quiet and regularity to grow on!

Schedule for Baby Two Months Old

6:00 a.m. to 7:00 a.m. Feeding, followed by toilet session if you've started bowel training. Afterwards, Baby may lie in his bassinet in the living room, and may or may not nap.

9:00 a.m. Concentrate or 1 teaspoon fish-liver oil as prescribed. Two to 3 ounces orange juice. Wheel into bedroom for short nap.

10:00 a.m. Bath, followed by feeding.

10:30 a.m. Sun bath on the porch or before an open window. Then Baby sleeps, either on the porch or indoors, depending upon the weather.

1:30 p.m. to 2:00 p.m. Feeding. Will probably nap after this.

4:00 p.m. Outdoors on the porch, in bassinet, or in buggy.

5:00 p.m. Exercise on the big bed.

5:30 p.m. Can be held or carried about house.

6:00 p.m. Feeding, followed by bed.

10:00 p.m. Feeding if he needs it.

Baby sleeps less as he gets older. This is to be expected. But opportunity should be given a baby of this age to get a nap before his bath, after the 10 o'clock feeding, and after the early afternoon feeding.

THE CHILDREN'S DISEASES

So-CALLED because they are so widespread and so infectious that few of us escape them in childhood, the children's diseases can be serious for infants and small children. Protect your baby and toddler from them if you can. If he's exposed, notify your doctor at once.

Diphtheria and smallpox have not been included in the list below, since your child may be protected from them completely by immunization. (See pages 100 and 101.) For those given here, no lasting immunization has been developed as yet. Attacks may be mitigated by toxins, vaccines or serums, in the case of most of the children's diseases, if your doctor is informed immediately after exposure or as soon as symptoms appear. The younger your child or infant, the more closely the children's diseases should be watched.

Whooping Cough

(For inoculation against, see page 101.)
Appears: Two to three weeks after exposure.
Symptoms: May start like a cold, with runny nose, slight fever (100° to 101°), slight cough. The cough gradually gets worse. After a week or so it may have the choking, strangling sound which is unmistakably whooping cough. At its height, the cough may cause vomiting.
Treatment: If child is exposed, call the doctor at once. He may wish to give whooping cough vaccine. Keep the child warm, but in a well-ventilated room. Bed rest is highly desirable during the acute phase for most children. If he loses a meal, give him another one, of solids, at once. Don't allow his stomach to remain empty.
Things to guard against: Pneumonia, later trouble with heart or lungs.
Duration of illness: Four to eight weeks. The patient must be kept isolated from other children for four weeks after the cough begins.

Measles

Appears: Ten to 14 days after exposure. It is most contagious before the rash breaks out.
Symptoms: Inflamed eyes, cough, fever which may go as high as 104°. (Babies tend to run higher temperatures than adults, so don't let it make you panicky.) Two to four days after the first symptoms appear, spots come, first on the face, and inside the mouth, then on the body.
Treatment: As soon as you know your baby or small child is exposed, notify your doctor. He may wish to give convalescent serum, made from the blood of a person recently recovered from the disease. If symptoms appear, put the child to bed in a warm, well-ventilated room. Protect his eyes from any glare, but it's not necessary to darken the room. Give plenty of fluids and a soft diet while the fever lasts.
Things to guard against: Pneumonia, ear and eye trouble, encephalitis.
Duration of illness: The rash is usually over in five days, but the danger of after-effects exists for some time. Keep the youngster in bed until his temperature has been normal for at least three days, and watch him for a week or two more.

Scarlet Fever

Appears: Two to seven days after exposure.
Symptoms: Painfully sore throat, fever, often vomiting, sometimes looseness of bowels. Very young children may have convulsions. Next a fine red rash appears on neck, chest, then on the whole body, and a red coating over the tongue, the characteristic "strawberry tongue" of scarlet fever. There may be a thick discharge from the nose and throat.
Treatment: Scarlet fever is one of the most dangerous of the children's diseases. Active immunization is possible, tho it is not permanent and hence is usually employed only in case there is an epidemic. However, convalescent serum or anti-toxin may be employed for temporary passive immunity following exposure. If your baby or small child is exposed, notify your doctor at once so that he may employ these measures. Scarlet fever is quarantinable and your child must by all means have a doctor's care. The sulfa drugs as well as convalescent serum have greatly minimized the suffering and after-effects of scarlet fever, but these must be administered only under doctor's orders, and carefully watched, especially with small youngsters.
Things to guard against: Swollen glands, heart disease, ear, throat and kidney trouble.
Duration of illness: Because of the danger of after-effects, especially great with scarlet fever, many doctors keep the patient in bed a full three weeks, even tho he is doing splendidly. Where there are complications, the time may be much longer.

Mumps

Appear: Ten days to three weeks after exposure.
Symptoms: Swelling of one or both sides of face. May be preceded or accompanied by difficulty in swallowing, headache, fever, and pain.
Treatment: Bed rest, light diet, mainly of liquids and soft solids. Avoid acids, hard foods, foods that must be chewed, and any with strong seasonings, as these may cause pain. Hot moist applications on the swollen portions may relieve the pain.
Things to guard against: Involvement of sex glands (rare with infants and small children); mumps meningitis.
Duration of illness: The swelling usually goes down in from a week to 10 days, but the patient should stay in bed for 48 hours after it disappears, and should remain quiet and isolated for a week after all swelling has subsided.

Chicken Pox

Appears: Two to three weeks after exposure.
Symptoms: May start with a chill, vomiting, or with a pain in the back. (Sometimes very young children become delirious or have convulsions.) Then small blisters appear. With the rash comes a fever, which goes to 101° or 102° (sometimes to 105°) and may last as long as five days.
Treatment: Bed rest as long as the fever lasts, and for 24 hours afterwards. A light diet of soups, cereals, milk and milk puddings, fruit juices. Itching may be reduced by sponging at intervals with a weak solution of baking soda, and applying calamine lotion. Keep the child's nails clipped short to avoid scratching.
Things to guard against: A healthy, well-cared-for youngster seldom has serious after-effects from chicken pox. The chief thing to guard against is pox, or scars, resulting from scratching.
Duration: The child should be isolated until the last scab drops off, usually about three weeks. He should then be thoroly bathed and shampooed before he mingles with other children.

CHAPTER III

Your Baby at Three Months

Development

Around the age of 3 months your baby may:

. . . begin to reach for things.

. . . recognize his parents or nurse, and be afraid of strangers.

. . . smile and respond to friendly overtures.

Formula Using Fresh Milk

(one day's supply)

24 ounces whole milk

12 ounces water

3 to 4 tablespoons Karo or

6 to 8 tablespoons Dextri-maltose

How to prepare: Method same as for formula on page 55.

Formula Using Evaporated Irradiated Milk

(one day's supply)

12 ounces evaporated milk

24 ounces boiled water

3 to 4 tablespoons Karo or

6 to 8 tablespoons Dextri-maltose

How to prepare: Method same as for forula on page 55.

(Please remember that the formulas above are for the perfectly healthy, normal baby who does nicely on fresh milk or irradiated evaporated milk, as the case may be. If he has any difficulty, be sure to see your doctor.)

He'll Need a Bed

Now's the time to shop for a regular baby bed, for Baby will soon outgrow his bassinet. The bed you select should be at least large enough for a 4- or 5-year-old child, so that it will last as long as a baby bed is needed, and there'll be plenty of room to stretch and exercise meanwhile. There are some models that can be converted later into single beds.

You may continue to use the bassinet for his waking hours, or for short naps. (He'll need the bed for his long naps.) The bassinet, after he's outgrown it as a bed, will also be fine for Baby's airings on the porch or under a tree.

He Should Have Toys

When Baby begins reaching for things and trying to grasp them, it's time to place one or two toys within his reach—a rattle, or a bright-colored knitted doll which he can easily hold. Don't hang bright objects above him in the crib for any long period, as they may excite him too much. The rattle and doll may be placed within his reach and he'll play with them or not as he likes.

Toys for the tiny tot. A soft ball he can grasp, a rattle, rag doll, toy animal, aid his mental growth

Leaving With Strangers

There may be one drawback to Baby's ready recognition of familiar faces—he may begin now or later to object to being left with strangers. You'll be very careful, of course, in your choice of the person left in charge during an absence. Don't, however, make the mistake of yielding to Baby's whim if he decides you shouldn't leave him at all.

Have the person who takes your place come in before your departure to learn the ropes, and if possible perform some operation for Baby while you're still there. Then when it's time, go. Don't become one of those unfortunate mothers who must sneak out the coal hole to get an afternoon or evening away from home!

Schedule for Baby Three Months Old

6:00 a.m. or 7:00 a.m. Breast feeding or formula.

8:00 a.m. to 9:00 a.m. One hour's exercise on floor or on big bed.

9:00 a.m. Concentrate or 1 teaspoon of fish-liver oil as prescribed by doctor.
    Two to 3 ounces of orange juice.

9:30 a.m. Bath.

10:00 a.m. Breast or bottle feeding.

10:30 a.m. to 2:00 p.m. Nap, on porch if possible, or in room with windows raised.

2:00 p.m. Breast or bottle feeding.

3:00 p.m. to 4:30 p.m. Out of doors.

5:00 p.m. to 5:45 or 6:00 p.m. On the floor or in play pen for exercise.

5:45 p.m. Breast or bottle feeding.

6:00 p.m. Bed.

10:00 p.m. Breast or bottle feeding.

CHAPTER IV

Your Baby at Four Months

Development

Around the age of 4 months your baby may:

. . . laugh out loud.

. . . reach for objects.

. . . hold toys.

. . . roll over.

. . hold his head up well.

The weight of the 4-months-old baby averages between 12 and 14 pounds.

Formula Using Fresh Milk
(one day's supply)
24 ounces whole milk
8 ounces water
3 to 4 tablespoons Karo or
6 to 8 tablespoons Dextri-maltose

How to prepare: Method same as for formula on page 55.

He'll probably take 6 to 8 ounces at a feeding. Increase the amount of milk 1 ounce each week.

Formula Using Irradiated Evaporated Milk
(one day's supply)

12 ounces evaporated milk

20 ounces water

3 to 4 tablespoons Karo or

6 to 8 tablespoons Dextri-maltose

How to prepare: Method same as for formula on page 55.

Formula Using Lactic Acid-Evaporated Milk

A slightly different method of preparation is used:

Mix together:
3 to 4 tablespoons Karo
1 teaspoon U.S.P. Lactic Acid
Enough boiled water, cooled, to make a pint in all. Pour 13 ounces (1 large can) of evaporated milk into the acid-sugar-water mixture, stirring all the while.

Both the milk and the acid solution should be cold. Divide into as many bottles as there are feedings during the day. Store in the refrigerator.

Play Pen a "Must"

It's time now to add a play pen to your list of equipment, as Baby's ready for his exercise periods on the floor. A good time for these periods is from 8 to 9 a.m., and from 5 to 6 p.m. It's fine to start them in a play pen, so he'll become accustomed to it early. (It won't hurt to start exercise periods in a pen even earlier if you wish.)

Whoever invented the play pen deserves a medal of honor, from both busy mothers and the babies themselves! From your viewpoint, the play pen tends Baby nicely for hours at a time while you do your work. From Baby's viewpoint, he learns to amuse himself, and it becomes an informal gym in which he can move about and develop his muscles as he likes and in his own good time.

When Baby's in his play pen, he can pull himself up and exercise his arms and legs whenever he gets ready. A word here about

You must have a play pen to help Baby amuse himself and let him exercise his muscles when he wishes to

urging Baby to do these things. It's a simple "don't." After a while when you hold Baby he'll begin pushing with his toes, trying to pull himself up. Some parents think this means he wants to stand up. It doesn't necessarily. It's simply his way of giving a workout to muscles which later he'll use in pulling himself up.

Place Baby in his play pen with his toys, and let him handle the sitting up and pulling up business in his own way.

There are several types of pens on the market. One model has a platform, raised a few inches above the floor. This places Baby above floor drafts indoors, and above damp or cold ground outdoors. You can also buy thick, non-absorbent, washable pads for the pen. Put the pen in a spot where it's out of drafts and where you can keep an eye on Baby. Place on the floor a pad or folded, heavy comforter. Over this lay a rubber or rubber-substitute protective sheet (if the pad

isn't non-absorbent) and then a clean muslin sheet over all.

He'll Like a Ball

Now, too, a soft rubber or woolly ball may be added to Baby's toys. When you place him on the floor for exercise, give him a rattle, soft doll, and the ball. Then leave him alone except for necessary care. Thus he'll learn to amuse himself early. He'll be happy in his pen and will be taking the first steps toward self-sufficiency.

Don't Hurry Sitting Up

Toward the last of this period, Baby will probably begin sitting up. Don't rush this, tho, or prop him up in a chair before he's ready. When he's strong enough, he'll begin the new activity himself.

Teeth on the Way

Your baby may get his first teeth in the fifth or sixth month, but the average baby gets them between the sixth and eighth month. There's little discomfort attached to teething for the normal baby of good habits and nutrition. You'll probably have no intimation of what's happening until the teeth appear, altho there may be some fretfulness. A teething ring can be tied to the baby's bassinet, so he can exert his desire to chew something. It should be boiled often.

Solid Foods

One mother said to me, "The advice we get is always 'the average baby is ready to eat this or do that at a certain age.' Won't you tell when it would be all right for babies who are advanced, rather than average, to do things? For instance, when would it be all right to start solid foods?"

A nationwide authority says that a healthy normal infant could probably tolerate sieved foods in small amounts almost from birth. We don't begin solids then, but the tendency has been to start them earlier and earlier, most doctors by the fourth month, many by the third. And there's no harm in beginning earlier still to accustom Baby to new tastes and feeding methods.

So if your baby is growing like a weed and digests everything that comes his way, there's no harm in trying solids any time now, unless the weather's hot. If they upset Baby, tho, drop them and wait a few weeks.

As early as the first month, some doctors start carrot or spinach water between feedings. This is simply the water in which these vegetables have been cooked. It's mildly laxative and accustoms Baby to the vegetable taste.

After Baby's taking this well, it's possible, if your doctor approves, to offer a few mild solids around the second or third month. A soft custard, or rennet custard, may be given first as a transition step. Bananas are excellent for this, too, when you can get them. Mash a ripe one (yellow flecked with brown) with a fork and beat it to the consistency of whipped cream. Babies love bananas.

A healthy, normal baby can start what we think of as the real solids any time he has become accustomed to these transition foods.

Prevent Eating Problems

Right now is perhaps a good time to talk a bit about this matter of foods and why they're so important.

You may already have heard rumors about eating problems from your friends with children. Eating's the great child problem after discipline. In too many cases the two are mixed up.

NOW IS THE TIME FOR YOU TO SEE THAT IT DOESN'T CROP UP WITH YOUR YOUNGSTER.

This is the time when your baby will build his food habits for years to come. He can learn now to take and like almost any healthful food that's presented to him. Or if allowed to get away with refusal of needed foods, he can become one of the finicky eaters who've caused so much parental grief in recent years.

Right now when solid foods are first offered is the time to see this matter thru. Usually babies like fish-liver oil, fruit juices, and the transition foods we've spoken of. But often the flag of rebellion goes up at the first bite of cereal, vegetable, or maybe egg.

It's well to remember that taste plays little part in this. Baby's taste buds don't develop to any extent until toward the end of the first year. Nerves in his tongue, however, are warning him that here's something with a different feel from the liquids he's accustomed to. A baby is the original conservative. He won't try something new unless it's practically pushed down his throat! Your job, therefore, is to get him to accept enough of a

new food so he can become used to it. Once this happens he'll like his cereal and vegetables, as well as his banana and fish-liver oil. But he can be a stubborn little rascal and it may take plenty of intestinal fortitude on your part to wear him down.

How to Offer a New Food

Offer a new food at the beginning of the meal when Baby's hungry. On no account nurse him or give him any of his bottle before the new food, or you'll defeat your purpose entirely. Offer a small amount of the new food. When a taste has been accepted, you can stop for that meal and offer the next food or the nursing or bottle as the case may be. Increase the amount of the new food a little at each offering until Baby's gradually taking the full amount.

It's very important not to feel any emotion or anxiety about this. With a small infant it's only necessary to be calm and persistent and Baby will accept new foods in the end. He may howl, but don't be disturbed. It's a necessary phase of his training. When the lesson's learned, any child is infinitely happier and healthier as a result. So stick it out!

The best way to hold Baby is half sitting, half reclining on your arm. Place a very small amount of the food on a teaspoon, after-dinner coffee spoon, or butter spreader (a *Better Homes & Gardens'* mother contributed the last excellent idea). Place the food so far back on his tongue that Baby can't spit it out. Be satisfied with a very small amount at first, increasing it gradually until he's taking several tablespoons of each solid.

Which solid food you offer first depends upon your doctor and the way your baby's constituted.

If more calories and Vitamin B_1 are needed, your doctor will probably prescribe a whole-grain or enriched cereal. If a bland transition

Hold Baby half-reclining on your arm when you feed solids. Slip food in small spoon into back of mouth where he can not spit it out

food, he may say gelatin. If he thinks your baby needs more iron, he'll probably say egg yolk, hard- or soft-cooked, or in the form of soft custard. If more vitamins, minerals, and a mild laxative are required, cooked sieved vegetables and fruits turn the trick. With many babies, it makes little real difference which of these foods come first.

Let's say that your doctor has decided to start your baby out first of all with green and yellow vegetables. You can offer a bit of sieved carrot, spinach, string beans, or asparagus tips just before the 2 p.m. nursing or bottle feeding. Gradually increase the amount until he's taking 1 tablespoonful. The canned, strained, or sieved baby foods are prepared in such a way as to conserve vitamins, and are easy to use. If you want to prepare your own, you'll find directions on page 176.

After Baby's learned to take various vegetables, begin a custard made with egg yolk just before the 6 p.m. feeding. Increase this gradually to 2 tablespoons. (See the recipes on page 178. Or you may get it canned.) Or your doctor may prefer hard-cooked egg yolk. Hard-cook an egg and put the yolk thru a sieve, or crumble it with a fork. Add enough formula to make it into a paste. Give Baby a small amount the first day, and increase it gradually until he's taking the whole yolk.

Starting Cereals

When Baby's accepted these two classes of foods, cereals can be started. You have a wide range of cereals to choose from. There are several special baby cereals on the market that are approved by the medical profession. These are ready for use as soon as water or milk is added. Then there are the cooked, canned cereals in the canned baby food lines. Some of these are cooked in milk. All are ready to serve. A third possibility are the cooked cereals you yourself eat. Directions for preparing these for Baby are on the containers. You may use them for Baby and the rest of the family, too. Cook the length of time prescribed for Baby. Then dilute Baby's portion with water or some of his formula.

All of these cereals, prepared according to the directions for baby feeding on the container, are all right for a normal, healthy baby. The only ones not to give are the ready-to-serve family variety, such as the various corn, rice, and wheat flakes, puffs, etc.

When your doctor gives you the go-ahead sign on solid food, ask him what cereals he'd prefer to have you start with.

Give Baby a tiny bit at first and work up to 1 tablespoonful just before the 10 a.m. feeding. Many doctors use cereal as Baby's first solid food, because the whole-grain and enriched kinds provide Vitamin B_1 which is particularly needed by the baby.

In introducing new foods, give one at a time and let an interval of several days elapse before trying another. Thus if Baby should be upset, you'll know which food is the culprit.

Schedule for Baby Four Months Old Beginning Solid Foods

6:00 a.m. or 7:00 a.m. Breast feeding or formula.
8:00 a.m. to 9:00 a.m. One hour's exercise on floor or on big bed.
9:00 a.m. Vitamin concentrate or 1 teaspoon of fish-liver oil as prescribed by your doctor. Two to 3 ounces of orange juice.
9:30 a.m. Bath.
10:00 a.m. One-half to 1 tablespoon of cereal. If your baby has a formula, serve 1 to 2 ounces, warm, on the cereal, and feed it with a spoon. If he's a breast baby, use boiled fresh milk. Breast or bottle feeding.
10:30 a.m. to 2:00 p.m. Nap, on porch if possible, or in room with windows raised.
2:00 p.m. One-half to 1 tablespoon of seived carrots, spinach, string beans, green peas, or asparagus tips. They may be diluted with a small amount of boiled, warm water and salted sparingly. Use the same can for not more than three feedings. Feed with a spoon. Breast or bottle feeding.
3:00 p.m. to 4:30 p.m. Out of doors.
5:00 p.m. to 5:45 or 6:00 p.m. On the floor or in play pen for exercise.
5:45 p.m. Boiled custard, 1 tablespoon. Breast or bottle feeding.
6:00 p.m. Bed.
10:00 p.m. Breast or bottle feeding.

CHAPTER V

Your Baby at Five Months

Development

Around the age of 5 months your baby may:

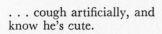 . . . laugh aloud and giggle.

. . . cough artificially, and know he's cute.

. . . drool—a sign that salivary glands are beginning to function.

. . . pull himself forward, trying to sit up.

Formula Using Fresh Milk

(one day's supply)

26 ounces whole milk

8 ounces water

3 to 4 tablespoons Karo or

6 to 8 tablespoons Dextri-maltose

How to prepare: Method same as for formula on page 55.

Fill up the bottles, for he'll probably be emptying them now at most feedings.

Formula Using Irradiated Evaporated Milk

(one day's supply)

13 ounces (1 large can) evaporated milk

21 ounces boiled water

3½ tablespoons Karo or

7 tablespoons Dextri-maltose

How to prepare: Method same as for formula on page 55.

The Lactic Acid-Evaporated Milk formula is the same as for the baby of 4 months, on page 93. Seven to 8 ounces are usually taken at a feeding at this age.

Schedule for Baby Five Months Old

If Baby's bottle-fed, he's now probably emptying his bottle at each feeding. He may also be given considerably more orange juice. The amounts of solid foods may be increased gradually.

6:00 a.m. or 7:00 a.m. Breast feeding or bottle.

8:00 a.m. to 9:00 a.m. One hour's exercise on the floor.

9:00 a.m. Concentrate or 1 teaspoon fish-liver oil as prescribed by doctor.
　　　　Two to 3 ounces orange juice or more.

9:30 a.m. Bath.

10:00 a.m. One to 2 tablespoons cereal fed with spoon. This amount means cereal as it is mixed and ready for the baby, not in the dry form.
　　　　Breast or bottle feeding. (Part of the formula may be fed with the cereal.)

10:30 a.m. to 2:00 p.m. Nap, on porch if possible, or in his bedroom with windows raised.

2:00 p.m. One to 2 tablespoons strained or sieved carrots, spinach, string beans, green peas, or asparagus tips. Feed with spoon.
　　　　Nursing or 6 to 8 ounces of formula.

3:00 p.m. to 4:30 p.m. Outdoors.

5:00 p.m. to 5:45 p.m. On the floor for exercise.

5:45 p.m. One to 3 tablespoons boiled custard.
　　　　Breast or 8 ounces of formula.

6:00 p.m. Bed in room by himself, with door closed and window open.

10:00 p.m. Breast or 8 ounces of formula if needed.

CHAPTER VI

Your Baby at Six Months

Development

Around the age of 6 months baby may:

. . . sit alone.

. . . get a tooth—maybe two— in the middle of his lower jaw.

. . . be more active; understand more, become a definite member of the family and an individual in his own right.

. . . show he has a temper if things don't suit him.

From now on you'll find this lusty chap a force to be reckoned with in family affairs. Six months represents completion of half that all-important first year, during which your child grows and develops faster than at any subsequent time. His progress mentally and physically will amaze and delight you.

Formula Using Fresh Milk

(one day's supply)

26 ounces whole milk

6 ounces water

3 to 4 tablespoons Karo or

6 to 8 tablespoons Dextri-maltose

Formula Using Irradiated Evaporated Milk

(one day's supply)

13 ounces (one can) evaporated milk

20 ounces boiled water

3 to 4 tablespoons Karo or

6 to 8 tablespoons Dextri-maltose

Formula Using Lactic Acid-Evaporated Milk

(one day's supply)

4 tablespoons Karo

1 teaspoon Lactic Acid, U.S.P.

Enough boiled water, cooled, to make 1 pint

16 ounces irradiated evaporated milk

All materials should be cold. Mix first three items together and pour into evaporated milk. Stir constantly.

Baby will probably take 8 ounces of formula at most feedings.

Program of Immunization

We parents are under an extra obligation these days to see that our children shall not have any preventable illnesses. It was bad enough that many children should have suffered unnecessarily. Now when the medical services are already carrying all the load they can possibly bear, it would be a catastrophe to add epidemics which might have been avoided by parental care.

We all know that no American child needs to have diphtheria or smallpox, two of the most dreadful diseases. A number of others can be cut down in virulence or brought under control if parents act quickly. Let's pay special attention to immunization, both to protect our children, and to avoid the drain epidemics would make upon doctors, nurses, and hospitals.

Make this *your* responsibility. Don't wait for busy doctors or health authorities to hound you into taking proper measures. Following is the age at which the normal baby or youngster may receive immunization, and the circumstances under which it is advisable. Acquaint yourself with the immunization picture, and get in touch with your doctor when a new form of vaccination or inoculation seems called for.

One way to keep your child healthy and happy is thru immunization against the most dreaded diseases

Smallpox. Babies may be vaccinated against smallpox at any age during an epidemic, but the routine procedure is to vaccinate anywhere between 3 and 12 months. The usual time is around 6 months. Now's a good time, therefore, to take up the matter of vaccination with your doctor. Your child should be revaccinated at 6 years, or if there is an epidemic.

Diphtheria. Babies are immunized against diphtheria before the first birthday preferably, but not before 9 months of age. Approximately 6 months after immunization, the Schick test is given to determine whether or not the child is immune. If the test is positive, your doctor will re-immunize. The Schick test should be repeated when your child is 5 or 6 years old to be certain immunity persists. If the test is positive, your doctor will re-immunize.

Doctors tell us, "Smallpox and diphtheria immunizations are to be regarded as 'must' procedures. Failure to protect children against these diseases is unjustifiable neglect."

Whooping cough. Vaccination against this disease is not compulsory, but is often desirable. It should be done around 8 or 9 months if your doctor feels it's desirable for your baby. Ask him about it, therefore, when you query him about vaccination for smallpox.

Scarlet fever. Immunization for this disease is effective, but is not recommended as routine procedure because of the large number of injections (five) required, and because there are often reactions. Moreover, the scarlet fever of recent years has been a mild type. If there should be an epidemic of any severity, however, immunization would be in order, but it shouldn't be started before your baby is 12 months old, and preferably not before he's 18 months. Its chief usefulness at present is for children in groups, such as nursing homes, orphanages, and sanatoriums. One week after the last injection, the Dick test is given. If the result is positive, the fifth dose is repeated.

Tetanus. Immunization against tetanus also is effective. There is a combined tetanus and diphtheria toxoid on the market which may be employed, or your doctor may give tetanus toxoid alone. If the latter, it's all right to give at any time after about 9 months of age. If your youngster is exposed to tetanus infection after he has received the toxoid—thru running a rusty nail in his foot, for instance—the doctor who takes care of him should be told about the tetanus toxoid inoculation. He will then give further toxoid, rather than tetanus antitoxin.

Typhoid. Children may be vaccinated against typhoid fever at any age if there's an epidemic. Ordinarily, however, it is not done unless a child has been exposed. Immunization probably does not last longer than two years, but is helpful in event of exposure.

It's Fun Helping Baby Learn

From now on the emphasis shifts a bit. Of course you continue Baby's physical care just as devotedly as ever, but to it are now added definite training duties.

If you've followed our suggestions thus far, Baby has established the habits of eating what's set before him, sleeping well, and amusing himself. Maybe he's also trained about bowel movements. Each month or two from now on will bring some new phase of training to build upon this fine foundation.

We assure you that if you deal with each at the proper time, you'll be astonished to see how easy training is. Many parents have discovered for themselves that there seems to be a period when a child is ready to tackle a certain learning situation. He can take it then in stride. Now science confirms this.

Psychologists who have studied babies and small children for years in the Normal Child Development Clinic at Columbia University tell us that there's a "critical time" in a child's life for learning each different habit and skill. This doesn't mean that he can't learn them later, but it will be harder for him, and harder for you to teach him, too.

Child indicates by signs, easily discernible to a watchful mother, when he's ready for a new type of learning, says Dr. Myrtle McGraw of the Clinic. Thus your baby will be ready for bladder training when he notices the puddle he has made on the floor, or listens to the sound in the stool. To attempt to teach control before he has any idea of what it's about would be futile. But to delay training too long after he has exhibited interest makes it harder for him to learn the lesson.

Children differ in the age at which the muscles and nervous system have developed sufficiently to permit a certain type of learning. Dr. McGraw therefore would rely upon signs such as the foregoing, rather than upon chronological age, to determine when it's time to start new training.

You, his mother, will soon become wise in detecting these signs if you're on the lookout

A popular arrangement is a low chair set in Baby's special table. Plenty of room for eating or play

Baby should have his own toilet seat, with back, arms, a footrest and strap to hold him in place

Furniture for a small child should be low and sturdy, for it may have to take much punishment

A high chair, if you have one, may be made into a low chair if you wish by sawing off the legs

for them. Study your baby, work with him, play with him. When he displays the awareness that shows he's ready for a next step in training, get busy!

Always remember to keep this training easy and fun. Expect Baby to make many failures before he masters a skill. He isn't failing deliberately, he simply has to learn, as you have had to learn in attempting something brand new. Crossness and punishments don't help when Baby doesn't understand, or isn't ready yet to grasp the lesson. Know your own baby, then be gentle but firm in working out the things necessary for his development.

We'll suggest the time at which he might be ready, so you can be on the lookout and prepared to provide the training indicated. If your baby isn't quite ready for the training we suggest at a certain age, let him take his time. If he beats the gun, sneak a look into the pages ahead and help him along.

The period looming ahead right now is that of "sitting up," when your baby's going to be ready for a whole series of new experiences and for a certain amount of independence. Independence is something you'll want to build for all you're worth, so you'll want to lay in the equipment your baby will soon be needing to develop new abilities.

Right Equipment Helps

When your baby of his own accord pulls himself to a strong sitting position, he's ready to leave your lap and arms, and sit alone for eating, bath, toilet, and for his play times. To make all this safe and comfortable for Baby, get him now, if you haven't already done so, the following items:

1. A play pen which can be folded up and used indoors or outdoors. The kind with a floor is especially good for outdoor use.

2. A toilet seat with arms, back, and a strap to hold Baby in. This may be placed over the stool in the bathroom or have its own pan enabling it to be used anywhere. Some models have folding steps, an aid to self-help when Baby gets big enough to walk and climb.

3. A safe chair in which Baby can eat his meals. We don't favor the traditional high chair, since so many babies have tipped them over and received bad falls. The high chair also presents a temptation to have Baby at the family table at mealtime, which often leads to bad eating habits. During the entire preschool period, Baby will be better off if he has his principal meals, or at least the

Accustom Baby to his new toilet duties by degrees. Let him examine the toilet seat before you place him on it. The first time you put him on, stay with him, hold his hand and get him used to it, then leave him

main part of them, alone and before the family eats. Whether you follow this plan exactly or not, your baby should at least have his meals alone during his first two years.

A low chair is preferable. It should have a tray or table which will serve the double purpose of keeping Baby in and giving him something to eat or to play on. There are various devices of this kind on the market. If you already have a high chair with eating tray, you can turn it into a low chair by sawing off the legs.

Bowel Training Easiest Now

You aren't to urge or hurry the sitting process, remember. Baby will do this himself as soon as he's strong enough.

When he's sitting up well, tho, it's time to start bowel training, if you haven't done so before. The first step is to keep a chart, for a week, of the times at which Baby has his movements. Usually these come, at least one of these comes, at a fairly regular time after the morning meal.

Whether your baby is already trained to the chamber or this is his first experience, the procedure is the same. Choose a day when he's feeling particularly well and happy. (Never start a new phase of training when Baby's fussy or tired or not quite himself.) Place the toilet seat with the footrest slightly extended, and the strap loosened. Sit down in front of it with Baby and help him get acquainted with it. When the usual time for the movement comes, lift Baby on, but the first few times don't fasten the strap, and don't leave him. Sit with him, making an occasional cheerful comment and holding his hand, until he's relaxed and at ease.

Indicate what is wanted. If the movement occurs, act pleased so he'll understand he has done what was expected of him. Leave him on the toilet seat long enough for the bowel to be evacuated. If nothing happens after ten minutes, take him off and don't put him on again until the next day at the same time.

It's extremely important to keep the toilet training experience a happy, easy one. It may take a long time for your baby to get the idea, and it will probably be some time after that before he has sufficient nervous and muscular control to prevent accidents. Never keep him on the seat for more than ten minutes and never scold, punish, or hurry him.

After he is having his morning movement in the stool or pan a reasonable part of the time, you may start trying to catch other movements during the day, if he has them. Use the same process—schedule the movement. Then put Baby on the toilet seat a minute or so before it usually occurs.

Praise accomplishment and ignore failures. Don't be angry or discouraged at a soiled diaper. You'll have these for a long time to come. What you're after now is to establish a healthful and cleanly procedure.

After Baby becomes used to the seat, you may strap him in and go out of the room, leaving him alone. Best move toilet paper and breakable objects out of reach! You can look in occasionally to see how he's doing. Five to ten minutes at a time is long enough for him to stay on the seat, unless he's in process of evacuation. Longer might produce antagonism.

After Baby seems to have caught the idea and has kept clean for some time, a new food may throw him off. It's not uncommon at all for a supposedly trained youngster to start having a movement during the night or early in the morning, before you get him up, or at unpredictable times during the day.

This can often be controlled by manipulating the laxative foods in Baby's diet. To control a too-early movement, try giving stewed fruit in the morning instead of at night. Extra movements may be cut down by staying away temporarily from the laxative cereals—such as oatmeal, Pettijohn's, Ralston's Wheat Cereal—and using, for the time being, only non-laxative ones such as Cream of Wheat, Pablum, and farina. You may also stop orange juice temporarily while Baby gets used to the new foods. Then begin the juice again in small amounts, gradually working up to full strength. After you've done that, you can introduce the full range of cereals again.

Praise Has Its Place

We've felt a bit self-conscious on the score of praise since reading a remark that many small children, when you tell them to be "good," think you mean for them to go to the toilet!

In the anxiety to get toilet training established, do we mothers make too big a fuss about successful accomplishment? "What's the place of praise in this and in other learning situations?" one mother has very properly asked.

Probably a child shouldn't be praised extravagantly for every small act of the day. Either it will make him a terrible egotist, or praise will lose its meaning.

Nevertheless, when your baby or child does perform creditably, don't hesitate to tell him so. When you first put him on the toilet, for instance, he has no earthly idea what you want. The occurrence of the movement is pure accident. But when you show him you're pleased, it helps him get the idea of what the toilet session is about.

We all like being praised. That's what most of us work for, at least in the beginning. When we find that a certain course brings us the approval of those about us, we try to continue that course. Your praise of Baby when he succeeds helps him know he did what you wanted, and encourages him to do it that way next time. Just be careful not to carry praise to the place where it's ridiculous.

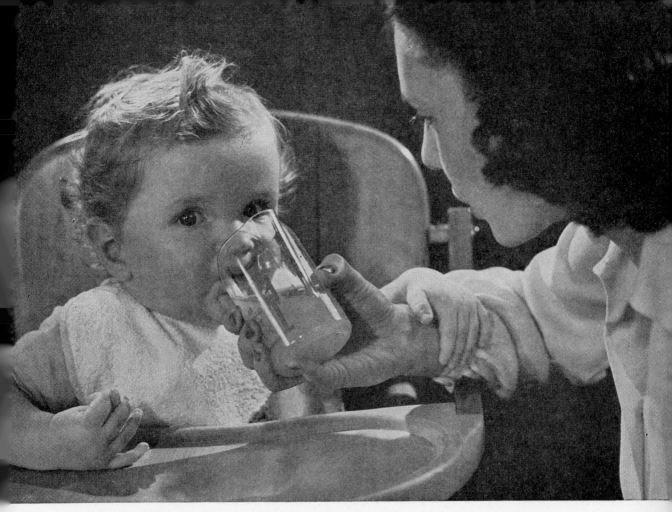

Baby can drink liquids out of a cup. Use a small cup or glass at first. One with a lip is best

What if the baby fails or disappoints you? The less attention called to this the better, for small youngsters love drama and are apt to repeat the undesirable conduct just to hear you sound off.

Not in toilet training alone, but in all future training situations, you'll find it's a good rule to praise successful accomplishment and to pass over failures. The youngster who gets recognition and satisfaction in doing the right thing has little temptation to make a practice of doing the wrong.

Ready for Cup Feedings

When Baby has learned to sit up strongly, he's also ready to learn to use a cup. This can be started by giving his orange juice and boiled water in a cup or glass. (A small one over which Baby's mouth fits is better, and one with a lip is best of all.) There'll be con-siderable spilling and leakage for awhile. One mother avoids the consequent mess by holding a saucer under the cup while Baby's learning.

Introduced in this way at 6 months or thereabouts, the cup or glass will soon be quite acceptable. From now on offer all fluids, aside from nursing or bottle, in the cup or glass. If Baby refuses it at first, persist quietly. Give his orange juice and water in this way and no other, until he takes them. Teach this lesson now, and you'll find that weaning, when you come to it, will be robbed of many of its terrors.

Many mothers find that their breast milk is beginning to diminish in quantity at about this time. If this happens (you'll know by your baby's failure to gain), after each nursing offer the formula for your baby's age, in a cup. (See formulas at the beginning of this chapter.) Let him take as much or

At any time after he's able to sit up strongly, Baby may have his bath in the family bathtub

Now that Baby's doing so many things, he may wear overalls or coveralls for his playtimes

little as he wants. As your milk gets less and less, you may give more and more of the cup feeding.

Don't start giving your breast-fed baby a bottle at this age. He's able to drink from a cup, and you'll save yourself much bother by using it, if complementary feedings are needed.

Baby's in the Big Tub

Our sitter-upper is getting big indeed, for now he can take his bath in the big tub! He'll love this, and how he'll splash and cavort! Place a towel or mat in the bottom of the tub so he won't slip. Test the water with a bath thermometer or with your elbow as you did with his own tub. Let him play awhile with celluloid fish or other water toys, then give him a regular bath. Remember tho that he's still a baby, and never leave him alone in the tub! Too many things might happen.

You'll probably find the bath table convenient for dressing and undressing as long as you can keep Baby on it. When he gets too lively, however, you'll have to put this handy object away for the next baby.

He Gets a Social Life

It's good for Baby to see some outside people, but his eating and sleeping schedule should on no account be disturbed. He can go visiting occasionally between 3 o'clock and bedtime. Visitors may play with him quietly during that period. He shouldn't be tossed, tickled, spoken to loudly, or made to laugh hard. These things are over-stimulating, and most babies pay for them with crying spells. It's nice for Baby to join the family circle while eating his zwieback and for a time

before the evening meal, but he shouldn't be overhandled or excited.

As Baby widens his contacts, shield him from people with colds or other infections. People, not drafts or cold air, give colds to babies. People also give them children's and other diseases. Don't let anyone with an infection near your baby.

Graduates to Overalls

Now that Baby's entering a more active phase, there'll be some changes in his wardrobe. The shirt and diaper remain his basic dress, but when Baby's on the floor and outdoors, little overalls or coveralls take the place of dresses or kimonos.

He may be outgrowing his nightgowns. When this happens, he's ready for sleeping garments with legs and feet.

In warm weather, a sleeveless cotton shirt or sunsuit, and diaper are quite enough. In cooler or cold weather, a sweater or coat, cap, mittens, and leggings may be added as needed to the coveralls. The whole purpose of dressing a baby, remember, is to make him comfortable. Clothe him as lightly or as warmly as is necessary for this purpose. A well-nourished baby is more likely to suffer from over- than from under-dressing. Here you will have to use your judgment and check indoor and outdoor temperatures.

These garments may be made of lightweight cotton or of flannelette and should be loose and roomy. It is good to have several changes.

Playtimes Are Scheduled

Your baby should now be put in his pen both indoors and outdoors (the same pen can be used) for regular playtimes with his toys—rattle, cloth or knitted doll, and a soft ball. A porch is ideal for his outdoor play, or in warm weather, the pen can be put on the grass. Be sure it's in the shade, if the weather's hot. Part of Baby's waking hours may be spent on your own bed (if it's well barricaded), for he's now very active and needs more space. The big bed, the play pen indoors, and the play pen outdoors will make Baby's waking time pass pleasantly for him and with a minimum of trouble for you.

How to Handle Fears

Baby's big enough now to be a member of the family, and around everyday living processes that may frighten him at first. The noise of the vacuum cleaner, the radio next door, or the swirling of bath water down the drain may elicit sudden screams from him.

These are things he'll have to get used to, so don't try to shield him from contact with them. Instead, show him by your cheerful matter-of-fact handling of the situation that there's nothing to be afraid of.

Pick him up in your arms and hold him while you show him how the vacuum works. Or watch the water run out of the tub, with him, and laugh about it as tho it were fun. Make your manner extremely reassuring, but not comforting for no hurt is involved.

Many mothers prevent fear of lightning and thunder by sitting on the porch with their babies while a storm is going on, laughing about it and showing that they themselves are enjoying the storm thoroly.

When Baby, safe in the circle of his mother's or father's arms, comes into contact with the thing he fears and learns that it doesn't hurt him, his fear is soon dispelled.

He'll Sleep Less

About now many mothers become alarmed because they feel the baby isn't sleeping enough. It's quite natural, however, for him to sleep less during the daytime. Many babies take only a short nap between breakfast and bathtime, and they may stay awake for the entire interval between the afternoon nap and bedtime.

Keep to the night schedule as before, with 12 hours in bed, and stick to the afternoon nap until your youngster enters school. If he spends the full time in bed, you may leave it to him how much of it he sleeps.

On the other hand, let him sleep as much as he wants to. Babies differ in the amount of sleep they need, just as much as in the amount of food required. If Baby gets sleepy at any time, put him down for a nap. If he gets fussy and irritable, the bed treatment is also desirable. Close the door of his room, so he may sleep if he likes. This is far better than walking him about, trying frantically to amuse or quiet him.

Night Wakefulness May Be Hunger

There is one point in connection with wakefulness that should be noted, however. At this time, as we said before, it's rather common for your milk to drop off in quantity. If your breast-fed baby begins waking and crying at night, or crying a great deal in the daytime, he may be hungry. Has his weight gain dropped off? Weigh him, with diaper on, before and after each feeding for a 24-hour period to see how much milk he's getting from you. If it's much less than 32 ounces in the 24-hour period, ask your doctor about starting milk in a cup. (See the directions on page 105 for cup feeding.)

If your baby needs more food, by all means give it to him. But if he's getting plenty and making his gains regularly, follow the suggestions we've just given for sleeping.

Tips to Make Eating Go Well

Feed Baby before the family mealtime in his low chair. Immediately after eating breakfast, he'll go to the bathroom for his bowel movement. After that he may, if you like, join the family circle by playing in his pen while the family eats. Don't give him food from the table.

It's a good idea to handle the evening meal in the same way with Baby going to bed immediately after his supper and before the family eats. This will be convenient for you, as well as very good for Baby.

Introduce any new food at the beginning of the meal when the baby's hungry. Give only a little at first, increasing until the required amount is taken. If Baby shows a disinclination for a particular food, give this food at the beginning of the meal, insisting that he take a small amount before going on to more acceptable foods.

Usually it's advisable to give his milk last, after the solid foods have been taken. With some babies, however, milk is least liked. When this is the case, it's proper to offer the milk first. There have been babies who had to have their desserts first because they liked them less than other foods on the menu!

Sometimes there's difficulty in striking a balance between milk and solid foods. You don't want Baby to get into the habit of filling up on milk at the expense of other needed foods, yet milk remains the principal food in his diet and will for some time to come.

First try offering the various solid foods at the beginning of the meal, as we've suggested. After he's taken a reasonable amount, offer the milk. One time he may refuse the milk altogether, then at the next meal drink two cups. As long as his daily intake of milk, including what is used in cooking for him, comes close to a quart, it's not necessary to worry. But if he consistently refuses milk, begin offering it at the first of the meal before the solid foods.

Also, use as much milk as you can in preparing his food—thru desserts made with milk such as custards, rennet mixtures, creamed vegetables, cream soups, cereals cooked in milk, and milk toast. His milk intake can be increased still more by using irradiated evaporated milk (diluted very little or not at all) instead of fresh milk for cooking. Most babies like the taste of evaporated milk. And if it's used full strength, Baby's really getting twice as much milk as he would from the same amount of fresh milk.

It should be possible in this way to get the equivalent of a pint of milk into his cooked dishes, on cereal, etc. Most children will drink two cups in the course of a day. This amount is quite satisfactory.

If your baby stubbornly refuses to take any milk over a period of several days, telephone your doctor and talk it over with him.

If Baby refuses food he has been in the habit of accepting, without fuss or emotion take all food away for that meal. Refusal of food by a baby of good eating habits is usually a sign of indisposition and the best treatment is to let him go without until he's ready to eat again. Should this continue for more than a meal or two, especially if the baby runs a temperature and appears ill, call your doctor. If there's nothing, or very little, the matter, Baby will probably make up for his fast at the next meal.

New Foods on His Menu

Don't force your baby to eat, beyond insisting upon a taste of a new food. Don't introduce new foods unless Baby's feeling well.

The half-year mark brings several new foods for your up and coming eater. Several new vegetables, liver soup, and beef soup may be added to the list. He'll have stewed fruit once a day, and likewise a simple dessert that's made with gelatin or milk.

Study the schedule on page 109, and give your baby all the foods allowed him now in rotation, to accustom him to a constantly widening range. When he's getting several accustomed dishes at a meal, it's a good idea to alternate in feeding them. That is, give a spoonful of vegetable, then one of dessert, and then back to the vegetable. Babies who eat their full helping of one food first and then clean up the next food have an inclination to continue the habit. No great harm is done, but this can be avoided by going from one dish to another during the early period.

Three Meals a Day

As was remarked earlier, babies are getting more and more precocious. They start various foods earlier and earlier, and occasionally we hear of small prodigies who are ready for three meals a day at the tender age of 10 weeks!

True, that's rushing things for most babies. However, they do make amazing progress on formulas and diet schedules that are well suited to their needs. Many babies are fully ready at 6 months for the momentous change to three meals, and some big babies are ready sooner than that.

Has your baby begun to lose interest in his 10 a.m. and 2 p.m. feedings, tho he's making his weight gains and is all right in every way? Then ask your doctor about exchanging the four meals a day he's been having for three. If he says yes, combine the 10 a.m. and 2 p.m. feedings into one dinner at noon or at 11:30—it's a good idea to use the earlier time for awhile, so he won't get too hungry.

You'll observe as you study the schedule that there's no actual change, just a rearrangement. Baby will have the same foods, but it has been found that many babies eat better from now on if their solid foods are spaced more widely.

Keep on giving Baby his meals alone, before the rest of the family eats. Place him in his low chair when he eats.

If there's a new food to be introduced, give it at the beginning of the meal when he's hungriest. Or if there's some food he doesn't like very well, give it first. Be content with a small taste of a new or disliked food. When he's taken it, give him one he likes very much, and let him have as much of it as he wants. This might be his nursing or bottle.

Suppose Baby persistently refuses to taste or take his food. Make no fuss of any kind but quietly take the food away, letting him go hungry till the next meal. Offer what's on the schedule for the next meal.

If he refuses two or three meals in a row, get in touch with your doctor.

Schedule for Baby Six to Eight Months Old—Four Meals a Day

6:00 a.m. to 7:00 a.m. Nursing or 8 ounces of formula. Bowel movement.

8:00 a.m. Nap in bedroom with window open.

9:00 a.m. Concentrate or 1 teaspoon fish-liver oil.
Two to 3 ounces orange juice in a cup.
Outdoors in play pen.

10:00 a.m. Bath.

10:30 a.m. Two to 3 tablespoons cereal with 1 or 2 ounces warm formula or boiled milk. No sugar. Nursing or bottle feeding.

10:45 a.m. Nap in bedroom with window open.

2:00 p.m. Two tablespoons green or yellow vegetable—sieved carrots, spinach, string beans, aspargus tips, fresh peas, or squash. May be served creamed, in vegetable water, or in meat broth. (See recipe section page 176.)
Liver soup, beef soup, or vegetable soup.
Zweiback or arrowroot cookies.
Custard, rennet custard, rennet custard dessert, or plain gelatin dessert.
Nursing or bottle feeding. He may take only about half a bottle at this meal, after eating the solids.

2:30 p.m. Outdoors in pen either on porch or in yard.

5:00 p.m. On big bed to exercise.

5:30 p.m. to 5:45 p.m. Held, or carried about the house.

5:45 p.m. One to 3 tablespoons custard or cottage cheese.
One to two tablespoons stewed fruit—prunes, pears, peaches, apples, or baked apple.
Nursing or bottle feeding.

6:00 p.m. Bed.

Schedule for Baby Six to Eight Months Old—Three Meals a Day

7:00 a.m. to 7:30 a.m. Breakfast:

Two to 4 tablespoons cereal, served with formula or boiled milk. No sugar. Enriched cereals or those made from whole grain are preferable. Milk toast or sieved ripe banana may be substituted occasionally.

Slice of toast or zwieback with butter.

Nursing or bottle feeding.

9:30 a.m. Orange juice—2 to 4 ounces in a cup.

Concentrate or 1 teaspoon of fish-liver oil.

9:30 a.m. to 11:00 a.m. Nap.

11:00 a.m. Bath.

11:30 a.m. to 12:00 N. Dinner:

Two to 3 tablespoons green or yellow vegetable—strained carrots, spinach, string beans, green peas, tomatoes, or asparagus tips.

Liver soup, beef soup, or vegetable soup.

Zwieback or arrowroot cooky.

Two to 3 tablespoons dessert—cornstarch pudding, custard, rennet custard, or rennet custard dessert, or flavored gelatin.

Nursing or bottle feeding.

1:00 p.m. to 3:00 p.m. Nap.

3:00 p.m. Milk, 4 to 8 ounces.

Zwieback, graham cracker, or arrowroot cooky.

5:30 p.m. Supper:

Two to 3 tablespoons boiled or baked custard (see recipe) or cottage cheese.

One to 3 tablespoons stewed fruit—prunes, pears, peaches, apple, baked apple, apricots.

Nursing or bottle feeding.

6:00 p.m. Bed.

CHAPTER VII

Your Baby From Eight to Twelve Months

Development

Between the ages of 8 and 12 months, your baby may:

 . . . sit up strongly with no support.

. . . creep and pull himself up. He may even walk, but don't hurry him.

 . . . pick up large and small objects in his hands and examine them carefully.

. . . understand many things you say to him.

. . . make sounds, such as da-da and ma-ma. He may say several words.

 . . . have two teeth and cut four more.

Your baby's development is rapid indeed during this period, both physically and mentally. And each new activity brings problems of handling, for which you'll want to be ready.

When He Starts to Creep

For some time you've been placing Baby in his pen both inside and outdoors. Besides getting him used to amusing himself, this has given him full opportunity to develop his muscles, as he couldn't have done if he were always kept in a bed or buggy. Around the seventh or eighth month he'll be able to pull himself over the floor, and soon make good speed. Babies creep in various ways, some sitting up, some on all fours, some on their knees. The method doesn't matter—any one serves the purpose.

At this time, let Baby creep about the house for certain periods when he can be watched. This gives him better use of himself and helps his mental development. He'll need to be protected, of course, from falls that might injure him, but if a hands-off policy is followed as far as possible, he'll soon learn to keep his balance and to pause at the top of flights of steps and the like.

Clothes for Creeping

The shirt and diaper remain his basic dress, but when Baby creeps he'll need something over his knees, if he hasn't had it before. The preferred garment nowadays for this period is the overall or coverall, mentioned in Chapter VII. These are made roomy enough to expedite diaper changing, and can be bought ready-made in cunning styles. You'll need a number of them, for the creeping stage is perhaps the dirtiest and messiest of all. But what a happy one for Baby, as for the first time he can explore under his own power this marvelous world into which he has come!

Eliminate Home Hazards

As soon as Baby reaches the place where he can move at will, go over your house and make sure there's nothing on which he can hurt himself.

Any poisons or medicines that you must keep should be locked up far beyond his reach. This applies even to aspirin, cough drops, remedies of any kind. Watch out for boiling liquids, hot coffee pots, buckets of scrub water. If you have a single-pipe register in the floor which gets very hot (it's much better not to have this kind where there's a baby) fence it off with the play pen during Baby's periods of creeping.

Keep all instruments with sharp points or ragged edges out of Baby's reach. From Grandmother's day comes the precaution of stowing dry beans, also, out of Baby's realm because they swell and cause real trouble if Baby sticks them up a nostril or into an ear.

A certain doctor, if he sees one of his children carrying a glass tumbler about, makes a practice of smashing it on the kitchen sink. That's to remind his wife of the danger to children of broken glass.

We don't want to be over-cautious, but these are a few elementary precautions to keep tragedy from your door.

Immunize for Diphtheria

At 9 months it will be time to have your baby immunized against diphtheria.

Strict attention to all details which safeguard child health are even more of an obligation in a period of emergency than in ordinary times. No child needs to have diphtheria if his parents will go to the small trouble and expense of having him immunized. Protect your baby now against this most dreadful disease.

Toys Aid Creeping

Baby's toys still remain soft ones, which he can grasp easily. They should also be washable, so knitted or rubber dolls and animals are suggested. Balls of various kinds—soft rubber, which can be grasped readily; woolly balls; bright-colored balls—will help in the first stages of creeping by giving Baby an incentive to go after them.

Baby Can Learn Not to Touch

Any time after about the ninth month, Baby may start pulling himself to his feet, holding to furniture, or to the sides of his pen. Again we say, this shouldn't be hurried or urged. When Baby's muscles are strong enough for this exercise he will begin it—it shouldn't be begun before.

And now you'll be confronted with your first great problem of management. As soon as your baby attains this stage, objects on tables are within his reach, and depend upon it, he'll reach for them. How shall you handle this?

There are two schools of thought on the subject. One is that the small baby can't be expected to leave things alone and that this indiscriminate reaching for things is a phase that will pass after awhile. Therefore, you should place breakable objects out of the baby's range during this period.

The other school says it's perfectly possible

Is Baby liking solids now? Then "dish up" his meal and give him spoonfuls of each food in rotation

Danger ahead for your household treasures! They need protection when the pulling-up stage comes

When he reaches this stage, your baby's big enough to have a playroom of his own, if it's nothing more than a fenced-off corner of the living-room. Here keep his playthings, and let him play just as he pleases

to teach Baby from the very beginning to leave your things alone. It's only common sense to put any irreplaceable articles beyond his reach, for accidents will happen. But many mothers have found it profitable to spend a week or more teaching Baby at the pulling-up stage not to trespass on forbidden knickknacks, for it saves much subsequent worry and strain.

The method is as follows: When Baby reaches the stage of creeping freely about the house, the only time that he can offend in this way—watch him. When he takes something from a table, say pleasantly, "That is Mother's." As you take the object from him, give him a paper, magazine, book, or object which

he may have, saying, "This is Johnny's." Replace the forbidden object on the table. Be at hand to do this whenever the need arises. Baby will learn, after not too many times, to leave forbidden things alone. At the same time, he'll be perfectly happy about the substitution. This method requires constant and patient work for a week or more to succeed, but once success is attained, it's well worth the effort.

Give Him a Playroom

Before your little fellow reaches the place where he's getting everywhere, he should be given a playroom, or play corner in a family room, where he can touch anything he likes. This should be on the first floor where he'll be near you as you go about your work. An older child would be content to play on another floor, but the youngster of this age is still too young.

Confine Baby in his playroom for regular play periods—a little gate or his play pen across the doorway will keep him safe and not give him the sense of being shut in that a closed door would. Given this room where he can have perfect freedom, Baby will obey the rules of the rest of the house with good grace.

His playroom may be anything from a cubby hole or breakfast room to a large, luxuriously furnished nursery. Your circumstances must, therefore, dictate the furnishings. The room shouldn't have a polished floor on which Baby will slip, or a nice rug which would have to be protected. The ideal floor covering is linoleum for it provides safe footing and a good surface for play activities.

The playroom should have an open cupboard or set of shelves (made from boxes, if you like) where Baby's toys can be placed in orderly fashion, within his reach. These are the essential furnishings of a playroom. Add to them as your purse and desires dictate. Any furniture you buy, such as small tables and chairs, should be strong and durable.

Let Him Amuse Himself

Continue his play periods by putting Baby in his pen, either indoors or out, depending upon the weather. Let him amuse himself with his toys. Go to him only to change him when he cries, or otherwise to attend to legitimate needs.

He Joins the Family Circle

In addition to the lesson of amusing himself, Baby also needs social contacts. He can

Baby's playroom should have low shelves for toys

have these in his journeys of exploration about the house. Also, there should be a period each day when he joins in family activities. (See the schedule on page 116.)

Don't Break His Sleep Routine

As Baby gets older, he'll sleep less during the day. His night sleep of 6 p.m. to 6 a.m., or 7 a.m., should be religiously observed, however, for years. His nap times will shift (see the schedule at the end of this chapter). But for his long afternoon nap, Baby should be put in his own room, with the window opened, door closed, and left there for the full period. If he cries hard, attend to his needs. But leave him for the full nap time. Don't begin now, or ever, that fatal practice of staying with Baby till he gets to sleep. Make him comfortable, and come out and close the door.

Time to Think About Weaning

After a baby is about 9 months old, breast milk is no longer adequate for his needs. Somewhere about this time, therefore, your breast-fed baby should be weaned, and the same procedure followed for the bottle baby. A rule rather universally observed is not to do this in hot weather. So if your baby's ninth month comes in June, begin weaning him in May. If it comes in July or August, and he's doing well on your breast milk, wait until cool weather to wean him.

His actual weaning should be gradual. If you've followed our feeding suggestions, your baby's already getting a good assortment of foods before his breast feeding, and he's using a cup for his orange juice and drinks of water. With this start, he'll slip easily into the new course expected of him.

The Milk You'll Use

When you decide the time for weaning has come, you will select the kind of milk you want to give your baby. Your choice may be guided somewhat by the circumstances in your community. As we've said before, irradiated evaporated milk has various advantages which make it especially valuable in a period of emergency. It keeps indefinitely when the cans aren't opened, and is always clean and germ-free. Moreover, babies and children like its taste and it agrees with them almost universally.

To wean your baby from the breast to

evaporated milk, dilute the milk with a slightly larger amount of boiled water. For this age, 17 ounces of boiled water to 15 of evaporated milk is a good ratio. Gradually use less water and more milk, until by the tenth month your baby is getting 16 ounces of evaporated milk to 16 ounces boiled water, or about the constituency of whole milk. Children can continue on evaporated milk, both for drinking and cooking purposes, as long as you wish. If the fresh milk supply is reliable, however, it's a good idea to teach children to take fresh milk at least by the time they start to school, for in social contacts that's the milk they will be given for drinking.

If you want to wean your baby to fresh milk, and there's a good and reliable supply of it available, boil the milk until your youngster is about 2 years old. Baby may be able to

He needs regular periods in his play pen outdoors

take the boiled fresh milk undiluted from the start, but if he has a disturbance of any kind, add several ounces of boiled water. Gradually drop out the water until he's taking the milk full strength.

Many babies take evaporated milk better than fresh so it's a good idea to wean to evaporated milk from the breast, even tho you switch to fresh milk later.

Don't put any sweetening in the cup feedings you offer for weaning.

Until Baby's about 1 year old, the milk as it comes from the refrigerator should be warmed to room temperature.

Weaning Your Breast-fed Baby

Begin by offering at each meal a cup of diluted (as above) but unsweetened, irradiated

evaporated milk, or boiled fresh milk, until Baby becomes accustomed to the taste. For this purpose it is permissible to offer the cup before the breast feeding. After he takes his first taste, he may have the breast. Next time let him have more of the cup feeding.

Carry the cup and breast feedings along together until Baby accepts the cup nicely. Then drop out the midday breast feeding. The next week drop out the morning breast feeding, and the following week the evening, substituting the cup of milk. At the end of a month Baby will be completely weaned without annoyance to anyone.

Care of Breasts

If your breasts cause discomfort as the feedings are dropped, a tight binder around them will give you relief. You can decrease your milk supply quickly by cutting down on your food and liquids. Get back to your regular amount of both. A mild laxative, which reduces bodily fluids, will also help.

Weaning Your Bottle Baby

Much the same method is followed as for a breast-fed baby. If your baby has been on an irradiated evaporated milk formula, it's not necessary to change. Merely drop out the sweetening and dilute the milk in the ratio of 17 ounces of boiled water to 15 of evaporated milk given for the breast baby. If you wean your baby to fresh milk, offer it boiled and cooled, full strength or slightly diluted, but without any sweetening. Substitute the cup for one bottle feeding, then another, as was done with the breast feedings.

It's important to Baby's wholesome development that you take him from the breast or bottle at the right time. Otherwise, he'll be retarded in an important phase of his growth and will continue in an infantile habit which he should discard. The longer the breast or bottle is continued after the ninth month, the harder it is to wean a baby.

It's not at all uncommon for Baby to seem to lose interest in milk somewhere around weaning time, if he didn't do so before. If this occurs, follow the suggestions we gave you in the chapter on "The Baby Six Months Old," to insure that he will get his milk ration anyway. Use all you can in cooking, and remember that undiluted evaporated milk gives Baby double nutrition for the amount he takes. One cup equals two of fresh milk.

Schedule for Baby Eight to Twelve Months Old After He Is Weaned

7:00 a.m. or 7:30 a.m. Breakfast:

Two to 4 tablespoons whole-grain or enriched cereal. Serve with milk or thin cream, no sugar. Milk toast or ripe banana (yellow flecked with brown) may be substituted. Egg, poached or soft boiled. (Give this for supper if you'd rather.)
Fruit sauce if desired.
Slice of toast or zwieback, with butter, if Baby wants it.
Irradiated evaporated milk, diluted as directed on preceding page, or boiled milk in a cup or glass—8 ounces or as much as he'll take. Use a small cup or glass, one with a lip if possible, until Baby becomes adept at drinking. Refill to get the 8 ounces.

After Breakfast: On toilet seat for bowel movement, with door closed. Leave him alone, but don't leave him on the toilet for more than 10 minutes unless he's evacuating. Duty done, he can return to his bed, or may visit with other members of the family from his play pen or the floor.

9:30 a.m. Two to 4 ounces orange juice, or as much as he likes. Concentrate, or one teaspoon of fish-liver oil, as prescribed.

9:30 a.m. to 11:00 a.m. Nap. It may be out of doors, with Baby's face and eyes shielded from the sun, or in his room with the window open and the door closed.

11:00 a.m. Bath.

11:30 a.m. to 12:00 N. Dinner:

Two to 3 tablespoons green or yellow vegetable—carrots, spinach, string beans, green peas, tomatoes, cauliflower, parsnips, squash, or asparagus tips. It may be served in 2 ounces of the juice in which the vegetable was cooked; creamed; or served in ½ cup of meat broth or soup. (Use the last at least 3 times a week.)
One to 2 tablespoons meat—scraped beef or beef juice, minced chicken, or liver (chicken or calf's liver).
One to 2 tablespoons baked or mashed potato, macaroni, spaghetti, or tenderoni.
Two to 3 tablespoons cornstarch fruit jelly, cornstarch pudding, custard, rennet custard; rennet custard dessert, flavored gelatin, tapioca, or rice pudding. (See recipe section on page 177.)
Milk, 4 to 6 ounces as desired.

1:00 p.m. to 3:00 p.m. Nap, outdoors again or in his own room according to the weather.

3:00 p.m. Milk, 4 to 6 ounces.
Zwieback, graham cracker, or arrowroot cooky.

3:00 p.m. to 5:00 p.m. In his pen, with his soft, easy-to-grasp toys. Either outdoors or in, according to the weather.

5:00 p.m. Clean him up after the afternoon's play—he'll need it! Then bring him into the family circle or let him creep about the house.

5:30 p.m. to 6:00 p.m. Supper:

Two to 4 tablespoons boiled or baked custard with toast; or banana or cottage cheese.
Egg, if none was given at breakfast.
One to 2 tablespoons or more of stewed fruit—prunes, pears, peaches, apple, baked apple, apricots. (If Baby starts having an early bowel movement before getting-up time, give the stewed fruit at breakfast instead.)
Milk, 8 ounces, or as much as he'll take.

6:00 to 7:00 p.m. Bed.

Allow no other foods than those listed above.
Baby may schedule his morning nap a bit differently than we have on the above outline. Let him take it at the time when he naturally falls asleep.

CHAPTER VIII

Your Child From Twelve to Fifteen Months

Development

If you've been following the feeding and training suggestions carefully, his first birthday should find your baby well trained in the habits of eating, sleeping, and play. He'll be happy and healthy. He'll have learned to accept necessary rules, but every day he'll be developing new independence, initiative, and self-reliance.

He'll have trebled his birth weight, and will have gained about 9 inches in height. He'll probably have six teeth. He'll be rosy and strong, and his flesh will be solid. He'll constantly be pulling himself to his feet.

At any time he may begin to walk. Again it's not wise to attempt to hurry the process. Your baby should now have a physical examination by a good physician. The examination should include a check of his feet and legs. Various foot defects can be easily corrected if special shoes are worn in early walking.

His First Shoes

If Baby's feet and legs are normal, his first shoes should have a soft, pliable sole. They should be designed to give him plenty of toe room. If the weather's warm, Baby can go barefoot.

Disciplinary Rules That Work

As your youngster grows in vigor, he'll more and more get into situations which require some action on your part. Decide now what that action will be and see it thru.

There are several rules of child management about which there can be no dispute:

1. You, Baby's parents, must be in agreement and must co-operate in whatever management plan you adopt.

2. The fewer words you use in handling a situation, the better. Small children don't understand language. Instead, they read your expression, voice, actions. Nagging is a thousand times worse than useless.

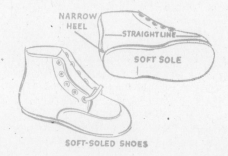

Baby's first shoes should have soft soles, narrow heels, and should be high to give ankles support

3. Be consistent. Nothing is more destructive of discipline than to allow a child to "get by" with something today, for which tomorrow you'll have to correct or punish him.

4. You'll avoid dozens of unpleasant situations if you keep to your schedule. The naughty child is very often the tired, hungry, or over-stimulated child. Feed your child at the right time; get him to bed at the right time;

handle him with tact and love; and he'll be happy and good for the most part.

Recognize, tho, that even the best of children, and those handled most wisely, have their off moments when they're disobedient, fretful, or naughty for no apparent reason. When these times occur, the most satisfactory course is to give a bath or sponge-off and put the child to bed, or isolate him until he's over his upset. In a usually happy child, these spells often betoken the start of a cold or other illness. The bed or isolation treatment is best, certainly, if your child is ill, and it's as effective as a spanking if he isn't. Should his trouble prove to be illness, you'll like yourself much better if you've followed the bed treatment, rather than the spanking one.

You may be tempted about now to stop observing the schedule as religiously as you did the first year. Baby's doing so beautifully, you may feel that a few slip-ups won't matter. Beware! The first thing you know every operation of Baby's day will cause a skirmish!

One of the common pitfalls into which many an unwary mother has fallen is to stay with Baby until he goes to sleep. What slavery you let yourself in for, if you start that! Don't yield to temptation in this, or in any other phase of the fine habits you've built, and you won't be wondering how on earth to get back on the right track again.

Keeping up the routine you've already established will take care of the necessary duties of Baby's life. If you perform the same operation at the same time each day, he accepts it as a matter of course. Thus, if every morning of the world you dress him after the morning bowel movement and brush his hair and teeth, the brushing becomes as natural to him as breathing. If you're haphazard about these matters, they often become a contest of wills that ends in some form of punishment before he gives in.

The well-trained, unspoiled, unabused child is anxious to do what you want him to do, as soon as he understands what this is. The whole attitude of the young child is of wonder at the world, of a desire to be one with it. He imitates you. If you do a thing twice a certain way, he wants to continue to do it that way. Our greatest ally in training is this desire to do what we want, and this imitativeness, provided we ourselves use them in the right way.

Parents who keep in close touch with a little child can teach him the right way to do each new thing before he has a chance to fall into a wrong way. Sometimes this is easy.

When you start bladder training, discard diapers for training panties. Put two-piece suits on boys

Sometimes it's more difficult, but it's always easier than to overcome a bad habit. Continue a careful schedule thruout the first two years and you'll be rewarded by an excellent set of habits and a co-operative attitude.

Punishment has little place in this scheme of discipline. Just go thru the proper routine without fail and without a break. Provide Baby with places to play, indoors and outdoors, where he can "let go" without colliding with adult requirements. Put him to bed at the proper times and feed him when the clock says his mealtime has arrived. Insist in a quiet, pleasant way that he do what must be done, and you'll discover that drastic punishments are not needed.

Ready for Bladder Training

Some authorities advocate that bladder training shouldn't be begun before the 15th or even the 18th month. As we've said before, tho, some babies are ready for a new phase of learning before the average. We mentioned earlier that when your baby notices the puddle he's made on the floor, or the noise of urination in the stool, it's a sign he may be ready for bladder training. Less frequent urination is also a sign. When he waits for longer intervals, it's evident that he can retain water longer in the bladder.

If you get these various signals from your baby during this period, it won't hurt to try bladder training in easy stages. Here's how to go about it:

Bowel training has already taught him what's expected when he's placed on the toilet, so the first big part of this job is already accomplished. For months he has probably been urinating when placed on the toilet for his bowel movement. Now begin putting him there for urination only at certain periods of the day—on arising, before and after each meal, before and after his nap, before going to bed. Don't leave him more than five minutes. If he fails, make no comment. If he succeeds, praise him.

When this procedure has become well established, begin putting him on the toilet every hour, or not oftener than every 45 minutes, during the remainder of his waking time. Continue your policy of showing no emotion when he fails or wets himself, and praising him when he succeeds. Keep the operation a happy one, without any tension. In time this course will get results, without annoyance to yourself or your child.

If your youngster gives no sign at this age of being ready for bladder training, don't try it yet.

Clothes During Bladder Training

When you decide to begin bladder training, remove Baby's diaper and substitute training panties. These are easily put off and on, and they encourage a youngster to keep dry, whereas the bulky diaper is really an invitation to wet. It will pay to get a good-quality training panty which covers Baby and is comfortable. Some mothers make training panties of the no-longer-needed diapers.

Thruout the training period, overalls or two-piece suits, with waist and panty separate, will be most convenient. If you buy a number of suits of the same color, the panties can be changed as they're wet without necessitating laundering of the whole outfit.

May Want Less Food

Don't bring your child to the family table, but continue to feed him by himself. At the first of the meal give him the food he likes least, whether it's vegetable, cereal, fruit, or meat. Give his cup of milk last after an adequate amount of solid food has been eaten— unless milk is the least liked food. If your child refuses milk or takes very little, add as much to his food as you can by cooking the cereal in milk, creaming soups and vegetables, and giving him milk desserts every day. Children often go thru phases of refusing milk, then come back to it with renewed zest.

At this age your youngster is easing off in the rapidity of his growth, and so he may not be as hungry as when he was gaining from a pound to two pounds every month. Keep up his food balance. Don't let him fill up on one food, or one class of foods, at the expense of others. But do let him decide whether he'll have one tablespoon or four of each.

You'll see that the amounts suggested in the schedule offer you some leeway. Many youngsters are given more food than they can eat, and the very sight of the heaped-up plate takes away appetite. Offer a small amount first, and increase it only if Baby indicates he wants more. If your child refuses his food, let him go hungry until the next meal. If several meals are refused, however, telephone your doctor and talk it over with him.

Never make the mistake of urging, begging, or threatening your child to get him to eat. He should have the privilege of going hungry now and then. It will give him a good appetite for the next meal, and a healthy respect for food.

Begin Chopped Foods

When your baby begins to boast a smile with teeth in it, it's time to start changing from strained to mashed or chopped foods. This, like weaning, can be done gradually and should give you little trouble. Anywhere between 10 and 18 months (depending upon how many teeth your baby has and what your doctor says) start introducing chopped foods in the same gradual way you did solids. The makers of strained baby foods also have a line of chopped ones in many interesting combinations. Or you may chop, or mash with a fork, the fruits and vegetables you're serving the family. Take Baby's portion out before seasoning to adult tastes, for he requires only about half as much salt and sugar and should have no spices at all.

Add a small amount of a chopped food to a serving of strained, preferably a strained food which your baby particularly likes. Gradually increase the chopped food, until Baby's taking his whole serving in this form. Then go on to another food.

Or you might first of all give some baked potato, mashed. After he's learned to take this well, introduce some chopped or mashed spinach, green beans, sweet potato, carrots, beets, or peas into the strained.

Chop or grind the meat you give your youngster until he's about 3 years old. He'll eat it better, and you'll avoid the danger of having a chunk of meat breathed into his windpipe. After you quit straining his cereal, take special pains to make it smooth.

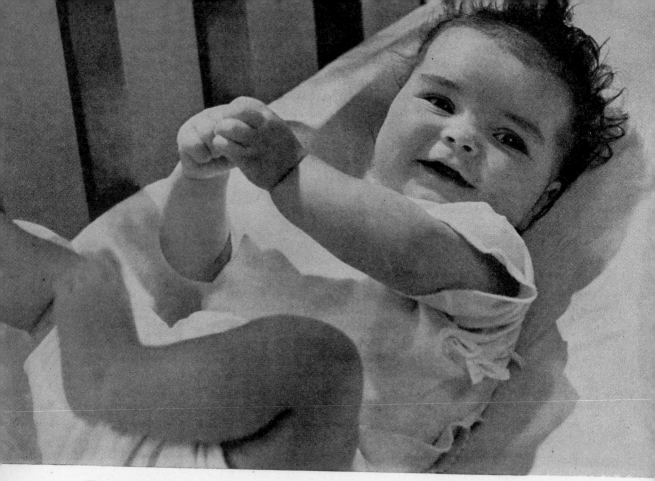

The right food plays a tremendous part in keeping your baby happy and good as well as healthy and strong

Your baby under 1 year needs every day:

Vitamin A—a minimum of 1,500 I. U. (International Units):
1 quart of milk provides about....1,500–2,100 I. U.
1 teaspoon of fish-liver oil........1,200–2,000 I. U.
2 tablespoons spinach...2,600–5,400 I. U.
2 tablespoons carrots.......470–850 I. U.

Thiamin (Vitamin B₁)—a minimum of .4 milligrams or 400 micrograms:
1 quart of milk (whole) provides 400–600 micrograms
1 portion (3 tablespoons) banana..50–100 micrograms
1 portion (3 tablespoons) tomato...30–52 micrograms
1 portion (3 tablespoons) oatmeal..52–116 micrograms

Vitamin C (ascorbic acid)—a minimum of 30 milligrams:
1 ounce fresh orange juice yields......52–56 milligrams
4 ounces fresh lime juice yield......38–120 milligrams
4 ounces fresh lemon juice yield......52–60 milligrams
4 ounces fresh grapefruit juice yield......38–41 milligrams
4 ounces tomato juice yield......21–29 milligrams

Riboflavin (Vitamin G)—a minimum of .6 milligrams or 600 micrograms:
1 portion (2.7 ounces) of liver yields about.........1,386–2,002 micrograms
1 portion (3 tablespoons) beet tops........156 micrograms
1 egg.....151–227 micrograms

1 quart of milk nearly ....1,872–2,304 micrograms

Vitamin D—a minimum of 400 I. U.:
1 teaspoon U. S. P. cod-liver oil contains about.....400 I. U.
3 drops of viosterol...400 I. U.
1 quart irradiated milk............—135 I. U.

Niacin (nicotinic acid)—a minimum of 4 milligrams:
100 grams (average serving) of string beans yield 5 milligrams
An average serving of lean beef..........7.5 milligrams
100 grams of wheat or bran flour......25–40 milligrams
An average serving of beef liver........17.5 milligrams

Energy Producers

● SUGARS ● CEREALS ● FATS

The energy-producing foods are *sugars*, *cereals*, and *fats*. Butter is needed both as a fat and as a source of Vitamin A. We've seen how sirups or sugars are used in the formula, and we met them again in desserts. The whole-wheat cereals, and the new enriched ones, are often chosen as a first solid food because they're easily digested and the Vitamin B₁ they contain is needed greatly by your energetic little fellow.

It's the burning or oxidation of these products in the body which produces the heat needed for growth, development, and bodily activity.

Body Builders

● MILK ● EGGS ● CHEESE ● MEAT ● FISH

The building top liners are *milk*, *eggs*, *cheese*, *meat*, and *fish*. They provide the materials for growth and physical development, and also repair wear and tear upon body tissues. We mustn't short-change Baby on building materials! And we can't have substitutions.

Body Protectors

● FRUITS ● VEGETABLES ● FISH-LIVER OILS
● VITAMIN CONCENTRATES

Body protection is furnished by *fruits*, *vegetables*, *fish-liver oils*, and *vitamin concentrates*. They contain vitamins and minerals which act as regulators of the body and growth processes, keep everything going as it should, and protect your child from sickness.

Fortunately, most babies love fruits and fish oils. It's in the vegetable realm that trouble most often pops up. So we'll have more to say about vegetables later.

122

Why Diet Is So Important

If there's a deficiency of any one of these groups or an excess of one at the expense of the other two, your child is bound to suffer. The consequences may not be apparent for some time and may be delayed because the body has material in reserve for such contingencies. But they'll turn up eventually.

Those who study babies closely find that the blood will show changes almost at once when the diet doesn't contain all the elements needed, the bones within three weeks, and all body tissues within six weeks. "If the child is well nourished," says one authority, "the reserves are used for superior growth, but if poorly, the body reserves are used for maintenance. How the baby has been fed is the measure of his happiness in early childhood; how the child has been fed is an index of health in maturity. A diet optimum in both quantity and quality yields buoyant health. If we want our child to be above average in health and growth, we should provide him with protective foods to make him so."

That's why it's desirable to teach your baby in the very beginning to take the whole gamut of foods allowed him. The only reason for reneging on any would be an allergic condition, which is shown by the fact that a food actually disagreed with him after he'd eaten it.

(Remember, it's the foods we like and eat that give us trouble. The commonest food allergies are among the most commonly eaten and best-liked foods—chocolate, tomatoes, wheat, celery. If your baby refuses to taste a food, it's probably not because he's allergic to it, but because he's still suspicious of the new and untried.)

A balanced diet is simply one that contains all the 50 food elements your youngster needs, and in such proportions that the energy-producing, body-building, and body-protecting ones balance each other. You're doing your dietary duty by him if you see that he eats every day:

1. Milk—boiled or pasteurized. 1 pint (minimum) to 1 quart (maximum). Butter—3 teaspoons daily.

2. Green or yellow vegetable. Portion: ½ to 1 cup. It's best to give two vegetables daily. They may be divided between dinner and supper, and should be sieved, mashed, or chopped according to your baby's age.

3. Egg—1 to 2 daily. The yolk is more valuable than the white. May be given at any of the meals.

4. Cooked fruit. Portion: ½ to 1 cup daily. May be given at any of the meals or for lunch in the mid-afternoon.

5. Meat, poultry, or fish. Portion: 2 tablespoons daily. Usually should be given at lunch time. Should be scraped, minced, or finely ground.

6. Fish-liver oil or vitamin concentrate 1 to 2 teaspoons of the oil or the amount of concentrate prescribed by your doctor. Should be given daily from November to May. Smaller doses may be given during the summer months.

7. Orange, tomato, or grapefruit juice, 4 ounces or more.

8. A serving of whole-grain cereal, or 1 to 3 slices whole-wheat or enriched bread.

The above foods provide the protein, minerals, and vitamins necessary for satisfactory nutrition and growth. Make sure that your boy or girl gets them.

A word of caution with regard to cereals, bread, and potatoes. These are valuable foods. But be careful not to let your youngster fill up on them and leave out some of the things on the list above.

He Can Eat All These

You've done a grand job up to now in building good food habits in your youngster. Now comes the final test. So far, the range has been rather limited, and confined mostly to foods that the majority of children seem naturally to like.

But now it widens out. Here's the list of foods your healthy, normal youngster is able to enjoy after he's 1 year old:

List of Suitable Foods for Child of One Year to Eighteen Months

Milk	Butter
Cream	Eggs
Buttermilk	Cottage cheese
Cocoa	Cream cheese

123

Vegetables

Spinach	Lima beans
Carrots	Squash
String beans	Beets
Green peas	Parsnips
Tomatoes	Brussels sprouts
Asparagus	Broccoli
Cauliflower	Swiss chard
Stewed celery	Lettuce
Cabbage	Onions
Turnips	Sweet potatoes

Meats

Beef juice	Bacon
Scraped beef	Lamb chop
Chicken	Roast beef
Turkey	Roast lamb
Liver (chicken, calf, beef, or pig)	Beefsteak
	Fish

Fruits

Orange juice	Stewed prunes
Grapefruit juice	Stewed pears
Orange (sliced)	Stewed apricots
Ripe apple, scraped	Stewed figs
Baked apple	Stewed plums
Applesauce	Stewed dates
Ripe banana	Stewed rhubarb
Baked banana	Cooked raisins
Stewed peaches	(seedless)

Cereals

—all cooked, canned, or prepared infants' varieties

Miscellaneous

White potatoes	Sponge cake
Macaroni	Jelly
Spaghetti	Custard
Tenderoni	Rennet custard
Graham bread	Rennet custard
Whole-wheat bread	dessert
Whole-wheat muffins	Unflavored gelatin
Corn bread	Cornstarch pudding
Crackers	Chocolate pudding
Graham crackers	Tapioca pudding
Zwieback	Rice pudding
Arrowroot cookies	Prune whip
Plain cookies	Ice cream
Angel food cake	Sherbet

It looks as tho he's practically grown up, doesn't it? This list doesn't mean that you must start now, this minute, giving your youngster all the foods mentioned. But some time during the next six to twelve months, do give him a chance to taste and to like each one. The child who eats everything set before him is a pearl without price in the home, a pleasure to take visiting, and far better fitted to meet life than the finicky feeder. Start now enlarging your fine, bouncing infant's food range.

How to Cook Vegetables for Small Children

Vegetables usually provide the greatest difficulty. The following cooking hints have proved helpful to mothers.

Small children don't like strong tastes, and they do like crispness and color. They require only about half as much sugar or salt as adults, and should not have spices or strong seasonings. So to have your youngster like the new vegetable you're cooking for him, use half as much salt as for your own taste, and just enough water to keep the vegetable from burning. Cook it fast, and just long enough to be tender and yet to retain some crispness. Pressure cookers do this job beautifully, but a well-covered saucepan works well, too.

Exceptions are strong vegetables such as onions, cabbage, cauliflower. Use more water and cook them in open vessels. It's more important at first to have your child like the vegetable than to save vitamins. That comes later, of course. Children like even onions—one of the least popular—when they're precooked three times, and very strong vegetables go down better when cooked in milk. (Don't serve the milk with the vegetable, tho.)

Many youngsters like certain vegetables raw better than cooked. After your child gets to be about 2 years old, you can cater liberally to this fancy. At present, however, there's danger of his getting slivers or chunks of food in his windpipe. An excellent food rule for children under 2 is "No food that won't melt." That bars raw vegetables for the time being.

Foods Should Be Easy to Eat

Most fruit should be cooked and chopped for the preschool child till he's about 3 years old. Exceptions which may be served raw are oranges, bananas, occasional very ripe apples, and peaches and apricots.

Keep your tapioca and rice puddings thin and creamy. Bits of chopped apple, pineapple, peaches, or raisins make them more interesting, and fruit bits in the bottom of the cereal or dessert dish make eating fun for your child.

Liver or salmon loaf should be made very moist—baking it in a pan of water helps. If the skins of apples are tough, pare before baking. Most youngsters like canned peas and spinach better than fresh, and canned peaches and apricots better than dried. They like frozen squash where they'll refuse fresh. Try yellow sweet potatoes, baked whole with no seasoning.

Youngsters usually like the flavor of irradiated evaporated milk, and this can be used freely, both for cooking and drinking. It has all the qualities of fresh milk, and in many localities is cheaper.

Offer New Foods This Way

And now for presenting a new food to your child. Choose a time when he's happy and all's well with him. Offer it at the beginning of the meal when he's hungriest and insist upon no more than a taste at first, but do insist upon a taste. No one can learn to like a food unless he tastes it. Moreover, refusing new foods can quickly become a habit which often extends to refusing familiar ones as well. After the taste, allow him to fill up on foods he especially likes. Never offer more than one new or disliked food at a meal.

This may sound like a lot of trouble. But having a youngster who won't eat this and won't eat that is far more trouble. The thing to work for at this stage is to have your child like all good wholesome foods, and look forward to mealtime as to a happy experience. When you achieve that, you've given him something of incalculable value.

He Shouldn't Eat These

Do not give your child of 12 to 18 months the following foods:

Tea	Eggplant
Coffee	Green corn
Hot fresh breads	Cucumbers
and rolls	Radishes
Griddle cakes	Condiments
Sweet cakes	Spices
Ready-to-serve	Nuts
cereals	Popcorn
All fried foods	Pastries
Gravies	Candy
Sausage	Berries
Salt fish	Fresh fruits, except
Corned beef	those mentioned
Dried beef	on page 123
	Melons

Teaching Mine and Thine

Full instructions were given in the preceding chapter for handling the question of household treasures exposed to your now active child. You'll remember we suggested keeping the baby in a play pen or fenced-off playroom except for periods of the day when he can be watched. Continue this course now that he's older. Let him roam freely about the house only when you can be with him. Show him what he may have and what he must leave alone.

Enough Teeth to Brush?

Between 12 and 14 months, your child will probably cut six more teeth. You can begin brushing them now, if you like. Get a tiny, soft brush for the purpose and begin by letting Baby see you brush your own teeth. Be very gentle about tooth-brushing and don't force the issue. Wait until your tot wants it done—as he will, from seeing you.

Schedule Until Bladder Training Begins

Until you start bladder training, continue the same schedule you have been using, except that you may add new foods from the allowed list. At any time now, your child may be expected to stop sleeping in the morning at the 9:30 to 11:00 period. When this happens, drop out the morning nap and let him spend this time in his play pen.

Schedule for Child Twelve to Fifteen Months Old After Bladder Training Begins

Keep in mind that it isn't necessary to start bladder training before the 15th month. If your baby has exhibited some of the signs of being ready for it, however, you may go onto this schedule any time now.

Choose vegetables, fruits, meats from the list of allowed foods.

7:00 a.m. Arises, to toilet at once to urinate. Into bathrobe for breakfast.

Breakfast:

> Two to 4 tablespoons any cooked or canned or prepared baby cereal. Serve with milk or thin cream, no sugar. Milk toast or sieved ripe banana may be substituted occasionally.
>
> Egg, poached or soft boiled. (May be given for supper instead.)
>
> One to 2 tablespoons fruit sauce. (If the baby has fruit sauce for supper, this isn't essential, unless there's a tendency to constipation.)
>
> Boiled or pasteurized milk, or diluted irradiated evaporated milk, 8 ounces, or as much as he'll take.

7:30 a.m. On toilet for bowel movement. Leave him not more than 10 minutes, unless he is evacuating. Dress him in his play clothes.

8:00 a.m. Now Baby may return to his nursery or high chair to munch a piece of buttered zwieback or dry toast while the family eats. If this was included in his breakfast, he can range about the house, provided someone watches him.

8:30 a.m. On toilet, not more than 5 minutes, then in playroom or outdoors, depending upon the weather.

9:30 a.m. On toilet.

> Four ounces orange juice or 8 ounces tomato juice.
>
> 1 teaspoon fish-liver oil, or vitamin concentrate as prescribed.

9:30 a.m. to 11:00 a.m. Nap or playtime.

11:00 a.m. On toilet, not more than 5 minutes. Bath.

11:30 a.m. to 12:00 N. Dinner:

> Two to 3 tablespoons green or yellow vegetables, or soup or stew containing these.
>
> One to 2 tablespoons baked or mashed potato, macaroni, spaghetti, or tenderoni (3 times a week).
>
> One to 2 tablespoons meat—scraped, minced, or ground.
>
> One to 2 tablespoons dessert.
>
> Milk, 4 to 6 ounces, or as much as desired.
>
> On toilet for not more than 5 minutes.

1:00 p.m. to 3:00 p.m. Nap.

3:00 p.m. On toilet, dressed.

> One cup of milk.
>
> Zwieback, graham cracker, or arrowroot cooky.
>
> Outdoors to play in play pen, or if weather is bad, in play pen or playroom indoors.

4:00 p.m. On toilet.

5:30 p.m. Allow 15 minutes for ranging about house. Watch to see that he doesn't get into trouble, and show him what he may and may not have.

5:45 p.m. Sponge bath, into bathrobe, on toilet.

6:00 p.m. Supper:

> Two to 4 tablespoons custard, banana, or cottage cheese.
>
> One to 2 tablespoons or more of stewed fruit.
>
> Egg (if not eaten at breakfast).
>
> Milk, 8 ounces or as much as desired.
>
> On toilet.

6:30 p.m. or 7:00 p.m. Bed.

Vitamin Needs

OF YOUR CHILD FROM ONE TO THREE YEARS OLD

Between these ages your child needs every day:

Vitamin A—a minimum of 2,000 I. U. (International Units)

Thiamin (Vitamin B₁)—a minimum of .6 milligrams. (This vitamin is needed in direct proportion to the total intake of food. Hence it must be increased during excessive activity. This means that your child should get more whole-grain or enriched cereal as he becomes more active. Not at the expense of other needed foods, tho. Proper balance should be kept at all times.)

Vitamin C (ascorbic acid)—a minimum of 35 milligrams.

Riboflavin (Vitamin G)—a minimum of .9 milligrams.

Vitamin D—a minimum of 400 I. U.

Niacin (nicotinic acid)—6 milligrams.

FOOD	AMOUNT	Vitamin A International Units	Thiamin (Vitamin B1) Micrograms	Ascorbic Acid (Vitamin C) Milligrams	Riboflavin (Vitamin G) Micrograms	Vitamin D International Units	Niacin (Nicotinic Acid) Milligrams per 100 grams
Apples	1 medium-sized	68–170	64	13			0.50
Apricots, dried	½ cup, packed	6,000–15,000	60–120	2–12	240–300		
Asparagus, green	12 stalks, 5″ long, cooked	300–700	15–180	15–40			
Bananas	1 medium-sized	160–400	50–100	7–8	45–80		0.62
Beans, navy	⅓ cup, baked	31–53	101				5
Beans, soy	½ cup	100	1,200		900		
Beans, string	½ cup, cooked	372–1,116	34–59	6–12	40–93		0.70
Beef, lean muscle	2.7 ounce	8–39	85–162		139–200		7.5
Beets	2 beets—2″ diam	100	25–95	3–5	125		.64
Beet tops	¾ cup (scant), cooked	10,000		35	625		
Bread, enriched	1 slice		40–180		40–140		.85
Bread, white	1 slice (1 ounce)		11–17		8–20		
Bread, whole-wheat	1 slice		62–104		26		
Broccoli	⅞ cup, cooked	3,000–9,000	80–100	50–130	200–500		
Brussels sprouts	⅔ cup, cooked	300–500	171	13–50			
Butter	1 tablespoon	490–700				8	
Cabbage, chopped	½ cup	21	36	13	69		0.3
Cabbage, buttered	½ cup, cooked	176	64	3	160		
Cantaloupe	¼ melon—5″ diam	400–2,400	50–65	26–34	75		
Carrots	½ cup	1,870–3,400	51–119	2–4	64–106		1.47
Cauliflower	1 cup, chopped	35–60	130–200	48–94	150–220		.57
Celery, green	4 average stalks	5–50	20–50	6–8	30–55		
Chard	⅝ cup, cooked	13,000–27,000		10–20			
Cheese, American	1⅛-inch cube	454–910	9–11		102–136		
Cheese, cottage (skim)	2 tablespoons	18–24					
Cranberries	1 cup, fresh	10–20		10–13			.13
Cream, heavy (40% fat)	2 tablespoons	600–750	7–10		36–48		
Cream, light (18.5% fat)	2 tablespoons	300–450	9–12		45–60		
Dandelion greens	⅝ cup, cooked	13,000–27,000	150–225	5–40			
Dates	14 dates	60–300	60–100				2.18
Eggs	1 medium	540–1,080	76–86		151–227	8	.085
Fish, lean (not oily types)	3 ounces		75–162				
Flour, white	⅞ cup, sifted		60–100		40		.73
Flour, whole-wheat	¾ cup, sifted		330–500		100–200		1.4–1.6

Note: The above tables containing the contents in foods of Vitamin A, Thiamin (Vitamin B1), Ascorbic Acid (Vitamin C), and Riboflavin, (Vitamin G) are printed by permission of American National Red Cross from ARC 725 Food and Nutrition. The Vitamin D contents are taken from our March, 1941, issue of *Better Homes & Gardens.* The amounts of Niacin (Nicotinic Acid) are used thru the courtesy of Dr. P. C. Jeans, who cites as his authority: Weisman, Harry A.; Mickelson, O.; McKibben, J. M. & Elvehjem, C. A. (J. Nutrition, *19,* 483, May 10, 1940)—Bacharach, A. L. (Nutrition Absts. & Reviews, *10,* 459, Oct. 1940)—Clouse, Ruth C. (J. Am. Dietetic Ass'n. *18,* 553, Sept. 1943). Amounts of Niacin are given for 100 grams, an average serving of most foods. In figuring vitamins 1000 micrograms = 1 milligram.

FOOD	AMOUNT	Vitamin A International Units	Thiamin (Vitamin B1) Micrograms	Ascorbic Acid (Vitamin C) Milligrams	Riboflavin (Vitamin G) Micrograms	Vitamin D International Units	Niacin (Nicotinic Acid) Milligrams per 100 grams
Grapefruit	One-half medium—4″ diam.	21	50–100	38–41	20–100		
Grapefruit juice, fresh	Juice of one-half medium grapefruit	21	50–100	38–41	20–100		
Ham, lean	3 ounces		540–1,285		180–270		
Kale	1 cup, cooked	13,000–27,000	120–190	50–100	400–600		
Lemon juice	½ cup		30–90	52–60			
Lettuce, green	6 large leaves	700–7,000	50–125	6–21	100–245		
Liver, beef	2.7 ounces	3,850–7,700	231–323		1,386–2,002		17.5
Milk, fresh whole	1 cup	384–540	96–156	5	468–576		08–.15
Milk, irradiated evaporated	1 cup (undiluted)	777–1,092	194–316		938–1,165	68	.7–1.6
Oatmeal, dry	3 tablespoons		52–116		30		
Orange juice	½ cup (scant)	50–400	75–145	52–56	28–90		
Oysters	4 large	150–300	200–300	3			
Peaches, fresh yellow	1 medium-sized	1,000–2,000					.95
Peanuts, roasted	33-35 single	108	150–180		60–150		10–13
Peas, green, shelled	½ cup (scant)	660–858	178–327	10–17	165		
Peppers, green	1 pepper—3–4″ long		20–30	90–150			1.2
Pineapple, canned	2 slices, 3 tablespoons juice	20–30	63	10	20–30		
Pineapple juice, canned	½ cup (scant)	40–60	50–100	5–10	20–30		
Pork chop (lean meat only)	2.4 ounces		483–996		155–175		8.6
Potatoes, sweet	½ medium, baked	850–4,250	77–115	6–13	68–85		.67
Potatoes, white	1 medium-sized, baked	26–43	81–140	6–13	34–68		1–1.2
Prunes, stewed	4 prunes—4 tablespoons juice	159–1,272	95–127	0–3	32–318		
Salmon, canned	⅝ cup	15–462			154	400	8
Spinach	⅝ cup, cooked	13,000–27,000	95–155	15–50	250–400		1.7
Squash, Hubbard	½ cup, cooked	2,000–4,000	48	3	81		
Tomatoes, whole, raw, or canned	½ cup	600–1,440	84–138	25–29	44–76		0.5
Tuna, canned	½ cup					50	
Turnips	½ cup	7–14	46–67	14–21	36–71		
Turnip greens	½ cup, cooked	8,190–17,010	87–113	13–38	473		
Whole-wheat cereal	¾ cup, cooked						.5
Yeast, compressed	1 cake		49–126		108–540	400	

Note: The above tables containing the contents in foods of Vitamin A, Thiamin (Vitamin B1), Ascorbic Acid (Vitamin C), and Riboflavin (Vitamin G) are printed by permission of American National Red Cross from ARC 725 Food and Nutrition. The Vitamin D contents are taken from our March, 1941, issue of *Better Homes & Gardens*. The amounts of Niacin (Nicotinic Acid) are used thru the courtesy of Dr. P. C. Jeans, who cites as his authority: Weisman, Harry A.; Mickelson, O.; McKibben, J. M. & Elvehjem, C. A. (J. Nutrition, *19*, 483, May 10, 1940)—Bacharach, A. L. (Nutrition Absts. & Reviews, *10*, 459, Oct. 1940)—Clouse, Ruth C. (J. Am. Dietetic Ass'n. *18*, 553, Sept. 1943). Amounts of Niacin are given for 100 grams, an average serving of most foods. In figuring vitamins 1000 micrograms=1 milligram.

CHAPTER IX

Your Child From Fifteen to Eighteen Months

Development

Probably by this time your child's walking. Don't urge him or insist upon it, however, if he doesn't seem disposed to as yet. When he gets ready, he'll do it.

He's also probably saying a number of words. But in this, also, babies differ quite normally.

Walking? Probably. But if not, don't hurry him up

Shoes When He Walks

Don't be in a hurry to change from his soft-soled, moccasin-type first shoe—or from bare feet, if the weather allows. While it's true that firm-soled shoes encourage walking, after all you're in no hurry for that. More important are strong, well-shaped feet for your child. Running barefoot or wearing soft-soled shoes, exercises all the muscles of his toes and feet, which in turn makes them sturdy.

If there's any fault in the way he stands or walks, special shoes and possibly exercises as well can usually do much to correct it. Consult your doctor about this.

Bladder Training Should Begin

If you haven't started bladder training before this—and many authorities consider it best to wait until about the 15th month—it would be a good idea to do so now.

Bladder training is probably the biggest single job in the training of a small child, but it's much easier if you understand and approach it with the right attitude.

In the first place, remind yourself that this is a trait your youngster is bound to acquire sooner or later, whatever you do or don't do. There's no need, therefore, to get worried or desperate. Success will come whenever your child's muscles reach a point where he's able to control elimination, and his nervous system is capable of comprehending that this is what he's expected to do. It will be a long time before he'll be absolutely perfect about it, and longer yet before he'll tell you when he needs to void. The responsibility is yours—not your child's. It's the mother who demands immediate and perfect results who finds this task a source of worry. If it is undertaken with understanding and patience, there's nothing to dread.

Psychologists believe that punishments, shaming, or other unpleasant associations with toilet training have an extremely unwholesome effect upon your child's later life. Whether this is true or not, rest assured that he'll learn as readily if he's dealt with kindly and patiently as if he is punished and harangued. It will make little difference in 10 years whether the lesson was learned in 3 months or 6, but a great deal whether it was taught with love and patience.

Pants Instead of Diapers

Discard the diaper, which, by its thick, soft mass is an incentive to be careless about wetting. Substitute training panties, which are made of knitted cotton and readily removable. The outer garment during this period should be in two pieces, for a boy, so that the pants also are easily taken off. A girl may wear a dress over her training panties.

Dig in now for an intensive campaign of putting your child on the toilet, regularly as clockwork, at certain times during the day. Your youngster now is trained as to bowels. He has learned, therefore, what is expected when he's placed on the toilet, and he'll urinate at these times. Tell him in terms you want him to associate with the act. Praise him for success, ignore failure or wet panties.

Place him on the toilet:

On arising.

Before and after each meal.

Before his bath.

Before and after his nap.

Just before going to bed.

When the habit of voiding at these times is well established, begin placing him on the toilet every hour during his waking times. If this seems ineffectual after a fair trial, shorten the intervals to every 45 minutes, but don't make them oftener. The idea isn't so much to catch every movement as to train him to a regimen. Placing him on the toilet too often will make him unhappy. In time he'll learn to wait for the expected interval.

An Alarm Clock Will Help

Watch the clock, for many youngsters are disturbingly punctual during the training period, and a minute's delay on your part may be fatal to dryness. Many mothers find it helps to set the alarm during this phase, to remind themselves of the hourly intervals.

Don't leave him on the stool for more than five minutes at a time. Usually you'll find that the child who has been bowel trained will void very quickly after being put on.

If he hasn't performed at the end of the five minutes, however, let him down. You may then watch him for signs, which every mother learns to recognize, and get him back on the toilet quickly when necessary. If he wets himself, display no emotion. Have him wipe up

the floor or otherwise help correct any damage as well as he can, but don't make it a punishment situation.

Some children begin rather early to indicate in some way or other when they need to go, but this isn't to be exptected until a youngster is at least 2 years old. Accidents will occur for several years, during stress or excitement. In cold weather, your child will wet more than in warm because there's less evaporation thru the skin pores. The big, robust child who eats and drinks heartily will wet more than the one with a small appetite. All these things must be taken into consideration and allowances made.

Even after he begins to tell you, the responsibility is still yours. Have him go to the toilet at regular intervals, tho these may gradually get farther apart. There will be a period during which the little chamber must accompany your goings abroad, if you are to be very long away from a toilet. You defeat yourself if you put on rubber pants for social occasions and let you child wet. This matter must always be on your mind, and the facilities at hand for attending to it.

He Needs Space for Play

Play will occupy an increasingly large place in your child's life. He should no longer be placed in the little play pen but should have a good-sized outdoor pen that's at least 12 feet square. It's ideal if you can fence in a whole back yard. In this inclosure there should be a sand pile equipped with a spade or shovel, and a toy truck or wagon. Both indoors and out, the push and pull toys fulfill the need of your youngster's growing muscles. At this age he'll enjoy putting things together, such as placing bottles in cans, and should have plenty of empty receptacles with which to work.

Snow fence is a popular material for a temporary pen, and it is usually available. An ingenious father can buy wooden laths and nail them to a board frame. Palings make a very neat enclosure.

For indoor play, your child needs a room, not too far away from your activities, where he can be confined with his toys for certain periods of the day. This room should contain a toy cupboard or shelves, low enough so he can reach his playthings readily; a small, sturdy table and chair; and any other furnishings you like. A gate or other barrier which keeps your child in but doesn't shut him away from you is needed to keep him in his room.

This type of sandpile is in a box slightly raised above the ground, with a wide rim for sitting on

Toy List Grows

This is the period for the development of the large arm, leg, and body muscles as opposed to the smaller muscles of hands and fingers. (That comes later.) There are a number of toys which help to do this:

Balls—Develop large muscles as your child runs after them.

Wheelbarrow—Develops large muscles.

Kiddie car—Develops large muscles thru footwork.

Rocking chair—Develops large muscles thru footwork.

Small stout wagon—Develops large muscles.

Pull toys on stout strings—Develop large muscles.

Heavy train (wood or iron)—Develops large muscles.

Doll carriage—Develops large muscles.

Stout chair—Develops large muscles.

Large blocks (no sharp corners)—Develop large muscles.

Nest of blocks—Develops large muscles, also senses.

Unbreakable or cloth doll—Develops large muscles, also senses.

Chair swing—Develops large muscles.

Linen picture books—Develop senses.

If it's possible, pets should be added to your child's collection. These are the most valuable playthings of all. A cat, dog, or tame rabbit is the best pet for a youngster at this age.

Playmates Add to His Fun

Your child will take pleasure now in the companionship of a youngster somewhere near his age, altho children don't begin to play together in the usual sense for some time to come. Each child will pursue his own individual activities, but will like the idea that the other is around. If there are no small children in the neighborhood with whom your youngster can play, arrange to have your friends bring theirs fairly often. Put the children together in the play yard and let them go their own way.

They can't be expected to know how to play with each other—that's something they have to learn by trial and error. They'll probably maul and manhandle each other before they discover that flesh and blood react differently from an inanimate object when hit with a shovel. If the children are approximately the same age, however, and fairly evenly matched, they won't harm each other and will learn by experience what they may and may not do.

To place a small child at the mercy of a considerably older or bigger and rougher one is hardly fair, tho. Be guided by your own common sense in this matter of playmates and the regulation of play. And don't be alarmed about seemingly cannibalistic or homicidal tendencies. Folks this little don't know their own power. When they get a healthy reaction from an equally sturdy contemporary, they find it out.

Keep His Food List Growing

Continue to widen your youngster's range of food likes by giving him more and more of the allowed foods listed in the preceding chapter. Continue also to progress from strained to chopped or ground foods. Work toward bite sizes, except for meat, which should be chopped or ground till your child is 3 years old.

In introducing a new food or one he doesn't like very well, insist that he take a taste. Then allow him to eat as much as he likes of the rest of a meal which includes several of his favorite dishes. Experiments conducted by nursery schools over a long period of time

He'll like the idea of another youngster in his pen

show that if a child has a chance to become accustomed to a food, he'll like it. But he has a better chance to like it if he takes it slowly, a little bit at a time.

During the present state, when food habits are still being established, it's helpful to present the new or disliked food (usually it's a vegetable) at the first of the meal when your child's hungriest. If he has already learned to take anything that comes his way, it won't be necessary to do this. Put on his plate a fair serving—about 2 tablespoons—of each of the foods for the meal. Give him a small glass or cup of milk—about 4 ounces—and let him eat and drink as he likes. As long as he takes some of each item, it's not necessary to worry about the amounts. He may have seconds if he cleans his plate. This time give him about 1 tablespoon each of the various items, and refill his glass of milk. Give dessert in proportion to the amount he has eaten of the other foods. Let him have as many refills as he wants, but in small amounts. And keep them in balance.

If you're encountering difficulty, however, in getting him to eat enough of one of the three food classes, continue to give him the food or foods he likes least (whether vegetables, milk, or dessert) at the start of the meal when he's hungriest. After he has taken a reasonable amount, bring on the rest of his meal.

In our schedule on this page we've listed first at each meal the foods which tend to be those usually slighted in child—and adult—nutrition. If your child eats these well and other foods not so well, reverse the order. If he eats all foods equally well, disregard this arrangement entirely, and set before him all the foods for the meal. In feeding him go from one to another, or if he feeds himself, let him make his own choices.

Continue to have him eat his meals by himself. He can now have his own little table and chair, and may want to feed himself.

When he starts reaching for the spoon, it's his sign that he is ready for this next step. Look out for a messy time, for his first tendency will be to turn the spoon upside down as he places it in his mouth. At first help him guide it. Encourage honest effort, but don't allow him to play with the food. When he starts this, or tires of the eating process, take the spoon away and finish feeding him yourself.

The schedule seems to call for a lot of baths during the day, but you'll find they're needed. At this age a youngster is a heavy wetter at night, and needs a morning sponge-off until he is taught dryness. After his morning, and again after his afternoon, play, you'll find he can use a bath with no trouble.

Schedule for Child Fifteen to Eighteen Months Old

The foods on this schedule may be selected from the list on page 123.

7:00 a.m. Arises, to toilet at once for urinating. Light sponge bath. Brush teeth, put on bathrobe for breakfast.

Breakfast:

Two to 4 tablespoons stewed fruit.

Two to 4 tablespoons cereal with milk or thin cream, but no sugar.

Milk toast or mashed ripe banana may be substituted occasionally.

Milk, 1 cup or as much as he'll take.

Bacon or toast, or both, if he's still hungry. The daily egg may also be given now if desired.

7:30 a.m. (or immediately after breakfast). On toilet for bowel movement, not more than 10 minutes, unless he's actually evacuating. Dressed for day, hair brushed.

8:00 a.m. Plays about the house or in his playroom, or sits in chair to eat zwieback during the family breakfast. Follow the arrangement which works best.

8:30 a.m. On toilet for urinating, not more than 5 minutes.

9:00 a.m. Vitamin D concentrate or 1 teaspoon fish-liver oil as prescribed.

Four ounces orange juice or 8 of tomato juice. More if desired.

On toilet again before being prepared for outdoors.

9:00 a.m. to 11:15 a.m. Plays outdoors in pen, being brought in each hour to urinate. Or plays in playroom, depending upon weather.

11:15 a.m. Bath. Dons bathrobe. On toilet.

11:30 a.m. to 12:00 n.
  Dinner:
  Vegetables or vegetable soup. (See list of suitable foods on page 123.)
  Meat or meat broth.
  Potato, macaroni, spaghetti, or tenderoni, 3 times a week.
  Dessert (see list on page 123).
  Milk.
  On toilet.

1:00 p.m. to 3:00 p.m. Nap. Arises. On toilet.
  Cup of milk, or graham cracker, or arrowroot cooky, or fruit.
  After eating, to toilet again. Dressed to play outdoors in pen.

4:00 p.m. Brought in to toilet.

5:00 p.m. Toilet again. He may now stay in the house, playing with other members of the family.

5:30 p.m. Light bath, on toilet. Dons bathrobe.

5:45 p.m. Supper:
  Creamed vegetable (different from the one served at noon).
  Poached egg if none was eaten at breakfast.
  Fresh or stewed fruit, according to the season.
  Whole-wheat or enriched bread and butter.
  Milk.

6:30 p.m. to 7:00 p.m. On toilet, dressed for bed. To bed in room alone with door shut and window open.

CHAPTER X

Your Child at Eighteen to Twenty-four Months

By now your child should be walking. If he isn't, take him to your doctor for an examination. Probably he's saying many words, and perhaps even forming short sentences. He's extremely active, and never still a minute.

If a girl, you may expect negativism to develop any time now. It will be explained in this chapter.

At this age he'll remind you of perpetual motion

Keep Good Habits Going

What all the foregoing adds up to is that now your job gets really interesting!

A normal child of 18 months is going to develop ideas and a will of his own. (We'll discuss that further under negativism.) He'll be as demanding as he is active.

You'll be tempted to relax the schedule somewhat—to let bedtime be later than it

should, to allow your youngster to dictate about his food. Don't, don't, don't! First thing you know, you'll find yourself the slave of a whimsical young tyrant.

One of the easy but lamentable errors to fall into at this time is to have your young one constantly under foot, getting into things, holding you at his beck and call. Don't let this happen, either. Keep your youngster in his playroom at regular hours of the day, with plenty of toys. You'll remember we suggested fencing off part of the downstairs to be used as a playroom when the play pen becomes too cramped. A breakfast nook or sunroom is excellent for this, but any room or corner of a room may be used. Have some barrier that will keep your child in but won't prevent him from seeing you and being conscious that you're near. Eighteen months is far too young for him to be shut off in an upstairs playroom, or confined behind a closed door.

Place your child in the playroom for regular periods when the weather's too bad for the play pen outdoors. You can drop by and chat with him now and then, and, of course, you'll observe the toilet times. But let him understand that you have your work to do, and he has his. Thus you'll not only free yourself of constant interference, but Son (or Daughter) will be taking another step along the path of self-reliance.

It's equally important to have regular periods each day when he's free to roam about the house, under somebody's watchful eye, and visit with the family. He mustn't be stuck off in a pen all the time, by any means.

Big enough to stand on
step or box for toilet

There should be places
for all his belongings

He'll run away unless
penned up or watched

But keeping this sort of thing to a regular hour does away with the constant importuning there will be if you always drop your work to act as entertainer.

Night Bladder Control

Bladder training continues to hold the center of the stage thruout the rest of this year. By the eighteenth month, if you started daytime training at 1 year or 15 months, your child is dry most of the time. But this is because you or someone else has the matter constantly in mind. This will have to be the case until your child is about 27 months old, or perhaps even older.

At about 18 months, a little boy can be taught to urinate while standing erect, and it's a good lesson for him to learn. At a time when you know he needs to go badly, hold the chamber or a milk bottle up before him, using the word you associate with the act. Or, if he's thoroly accustomed to the toilet, have him stand on a box before it. He may refuse for some time. But persist, doing it at least once a day, and presently he'll get the idea. The convenience of this method is obvious in the case of a boy, besides being a psychological step forward for him. When this lesson is learned, the pants with an opening in front can be used. Great stress can be laid upon the fact that he's a big boy now!

When daytime control is well established, and not before, night training should begin. This will occur at about the eighteenth month if the schedule has been faithfully followed. It will facilitate matters if you take away the evening cup of milk, giving no liquid after 4 o'clock. If he wants a drink badly, give him a small one.

Method:

1. When night training begins, remove his diaper, as for daytime training.

2. Take him up at 10 o'clock and have him urinate, being sure he's thoroly awake and knows what he's doing. If he has wet, put a dry sleeper on him, and dry his bed. If he's consistently wet at 10, take him up at 9 o'clock, but not before.

3. Take him to the bathroom the minute he wakens in the morning. This is usually the most difficult time to catch, for a child usually voids as his first waking act. You must be on the alert to anticipate this. If your youngster wakens at 6 o'clock and voids, get him up at 15 minutes to 6. He can then be put back in bed until the hour for rising. Some of your sleep will have to be sacrificed during this period—there's no escaping it. But having your little fellow's bed dry most nights after his second birthday is well worth the effort. If he's wet when you go to him in the early morning, you'll have to get up with him sometime during the night. About 1 a. m. is usually a good time. As he learns bladder control, this time can be omitted, just as the night feedings were.

As in the case of the daytime wetting, accidents aren't cause for concern. Gradually your child will learn control and the advantages of dryness over wetness, just as he learned during the day.

Orderliness Now

Now's the time to teach orderliness. The first step is to be orderly yourself, for a child at this age sees everything and is as imitative as a monkey. If you haven't had it before, you should by all means now have a regular place for your youngster's every possession and be strict in returning it there after it is used.

Clothes: There should be low hooks and hangers for your child's clothes—in his bedroom for his suits and underwear, and in the downstairs coat closet for his outdoor wraps. Have a hook for each article, and take pains as you remove each piece of clothing to hang it on the proper hook. Your child will quickly learn where each belongs, and will run and get it as needed. The next step, to be made when your little runabout is about 2 years old, is to teach him to hang the garment on the designated hook. Observe the rule yourself, and you'll have little trouble getting him to do so.

Toys: Remember how we've said that from his first birthday your child needed his own room or corner with shelves or a cupboard for his toys? The toys should be placed in the same spot each time. Begin at 18 months to put things away as he's thru playing with them, and call his attention to what you're doing. Presently he'll want to help a little. Show him where to put each toy and pleasantly insist that it be put there. Extend this until, around his third year, you hold him responsible for putting each toy in its proper place after he's finished.

The important thing to remember is that orderliness comes as a result of orderliness in the home, plus training at the proper time. This period is the proper time for the training.

How to Teach Obedience

Some conscientious parents are confused as to how much they should expect in the way of obedience. Do modern methods mean that a child shouldn't have to obey?

Not at all. Obedience to properly constituted authority is one of the lessons each of us must learn. You, his parents, are the first authority with which your child comes in contact. If he learns early to accept and to obey your reasonable commands, delivered in a pleasant and courteous way, he's all set to accept the authority of the school when he comes to that, and of society when he's old enough to come under its laws and rules.

The child who has learned to obey necessary commands while allowed as much freedom of choice and action as is possible at his stage of development, runs no danger of becoming an automaton. Rather, he's relieved of useless rebellion against necessary operations in which the undisciplined and disobedient child wastes much of his energy.

He's free instead to use his strength and ingenuity in ways that are more profitable.

Around the 21st month, you can occasionally give him a simple command, helping him by your gestures to know what you mean, as "Pick up the paper, please." Say it very pleasantly and courteously, and show him what you mean until he gets the idea.

Give few commands, now and from now on, but when you do give one, see that it's carried out. Make a request or command to your child in as polite and courteous a way as you would to any adult of your acquaintance.

Make it definite and firm, however. Don't ask a child if "he'd like" to do this. It's too easy for him to say he wouldn't.

A pitfall into which it's easy to fall is that of so-called "reasoning." Children at this age are too young to reason, but they learn quickly that they can get control of the situation by arguing and resisting. They've a whole bag full of tricks! You should have a reason for your command, of course, and it's all right to explain it—once. That, however, should end all discussion. If your command's worth giving, it's worth obeying without debate. If you start refuting a youngster's objections and go into lengthy explanations, first thing you know you'll have an argument over every simple operation.

Teaching obedience doesn't mean that you should regiment your youngster and his every deed. Allow him as much freedom of choice and action as you can. Study to make the doing of necessary things pleasant for him. But don't be afraid to tell your child, quietly and courteously, to do the things he must do. And then to see that he does them!

Play Pen for the Runaway

It's normal for the active, bright runabout to begin running away during this period. The answer is not punishment or admonition, for the child this age can't remember. Putting him in the play pen is the way to handle this problem. By the age of 3, when it will be almost impossible to confine him, he'll be old enough to learn to stay within bounds. Until then, it's your place to see that he is safely confined or constantly watched.

When Training Hits a Snag

Your youngster is now in the full swing of one of his most active periods of growth and learning. At a year, he was a baby. When he's

2, he'll be running everywhere, talking, feeding himself, making some moves toward dressing himself, helping to look after his belongings, and toilet-trained except for occasional accidents. In a year's time he changes from a baby to a child.

With so many things for him to learn, it will be helpful to stop and look at the way youngsters this age do it. Recent information has come from scientific laboratories about this. It will help you with problems that have stumped many parents before you.

We've seen that there's a time when your child is ready to take on easily and quickly each new habit, skill, or accomplishment. It's the time when his muscular development and his nervous system have caught up with each other, and he's bursting to try the new powers laid open to him. We've seen that when he reaches for the spoon, it's his sign that he's ready to feed himself. Likewise, when he begins to recognize the articles of his clothing and to take an interest in dressing, he'll be ready to begin dressing himself.

Thus it is with all the skills and activities, which will be opening up gradually to your child in the years to come. It's your job to keep close enough to him so you'll catch the signals when he gives them. As you follow his development, you'll get more and more adept in interpreting them, and in helping him develop the skill or ability for which he's ready at the time. Don't urge or rush him into an activity for which he isn't ready. But when he shows the go-ahead signal, drop everything else and go ahead with him for all you're worth!

But there's a second thing. You must understand that after your child has mastered a skill or habit, there will be periods of regression. Parents have been up against this from time immemorial, but haven't known what it meant. They have probably thought their youngster was being deliberately naughty because he had already shown that he understood what was wanted of him.

But according to Dr. Myrtle McGraw of Columbia University's Normal Child Clinic, the regressions are just as much a sign of development as are the increases in skill.

We've known for a long time that most toddlers break down in their toilet habits around the 18th month. To mothers and fathers, this often looks like deliberate wickedness, and countless home battles have raged in consequence. But let's see what else is happening. The toilet miscreant is learning to talk—a tremendous new experience. Perhaps he acquires a word for voiding. When he does that, he'll probably quit the gesturing upon which you've been depending. Or he may say the word for voiding all right, but only after the act has begun. It takes time for both speech and bladder control to become co-ordinated to the place where your child can express his need in words before he urinates.

The same is true of self-feeding. After your baby has learned to carry the spoon nicely to his mouth, he begins throwing and splattering the food around. (That's something else that has been misunderstood by the adults within firing range.) But notice that he'll also begin to pick up crumbs between his thumb and fingers. This is another stage of development. Part of his food should now be given in small bites or pieces that he can pick up with his fingers, thus using his new ability.

After a youngster gets to be about 3 years old, new experiences and impressions are coming so thick and fast that often he forgets to eat at all for a time, he's so busy telling you about them. But in time he'll learn to talk and eat at the same time.

Ahead of you is a long, patience-taxing period of letting your child learn to dress himself. You stand by, tho it kills you, letting him puzzle out buttons and ties that are problems for small, awkward fingers. And then about the time he gets so he can do it pretty well, he'll lose all interest and dawdle till you'll be distracted. But that's all part of the picture.

Learning to dress himself is a long, slow process

"Your child has an indomitable urge to exercise his newly developing function," says Dr. McGraw, "but once he has acquired a degree of efficiency, he grows indifferent toward it and directs his energies toward some new type of learning. Recognition of this fact may avoid storms and tantrums. When peri-

Just as he's learned to feed himself fairly well, your rascal will start throwing his food around

ods of regression come, look for rapid development in other aspects of the child's behavior."

The same laws govern learning later on in sports, the arts, and all kinds of things. "We don't begin to develop the potentialities of our children," says Dr. McGraw. "As each stage of development looms, provide the opportunity for the exercise of new powers. The first 18 months in general are a time of marvelous motor development. The baby can learn to climb and swim, even to roller skate, more easily then, in all probability, than ever afterwards. During the last part of the second year, speech develops. That is the time to talk and read much to your child. From then on, it's a constant unfolding."

Expect that once a new thing has been mastered, something else will come along to claim your child's interest. Don't be disappointed if he drops the first thing. Soon he'll develop to the point where he can co-ordinate the new with the old, and the old skill or habit is there again, good as ever.

When we understand the reason back of the regressions which are bound to come, it's easy to see why calmness and patience are better parental methods than crossness and punishments.

If Toilet Training Breaks Down

One of the most annoying regressions is that in toilet training. Somewhere around the age of 18 months, many excellently trained chil-

dren revert to baby habits in this respect. Because this is so disconcerting socially, parents have a tendency to bear down heavily with punishments or perhaps keep the youngster on the toilet for long periods. The result is that a great many youngsters acquire at this time an aversion for the toilet itself and the whole business. They'll go to fantastic lengths to keep from eliminating when on the toilet, only to do so as soon as they're released. But that is because the parents themselves have turned it into a battle of wills.

What should you do?

Keep calm and unperturbed. You know this is only a passing phase, for normal human beings in a state of civilization accept toilet taboos if they accept nothing else. Go back to your training method again, just as you followed it in the first place. Watch the clock, make it your responsibility to see that he goes at regular intervals. Remain cheerful and pleasant. Don't keep him on the toilet for more than five-minute intervals, and don't put him on oftener than every hour. If he offends, have him help clean up the mess as much as he can, and pleasantly remind him to let you know when he needs to go to the toilet. Soon he'll be back on schedule again.

Many parents have the idea that it's harder to retrain a child for the toilet than to train him in the first place. This isn't so. It only seems harder because it's a long, hard job that you thought you were done with. Your child isn't being deliberately naughty. If you remain pleasant and keep toilet times on your own mind instead of expecting him to do so, the regression will soon be a thing of the past.

There may be one or more regressions later as your youngster gets particularly absorbed in some new phase of learning. In cold weather when he's playing out of doors, urination will be likely to be more frequent and you may have to watch him more closely.

Usually by the age of 3, however, daytime cleanliness is permanently established, nighttime dryness by 5. Even a well-behaved preschool child will wet the bed when he has a cold, or some other illness, but will stop as soon as he's well again.

When He Says "I Won't"

Another phenomenon of the period between 18 and 27 months is negativism. This is very disturbing to parents simply because they don't understand it.

When negativism hits your happy home,

your formerly amenable, obedient, well-trained youngster suddenly will start "no"-ing every proposal you make. "No, no!" and "I won't!" will seem to make up his entire vocabulary. He won't eat his dinner, take his nap, go out in his play pen, or pick up his toys. Or so he says. He'll probably back up his remarks with a temper tantrum, and if it gets results, he'll keep right on having tantrums.

"If I can't control my child when he's 18 months old, what will happen when he's 18 years old!" is a common fear of parents when this phase strikes.

Don't worry. Negativism is one of the steps in development described by Dr. McGraw. As your child's powers increase, he naturally wants to try them. He'll make an all-out effort to take the control of his schedule and of his life in general into his own hands. If he succeeds, as too many children do at this age, he'll be as unhappy as the folks around him, for no child of 18 to 27 months possesses the judgment to run his own life.

What to do? Again, keep perfectly calm and cheerful. Soon you'll learn that the "I won't" is only lip deep, and that he'll do what you want him to do if you don't argue, but insist by your actions. If he refuses to do what you tell him, take him by the hand and pleasantly but firmly lead him thru the motions.

Pay no attention whatever to what he says, let the "No, no" go in one ear and out the other.

Often you can divert his mind by making a game out of what you want him to do. If he says he "won't" go to bed, don't argue. Say, "Let's see who can get up the stairs first." Children are tremendously suggestible. They respond miraculously to play ideas when you yourself are poised and unperturbed.

At the same time, make your commands just as few as possible. You want your child to be independent, and he can become independent only as he's allowed to take on responsibility for his own affairs. Unless it's a matter of his health and welfare, as food, sleep, and safety obviously are, give him as much freedom as you can. Just don't let him get the whiphand in matters he's not qualified to handle.

This is another place where common sense must be the judge. As incidents arise, you'll have to decide whether they're important or trivial. But you can follow the general plan of insisting upon obedience when it's absolutely necessary for your child's health, well being, and safety, and letting him have his head in most other things.

As a rule, girls show negativism somewhere around 18 months, and are coming out of it when they're 27 months old. Boys usually start it at about 27 months.

The Inevitable Temper Tantrum

The happiest and most wisely handled child in the world may have a temper tantrum sometime during this period of trying out his own powers. Pay no attention to it, unless it's to remove your youngster to his own room or some place where he won't bother anyone else. He shouldn't be allowed to get his own way by means of a temper tantrum. If he's simply trying you out, he'll quit when he finds that the tantrum gets him nothing except exile from the family circle. If the first tantrum works, naturally he'll try more and more. Children aren't dumb!

Children also however, have tantrums when they're tired, over-stimulated, or ordered about too much. Have you yielded to temptation and broken his bed and nap times? Are you directing every detail of his day? If you can answer "no" to these questions with a clear conscience, just smile up your sleeve when your youngster pulls out this old trick, and make sure it wins him nothing. Have you, however, been letting him overdo, subjected him to too much excitement or stimulation? Are you treating him like a baby with no mind or will of his own? If so, take the tantrums as a signal to change your ways.

"Tell Me a Story"

Any time now the story hour may begin. The yearling-and-a-half won't understand much of a story, but loves to look at pictures. The last 15 minutes before bedtime, when he's all ready to be popped between the covers, can be spent in looking at the pictures and telling what the objects are. Or you can play records on the victrola. (See lists of books and records beginning on pages 185 and 188.) This can be varied with songs, with or without the piano. The story or music hour will prove a precious custom both to you and to your child.

When He Feeds Himself

Continue to feed your runabout before the family meal, and apart from the family so he'll be quiet and bothered as little as possible.

He should have his own little table and chair. They can be in the playroom, nursery, or kitchen, whichever's most convenient. Floor-coverings must be taken into account, for there'll be much spilling.

After your youngster begins to feed himself, the kitchen is an excellent place, for he can eat while you're busy getting the family meal. You're at hand to help if help is needed, but you aren't giving your whole attention to him. This is desirable.

As he shows an inclination to feed himself, let him do so. Help him only as he needs it, letting him carry on as long and as well as he can. When he tires, take the spoon and finish giving him the meal yourself. Don't let him play or dawdle over his food, but don't urge or coax him to eat.

Set before him about 2 tablespoons of each food (unless he's a very hearty eater, in which case it may be more), and a small glass of milk. If he cleans his plate and asks for more, give another round of small servings, and fill up his milk glass. If he eats all his solid foods well, it's all right to place a cute little pitcher on the table and let him fill his own glass.

If he has a tendency to fill up on milk and slight his solids, however, give the plate of solids first, and withhold the milk until a reasonable amount of the solids has been eaten.

How *Not* to Have an Eating Problem

A good many youngsters, trained to good eating habits, become problems at this time simply because their parents don't understand that there are normal setbacks in physical growth, just as in learning. Let's see now how children grow.

During his first year, your fine infant gained at least 14 pounds, which required a lot of food. But in his second year he'll probably gain only 5 or 6. It's logical, then, that his appetite also will slacken, for children eat to grow—they don't grow to eat.

Not understanding this, parents are prone to be worried when their child's interest in food lessens. They start urging, pleading, even threatening the youngster to eat more than he really wants.

Left to himself, your child at this period will probably pick at his food for a few meals. Then, getting really hungry, will eat everything in sight for a few days. Over a year's time, the resulting food intake is the same as if he had eaten three good meals every day.

Temper tantrums come with this age. Smile to yourself, otherwise ignore them. He'll soon give up

Your toddler will eat best at his or her own small table before your meal. Kitchen's recommended spot

He'll probably want to feed himself, but may tire and start playing. Signal for you to finish feeding

The story hour can begin any time now. One of happiest parts of day for youngsters and for you also

But when parents try to bribe, coax, and tease a set amount of food down every day, the child never has a chance to get hungry. Often he gets so he hates the thought of food. "I don't believe he'd care if he never ate," is a frequent complaint of parents of pre-school youngsters. To a certain extent it's probably true.

Let your watchword from now on be "don't force him to eat." His appetite may be bird-like at times, and for some time to come, but when he reaches the pre-pubertal growth spurt, he'll make up for it.

And don't let him fill up between meals on bread and butter, candy, and cookies. Confine his eating to mealtimes, except for what's called for in the schedule. Then you can safely allow him to eat as little or as much as he wants of his balanced menu.

Place before him on his little, attractively set table, small amounts of each of the foods on the diet schedule. Then let him alone.

If he cleans it up and wants more, give him more in small quantities. Give dessert in pro-portion to the food he has eaten. That is, if he eats only about a tablespoon of other items, give him a tablespoon of dessert. If he has re-fills and gets 4 tablespoons of the others, give him 4 tablespoons of dessert. Thus the food balance will be maintained, however small or large the amounts he eats.

If he tires of feeding himself, it's proper to take the spoon and finish as much of the meal as he wants. But don't urge upon him food that he obviously doesn't want.

At the end of half an hour, dismiss him quietly and pleasantly from the table even tho he has eaten nothing. If he has eaten well, compliment him. If he hasn't, ignore it. Keep mealtime a pleasant, happy experience to which your child looks forward. Never let it become an issue.

Says the American Academy of Pediatrics, "Parents should be made to understand that it is their duty to decide what and when the child should eat, but that it is the child's prerogative to decide how much of it he will eat. Missing a meal now and then is not a matter of great seriousness, but it is an excel-lent means of stimulating an appetite."

Between Meal Sweets Spoil Appetite

Still another pitfall looms at this age. Dur-ing their child's infant years, most parents are conscientious about following the diet sched-ule given them by the doctor. But when Baby turns into a runabout with teeth and the ability to eat most of the foods on the family menu, he's exposed to a deluge of candy, ice cream, soft drinks, cookies and the like. As someone has observed, the one idea most people have of the way to be good to a child is to feed him something, and in most cases it's something sweet or rich. Thus children learn quickly to want the sweet, pleasant-tasting foods, and to reject those not so exciting. Un-fortunately, the carbohydrate or energy-pro-ducing foods taste better than the body-building and body-protecting ones, so many children grow up starved in minerals and vitamins because they are gorged with sweets.

Don't fall into that trap with your young-ster who has come along so nicely. Keep to the foods in the schedule which follows, and insist that friends, relatives, and neighbors shall not feed your child between meals. They mean well, but that's no reason why you should let them overthrow the splendid food habits you've built so carefully and laborious-ly. Keep up the good work!

Weight Isn't All

We've said little about growth since the end of the first year. If your child is given the care we suggest, he'll be well nourished. There'll be no need to watch the scales. We will put our emphasis upon giving him the proper food, rest, and outdoor life—that done, his growth will take care of itself.

After his first birthday, as we've seen, the gain is much slower. His weight on an aver-age is 21 pounds at 1 year, and 27 at 2. His height on an average is 27 inches when he's 1 year old, 31 inches when he's 2.

Much more important than weight and height are his posture, the color and bright-ness of his eyes, the strength of his muscles, the solidity of his flesh, and his animation and happiness. If these are all good, your child is all right whether he's above or below the average of the tables.

A good deal of grief has been caused in recent years by mistaken attempts to have every child conform to averages arrived at by lumping together the measurements of many children. Now parents are warned against this.

Children born of tall, thin stock are likely to weigh less than the average. Chunky little folk will probably weigh more. Be pleased with your child as he is, so long as he's bright, healthy, peppy, and happy, and eats with appetite the foods that are good for him.

Schedule for the Child Eighteen Months to Two Years Old

Stressing orderliness and night bladder training

The foods on this schedule may be selected from the list on page 123.

5:45 a.m. Take him up to urinate. (The time will depend upon when your child usually wakens. It may be earlier or later than this.) Put him back to bed, in dry sleeper and dry bed.

7:00 a.m. Rises, urinates, gets light sponge bath, dons bathrobe. Breakfast, eaten at his little table, in his little chair. Let him feed himself, if he wants to.

Stewed fruit.

Cereal. Your child at this age may occasionally have ready-to-serve cereals (such as corn flakes), in addition to the cooked, canned, and special baby cereals he has been eating. Use them sparingly, however. He may have a teaspoon of honey on his cereal once in a while.

Bacon and toast if desired.

Milk.

7:30 a.m. On toilet for bowel movement. Following this, dress him for day. Brush his hair and teeth as part of the dressing process, hang nightclothes and bathrobe on special hook.

8:00 a.m. In playroom, or eating zwieback while family has breakfast. Have him help put away his toys as used.

8:30 a.m. Urinates.

9:00 a.m. Concentrate or 1 teaspoon fish-liver oil.

Four ounces orange juice, or 8 ounces tomato juice—more if desired. Urinates before going out to play in pen or fenced yard.

10:00 a.m. Brought in to toilet.

11:00 a.m. Brought in to toilet. May stay in now.

11:15 a.m. Bath, with clothes hung on special hooks as taken off. Afterwards he dons pajamas and bathrobe.

11:30 a.m. Lunch:

Vegetables or vegetable soup.

Meat or meat broth.

Potato, macaroni, spaghetti, or tenderoni 3 times a week.

Milk or gelatin dessert.

Milk.

12:00 n. On toilet. Put down in room with door closed and window open.

2:00 p.m. to 3:00 p.m. Wakes, placed on toilet, then dressed for play. Cup of milk.

3:00 p.m. Urinates.

4:00 p.m. Urinates. May have cup of milk now as it will be withheld at supper, but he need not take it if he doesn't want it.

5:00 p.m. Brought in from outdoors, urinates, plays about house and joins family.

5:15 p.m. Light bath (as needed). Dons pajamas and bathrobe.

5:30 p.m. to 6:00 p.m. Supper:

Creamed vegetable.

Poached egg.

Fresh fruit in season.

Cottage cheese may be given often.

No milk for convenience in night bladder training.

Urinates, dresses for bed.

6:00 p.m. to 6:30 p.m. May play while Daddy eats his dinner.

6:30 p.m. to 6:45 p.m. Story or music hour. Daddy will enjoy presiding.

7:00 p.m. On toilet again, to bed in room with door closed, window open.

10:00 p.m. Taken up, thoroly wakened, placed on toilet to urinate. Afterwards, given dry sleeper if necessary and bed dried. It may be necessary to do this at 9:00 instead of 10:00.

1:00 a.m. Roused to urinate if ordinarily found wet at 6:00 a.m. Otherwise let him sleep thru.

The cereals, meats, vegetables, fruits, and desserts listed on the schedule may be selected from the list of suitable foods on page 123. It's a good idea to teach your youngster to eat as many of these as possible.

If needed, one-half hour may be allowed for supper. The story hour may gradually be extended to one-half hour. Please don't feel it's necessary to follow this schedule as if it were a railroad timetable.

SECTION THREE

Your Child
From Two to Six Years

The Gate Begins to Open

Your adored and precious baby has left your lap. He's an eager little runabout, going everywhere, wild for experience and adventure. You couldn't keep him sheltered in your arms if you tried. He's on his way!

You have a right to be proud and happy because the love and care you've lavished upon him have provided him with so healthy a body, so eager a mind.

Now comes the question, "How can I best fit him for what lies ahead?"

We have seen in the past that the world can change overnight from a safe, pleasant place to one of grim effort, sacrifice, and hardship. Fathers and mothers can't be blamed for wondering whether the gentle philosophies which have dominated child-rearing these past years will prepare children adequately for such a world. It's natural that we should ask ourselves whether sterner attitudes and punishments are called for.

But let's stop and consider. The boys who accepted the disciplines of the last war so splendidly and who endured hardships we can never know, were reared by that philosophy. It has proved itself under fire.

A wise man has pointed out that a gardener doesn't expose his tender spring seedlings to frost and chill, just because he knows winter is coming. He doesn't keep pulling and tugging them up by the roots to accustom them to future hurricanes.

Instead, he cherishes them with the utmost tenderness, so they'll have a chance to grow sturdy and strong before they meet the storms. He knows such care will give them the best chance to survive.

Thus it should be with our children. The colder and harsher the world outside, the more they need warm affection in their own homes. Don't be afraid to love and cherish this precious little chap. Don't give up trying to see things from his viewpoint. Don't give up working problems out in a gentle, understanding way. These will do for him what the glass covering of the hothouse frames does for delicate plants. Warmed and sheltered by your love, he'll have a chance to strike deep roots and to stand staunchly when the protective covering is removed.

Adorable as he is, your little rascal is going to try your patience many times during the next four years. In days of strain and anxiety, there will be a tendency to expect too much of little folks. Don't fall into that error. Don't allow yourself to get stern or cross or frantic when your preschooler merely acts as any preschooler will. Keep your poise and your sense of humor. Keeping them for your child's sake will help you keep them in dealing with the real problems that press in from outside your home.

Enjoy him! Two to six is one of the most entertaining and intriguing of the ages of man, if you hold fast to your perspective. Let no unfounded worries rob you of the pleasure and fun you should find in your preschooler.

Strengthen your child by encouraging him to be self-reliant, independent, and responsible for his own needs. Insist upon the health habits which will keep his body strong and fit. Provide the means for turning his interests and abilities into skills and definite knowledge.

When he passes at last thru the gate of adolesence into maturity, from the shelter of your home into the unknown, he'll be strong, confident, and fearless. He'll be kind and generous because he himself is rooted in love and in gentle ways. In short, he'll be the kind of lad you'd like him to be!

CHAPTER I

Your Child From Two to Three Years

If you've followed the suggestions in Section II, we can give you a pretty accurate picture of your youngster at 2 years.

Physically, he's:
. . . more than 31 inches in height.
. . . more than 27 pounds in weight.
. . . the proud possessor of from 12 to 16 teeth.
. . . rosy, sturdy, running and playing tirelessly.
Mentally, he's:
. . . happy and cheerful.
. . . says many words and makes a few sentences.
. . . understands much that's said to him, and sees everything.
Good habits have gotten a start. He:
. . . eats what is set before him. Perhaps he feeds himself.
. . . goes to bed cheerfully.
. . . plays happily by himself, both indoors and out.
. . . is trained as to bowels; has daytime bladder control, and is fairly well trained in night bladder control.
. . . accepts the daily routine of bathing, dressing, and brushing hair and teeth.
. . . knows where objects belong and can help to put them there.
. . . obeys simple commands.

The foundations for all the fundamental habits—those things which a child should perform instinctively, without thought and without conflict—have been laid, just as we must learn to shift the gears almost by instinct in driving an automobile. Thus are his energies released for activities which will foster his native abilities and capacities.

From now on your child's mind will develop at a pace that will delight you. Don't force him, but give him the materials that

Preschoolers think it's fun to wash dishes and do similar household tasks. Provide a stool or a box on which yours can stand, and permit him to help when he asks to

will aid its development when the time is ripe. (See list of playthings and play materials on page 164.)

Keep Him on Schedule

The schedule remains the same as to meals, nap, and bedtime. Observe these as faithfully as you did when your child was an infant, and he'll continue to be happy, healthy,

Learning to dress himself is a long, intricate process. You can help by stimulating his interest in it

and, for the most part, well behaved. It's a common weakness for parents to relax the routine as the infant becomes the toddler. And right there countless behavior difficulties get a start. Many of them can be avoided if you continue to see that your youngster eats the right things at the right time, and goes to bed at his bedtime. If you have held to the schedule so far it will be easy to continue, for both you and your child will have learned the habit of regularity.

Let me repeat that your child's day may begin at 6 a.m., 7 a.m., or 8 a.m., and end at 6 p.m., 7 p.m., or 8 p.m., according to your convenience. By all means arrange it so that Dad can have plenty of time with his youngster. But whatever your child's schedule is STICK TO IT!

Provide Playmates

From 2 years on, your child needs contact with other youngsters. This is as essential to wholesome development as are food and sleep, and you must provide it in some way. If there are no children in the neighborhood, arrange frequent visits with friends who have children the same age. You'll find the ideal social contact for your youngster in a good nursery school, if you're fortunate enough to be near one.

Social development is a learning process and, like any other, goes thru distinct stages. Your 2-year-old is largely non-social. He plays by himself, and doesn't concern himself with the children around him unless they interfere with him in some way. Yet he needs the chance to become accustomed to his contemporaries.

Pretty soon you'll find him stopping to watch the others, and he'll do this more and more frequently. Next he includes one or more other youngsters in his play. His first advances are apt to be physical—pushing, pulling, or hitting. He uses playmates as he does the rest of his environment, and with no more ill will. He must learn from sad experience—for his victim will hit back—not to trespass upon the rights of others. Presently he's playing with another child in co-operative enterprises. Gradually the group enlarges and, by the time he's 3, your little fellow should be a happy member of a neighborhood "gang" of small children.

It's an advantage for him to play with both older and younger children. That way he learns both to follow and to lead.

In your child's social contacts interfere just as little as you can, once you've provided suitable playmates. Let him attack his problem of social learning in his own way, pick his own chums and form his own groups.

Self-Reliance the Keynote

One of the principal goals of this period is to develop your child's self-reliance. He has already learned to feed himself, or he's rapidly learning. In the same way he'll want to perform from time to time the other operations of his daily routine. He'll try to lace his shoes, put on his stockings, etc. At first these efforts are futile and of short duration. Wait patiently. The attempts will grow more effective, and soon, with a little help, your child can really perform the function. Each step of this sort is of incalculable benefit to him. You can't make better use of your time than to stand aside while his awkward little fingers work out the problem.

He Learns to Dress Himself

Learning to dress himself is a long, intricate process. It must be taken gradually, else your runabout will tire of it. Undressing himself is much easier and should come first.

This phase of learning is divided into three main periods. At 2 years, most youngsters have no interest in dressing themselves, and lack the ability to do it. Your child is ready to begin dressing himself when he starts to identify the parts of his clothing and to know where they go. At first, tho, he's able to do little more than to get out of his clothes and put them away.

Your role in this first stage is to provide clothing he can manage and to stimulate his interest. Keep his attention on the job in hand, prevent distraction and play, direct him in the simplest parts of the routine. Let him think he's doing a great deal himself, even tho you do practically everything. If kept busy, he'll feel he has accomplished a great deal.

The second phase occurs when he develops an interest. Now your role becomes one of instructing, and assisting only as much as is absolutely necessary. This period requires much patience, for you're able to get him in and out of his clothes much more rapidly than he is himself. Only as he does it, however, can he advance in skill, and in the desire to handle the matter himself.

Send the youngsters to bed on the dot thruout preschool years. It keeps health and dispositions good

The third phase is the regression of which we've spoken before. (See page 138.) As he becomes fairly adept in dressing himself he loses interest. By this time, however, he has become good enough so that he can do it with comparative ease. Your role now is to direct the proceedings, to keep him on the job, and to maintain order. It's an excellent idea to have a bit of mending or a similar task to occupy you. Thus you can keep an eye on proceedings without seeming to give him any more than casual attention.

If you follow these directions, your child will be able to dress himself fairly well by the time he's 3, except for difficult fastenings.

He can't be expected to manage things like back buttons before he's 4 or 5. His clothing at this time should, therefore, fasten in front

Your 3-year-old can button things that aren't too difficult to reach. Clothes now should fasten in front as far as possible and be easy to manipulate

and have, if possible, seats that pull down instead of unbuttoning. Praise the child's accomplishments when they show real effort on his part, even if what he does seems trivial from a grown-up's point of view.

He'll Enjoy Washing Himself—at First

It's easier to teach small children to wash than to dress themselves, for they love to play in water. The task here is not so much to develop your child's interest as to transfer his delight from mere dabbling in water to getting his face and hands clean. Supervision of the "washing-up hour" will be necessary until he's about 4.

The first step is to set up washing arrangements a small youngster can use without your help. Provide a low bench, wash basin,

and low mirror in the kitchen, or put a box or steps in the bathroom on which he can climb up to the lavatory. Place a mirror where he can see himself as he makes his toilet, and have hooks he can reach for his washcloth, towel, comb, and toothbrush. In the early stages, it's a good idea to have these

Arrangements which will help your child look after himself. Chains keep toilet objects off of floor

articles on strings or chains to help him return them to the proper hook, and to prevent his throwing or dropping them on the floor.

Your emphasis will be upon his finishing the job speedily and effectively. Let him have water now and then to play in as part of his play equipment, and stress that washing-up times are business. Your standard of cleanliness must not be too high at first—you can polish him off in the daily bath. So far as his own efforts are concerned, independence is more important than removing all high water marks, and will be for some time to come.

Toilet Routines

If you've followed our training routines, your youngster by this time is probably dry most of the time. It's still desirable, tho, for you to keep the responsibility for toilet functioning. Continue the toilet schedule you've had before (see schedule on page 143), but lengthen the intervals by 15 minutes during his waking hours, then another 15 minutes, and so on until he's waiting two hours.

Is Negativism Still With You?

Little girls are usually at the peak of

Every youngster loves to dig in the dirt, and your child should have a garden plot of his own in his play yard, if it's at all possible. Give him a set of small garden tools, and let him plant and tend his seeds. For tiny gardeners, choose those which appear soon—radishes, lettuce, beans, and the like. Then he won't have to wait too long to behold results

negativism at the age of 2. Continue to follow the suggestions given on page 139 for treating this phenomenon, and otherwise ignore it. Little boys usually begin it somewhere around 27 months. So if your usually sunny, affectionate, amenable youngster suddenly stages a one-man rebellion, don't let it worry you. Quietly see that necessary commands are carried out, and pay no attention to verbal defiance.

Play Is Part of Learning

One of the important ways in which your child is educated is thru his play. If directed adequately, it leads to the formation of habits of concentration, discrimination in choice of activities, and eventually to the development of your child's individual interests and abilities.

You help his development in many ways when you furnish an adequate place for him to play, both indoors and out, and a good choice of toys and materials for him to use. His outdoor play yard should be fenced until your child is 3, if you can possibly arrange it, for he can't be expected to stay within bounds much before that age, and will be constantly running or wandering away if he has the chance. If you can't have a fence, set certain boundaries, and have someone there to see that he stays within them.

Have his play yard where you can see what's going on by glancing out of the kitchen or dining-room windows. Thus you can keep a check on things without interrupting your work.

Something to climb on should be included in equipping the play yard. A jungle gym is ideal, but a firmly piled group of logs furnishes much pleasure

In planning his play yard, leave plenty of space for running and for vigorous play, and include something your youngster can climb on. (Children at this age are little monkeys. You'll be picking yours down off the top of the piano, and every ladder he sees will be an invitation.) This is an activity to encourage, not discourage. Your youngster should not climb on your furniture, but provide things of his own that won't break or tip over. Very small children perform miracles of balancing on an apparatus like the jungle-gym, and firmly piled logs over which your little tot can scramble will entertain him endlessly.

Play apparatus and materials for this age, and the purpose each serves in a child's development, are listed on page 164.

A good general rule for handling his play is to furnish the best equipment you can, then stay out of the picture except to keep him from actual harm. Allow him to choose his activities and to drop them when he gets tired or bored. Thus he has a chance to pursue and to develop the interests that will be peculiarly his.

Don't hesitate, however, to use your own good judgment about this as about other matters. There may be situations where a little help or a suggestion from you would enable your youngster to get more value from what he's doing. If that seems to be the case, give it. Just take care not to dominate his play, or to make him dependent upon you.

If he does well, commend him, but don't overdo praise, as we've said before.

Your 2-year-old goes quickly from one object to another without plan. But let him alone, and by the time he's 4 he'll be making intelligent selections of play materials, spending considerable time on one activity, and going from one play sequence logically into another.

Should Pick Up Toys

Tidying up after play is part of your youngster's education. He should help at 2, even tho he only puts away one toy. Gradually he can take care of more and more. In nursery schools, youngsters 3 years old and older are required to replace a toy when they're thru with it, before taking down another. Few mothers, however, have time to enforce this rule, and if your child picks up his toys at the end of a play period and puts each back in its proper place, he's doing well enough.

Young children get very intent on their play—the beginning of the habit of concentration, which we've mentioned. This is a desirable trait and shouldn't be broken. Allow your child 5 or 10 minutes in which to conclude the thing with which he's busy.

Taking things apart is as much a part of play to the 2-year-old as putting them together. Tearing them down is as much fun as building them. Give your youngster plenty of toys that he can take apart, and teach him to respect the others. Keep them in his own play places, where they can't harm your furnishings or house, and let your small experimenter carry on such researches as occur to him. (Within the limits, as we've said before, of his own personal safety and that of his playmates.)

Disciplining the Runabout

Carrying thru your youngster's daily routine and keeping faithfully to his schedule continue to be main props of discipline. Providing a proper place to play indoors and outdoors, as we've just suggested, is another. See that your child gets enough sleep and rest, proper food, has plenty of opportunity to play vigorously in the open air and plenty of things with which to amuse himself. Handle him gently, courteously, and with understanding. Do these things, and your child will be happy, healthy, and pleasant to live with most of the time.

Yet, being human and very inexperienced, he's bound to err at times. Situations are sure to arise in which you'll have to divert your youngster from a non-social, non-productive way of doing things. And the brighter and livelier he is (the way you want him!) the bigger handful he's going to be. Keep in mind, however, that what you're after is not to get even with him for any annoyance he may cause but to help him learn ways of doing things that are acceptable to society.

Various means may be employed to teach this lesson, but whichever one you use, your own attitude must always be the same. It must be:

1. Impersonal. You require your child to do what you tell him to do not because YOU want him to, but because it's the right and proper thing for him to do. Your own feelings don't enter in at all.

2. Expectant that he'll do what you tell him to.

3. Firm. If he fails, see that consequences are administered. What these consequences are should depend upon the child's misdemeanor and upon his understanding of what he has done. They should be logical, growing naturally out of the child's own conduct.

For example, if your child throws his food on the floor he'll have to clean it up, and possibly go without that particular food for the next meal. If he defaces something, he must repair it as well as he's able.

Your judgment will have to dictate the consequences, depending upon what the offense has been. But always impersonally and without anger.

Suppose he refuses to obey your commands? Removal from the family or play group has proved ample punishment in countless cases, and it has all the virtues we've just described.

Help Your Child to Love Books and Music

Giving your baby the best possible start from the standpoint of health and habits has been your main preoccupation, naturally, for the first year or two of his life.

But now comes the time for which you've perhaps been impatiently waiting. You can introduce him to the world of books, music, and art, and a thousand other things which give pleasure and meaning to life.

Of course your 2-year-old won't be able to appreciate Shakespeare, symphonies, and Rembrandts right off the bat, any more than he can play football. But he can and will en-

Tho you can only pick out a melody with one finger, your little fellow will prefer your playing to Paderewski's. Here's use for your talents and appreciation no mother can resist

joy stories, music, and pictures which are fitted to his stage of growth.

If you love these things yourself, the story or music hour will probably prove to be the happiest time of the day for you and your youngster, since there's no pleasure more keen than sharing things with those we love.

Moreover, it's one of the pleasantest times of companionship. Your little fellow is bathed and clean and all ready for bed. In slippers and bathrobe, he snuggles against you while the two of you pore over books or listen to the music.

Just don't hurry him along too fast in the realm of books and music. Always remember that children have their own ways of learning and their own times for doing it. Perhaps you have had this experience with such a favorite as "Alice in Wonderland." It was a high spot in your childhood, and you couldn't wait to have your child love it as you did. So you introduced it too early and tried too hard to sell it. Result—the child refused to have anything to do with Alice. To this day, that marvelous whimsy of Lewis Carroll is unknown to him.

The better way is to provide a plentiful supply of enjoyable books and stories for each stage, then let your youngster choose the ones which attract him. How preschoolers react to books at different ages and how to interest them in books was told most interestingly by Louise Bechtel in "The Horn Book Magazine," September-October 1941. Thru the courstesy of the Horn Book, Inc., we reprint the following excerpts:

First Experience With Books

"In my little book room at home, the majority of children 'before 5,' if left alone, simply slam over the pages of one book after another. They shout or sing if some single picture catches the eye. They look up away from the books for something active to happen in the room. Suppose I gather them on the sofa and read, showing them the picture slowly: then the brighter ones respond, but half still squirm and shout in irrepressible spirits about nothing at all. But if I have found a very good story, and *tell* it, stopping frequently with a question or a chance for imitation, the audience is absorbed. *That* is the story they want again next time. Meanwhile, of course, an unusual child may have crept off alone with a book she loves, to apply her more mature powers of eye and mind, murmuring her own tale to herself as she fingers the lines of the pictures lovingly.

"Only the home can have the greatest pleasure of discovering books. Mothers *could* have the same fun the school has, with experiments in story telling. But parents are still apt to push small children too fast in language process and picture appreciation.

"Well, let us turn to the books. The first 'book,' we all agree, is a recognition book of simple objects. Babies of 2 love to pull apart the big color advertisements in a magazine. Years ago they were given the Steichens' *First and Second Picture Books*, which still are popular. The objects portrayed should be those really familiar to a baby, for this book is merely a tool for talking. At this age of 2, most words are sound, not meaning; most nonsense verse and songs are not understood in the adult sense, yet can be a very quickening influence, or a soothing one, or a source of laughter.

"Then come the very first stories, at 2 and 3 years old. No one who has not worked daily with children will believe how simple they should be. To say that 200 words is long enough puts it too easily. The point is, much more, the utter simplicity of word and content. In these first experiments in attention, as opposed to songs and nonsense verse, there should be a delicate balance of reality—something that could happen to you—and of nonsense and action.

"At 3 and 4 years old, attention has grown in power, and we meet more sharply the problem of style. The body which has been developing an exciting lot of varied responses, the mind which has heard songs and poetry, quickly feel the wet blanket of dull prose. Then there is the matter of the 'comeback,' the question or pause for answer or imitation that lets the small child actively enter the story, as he longs to do.

"We know how the really good story has to be told over and over—how it is chanted with the book upside down. It ought to be very good!

"Then, toward 5, horizons have widened, one can sit more quietly, one can listen longer. We have gathered a few criteria for style for these years: rhythm, repetition, brevity, sensory range, 'comeback.' As to content, we all agree on those elements of 'just like me,' of humor, the love of bump and fall and grimace that mark this primitive age, and we are apt to differ only on the fantastic.

"Only Mother's experiments unlock attention and imaginative response. But she must realize that these early steps are important—that it does count enormously to *tell* stories, each year a bit longer; to read poems, each year with more variety; to have the child treasure lovely books. With a little investigation, she will soon see how one writer speaks of 'here and now' very dully, and another so well that it is the beginning of literature.

"Mother or teacher, she will be amused at discovering the stories a child likes, those he does not, and why. As the child's sensitiveness and appreciation grow, she will know that the audience for good books has a new recruit."

Music Appreciation Begins

Quite as gradual will be the growth of your youngster's response to music. Heavy operatic numbers and subtle symphonies are as far beyond his ken now as is driving an automobile. But he'll love listening to a wide variety of other types of music. (See suggested lists of records beginning on page 188.) There are many classical and semi-classical pieces, tuneful and rhythmical ones, which delight quite small children. There's descriptive music, such as "Hunt in the Black Forest" and "In a Clock Store." There are countless topical and nursery songs.

A phonograph selection of records he can enjoy is an invaluable aid in developing your

Small youngsters like doing things to rhythmic music, and after a while you'll find them singing simple tunes heard on records or radio. Thus appreciation leads to participation

child's love for music. He can soon be taught to run the machine himself, and can put on the records he wants to hear. Steel yourself to have him play his current favorite dozens of times in a row, for that's the way he likes to do it. But that's also the way he'll learn to carry a tune and to get pleasure from music.

He'll be especially pleased if you sing and play to him yourself. If you can do no more than pick out a melody with one finger, here's an audience that will prefer your playing to Paderewski's!

Then there's the very simple music in which your child himself can begin to participate. Most children can't carry a tune much before the third or fourth year. But at any time you may find your youngster joining in when you sing a simple song, or when he hears one on the phonograph. At first he may repeat only parts of songs in a monotone, and at his own rate. Let him improve in his own way. The ability to carry a tune and to keep time develops slowly in most youngsters, and then it's largely the result of interest, imitation, and practice.

Your youngster will also learn to like doing things to rhythmic music. For this purpose, the tune should be easily recognized, the beat accentuated, and the selections short. (See lists of rhythmic and marching pieces on pages 185 and 188.) Let him interpret this music in his own way—running, jumping, trotting, or galloping like a horse, "flying," "swimming," or "skating."

Simple instruments help keep up the interest in rhythm—drum, tom-tom, cymbals, triangle, bells, and tambourine. One or several of these may be acquired to help your youngster express what the music makes him feel.

Whether he has any musical ability or not, and whether or not he does anything with music in later years, he can get infinite pleasure from it if it has been presented to him as a pleasurable experience in early childhood.

Another Baby on the Way?

Perhaps it will be your good fortune to learn that another baby is headed your way. The second arrival often appears at just about this time. It's your wish, we know, to handle this matter in the best possible manner from the standpoint of the Crown Prince, who up to now has ruled as an absolute sovereign in your affections and in your household.

A child this young is not likely to notice anything. Shortly before the time you expect to be confined—very shortly, for 2- to 3-year memories are brief indeed—tell him that a small brother or sister is expected, and that you'll go to the hospital for the event. Show him the things you and he and Daddy have ready for the new arrival, make him a full partner in the enterprise. Stress that it's "our" baby, Johnny's as much as anybody's.

If he asks questions about where the baby came from and how it's going to get here, that will be your first opportunity at sex instruction. Answer each question very matter-of-factly, but briefly, and tell no more than he has asked for.

When you bring the new baby home from the hospital, you'll take pains, of course, to see that Big Brother or Big Sister isn't crowded into the background. Yet don't go so far as to crowd the new arrival into the background in order to avoid jealousy. Some parents, anxious to keep the first from feeling slighted, have actually slighted the newcomer. That develops selfishness in the older child, and hence he's quite as unhappy as tho he had been ignored.

Your first-born must learn that life is a process of sharing. Consider his rights and feelings, but not at the expense of the baby's place in the family. Give each his just due, and make the elder a sharer, insofar as it's possible, in both the pleasures and the tasks arising out of a baby in the house. Such a course builds happy relationships and is the best insurance against jealousy.

Feeding Your Preschool Child

Your youngster's diet is altered very little from what it has been thruout the last six months, and will change very little for four years more. Choose his foods from the allowed list on page 123, with the exception that he may now occasionally have the prepared family cereals, such as corn flakes. He should still be guarded from rich, greasy, spicy things, from pastries, and from any but the simplest sweets and desserts.

Keeping His Foods Easy to Manage

In preparing foods for your child from 2 to 6 years old, continue to make them as easy to handle as possible, and as appetizing as you can. A child of 2 with good teeth may eat raw vegetables and will like them this way.

Wash carrots, lettuce, celery, turnips, cabbage, rutabaga, and cauliflower, remove any tough spots or woody leaves or fibers, and cut into attractive sticks or break into leaves and flowers. Soak them in cold water until very crisp, then serve as one vegetable at the meal.

Preschoolers gobble tiny sandwiches of whole-wheat bread, buttered (cut a regular-sized piece of bread into quarters) and filled with bits of raw vegetable or fruit. Any you have on hand may be used this way—apple, carrot, tomato, lettuce, cabbage, celery. Prepare the vegetables or fruits as above, and cut into thin slices or easily managed bites. Such sandwiches should be passed only after your child has eaten a fair amount of his meal, for the preschooler will fill up on bread if you'll let him, at the expense of other foods.

Make cream soups thick enough so they won't slip from the spoon. Cut or chop such foods as tomatoes and spinach to make them easy to manage.

Cereals and starchy desserts such as corn-starch, tapioca, and rice puddings shouldn't be made too thick. Children like these dishes best when made with about one-half the amount of cereal or starch called for in adult recipes.

In seasoning, use no pepper or spices. Use one-half the amount of salt you would for adults and not too much sugar.

Make meat, liver, and fish loaves very moist, with plenty of milk and several eggs in them. Place the loaves in a pan of water in the oven while cooking.

Your child at this age needs an egg every day, two vegetables other than potato, and two fruits (unless there's a tendency to loose bowels).

Include three-fourths to one quart of whole milk every day in his diet. It's not necessary that all this be drunk. Part may be used in the cooking.

Serve fish once a week, liver about twice a week. Two teaspoons of fish-liver oil or the amount of concentrate prescribed by your doctor should be given daily during the winter months and 1 teaspoon of fish-liver oil and concentrate as prescribed in summer.

Food between meals? As a general rule—no. If your youngster's very hungry, however, a snack is permissible if you're sure it won't interfere with the next meal. A cup of milk, an apple, or a graham cracker makes the best "snack." A whole-wheat sandwich is good, also.

Planning His Meals

We give you two weeks' menus, one for winter and one for summer, to show how your youngster's daily food needs may be combined appetizingly into three meals. For the dinner menus we want to give credit to "Your Child's Food" by Miriam E. Lowenberg, published by Whittlesey House, McGraw-Hill Book Company, Inc. (Recipes for the dishes mentioned in these menus, prepared in the way small children like them best and endorsed by the *Better Homes & Gardens'* Tasting-Test Kitchen, will be found in the recipe section beginning on page 182.)

These are offered only as suggestions, and the menus may be varied greatly according to your preferences and to the foods you can obtain. They give the principal meal at noon. This is not necessary, unless you find it more convenient to have the principal family meal at noon. If you have your large meal at night, your preschooler may have his then also. The sort of menu suggested for supper may then be served him at noon.

Because of seasonal conditions, it may not be possible to get, at all times of the year, all the variety of fruits and vegetables we should like to have. In such cases, substitute others. Tomatoes, for instance, are a satisfactory substitute for citrus fruits. If you'll consult the vitamin tables on pages 127 and 128, you'll be able to select those foods at your disposal that will best supply the needed vitamins and minerals.

One Week of Winter Menus for Child From Two to Six

Monday

Breakfast:

Orange or Tomato Juice

Oatmeal (2 to 4 rounded tablespoons) With Whole Milk

Buttered Graham Toast   Milk

Dinner:

Meat Loaf   Creamed Carrots

Buttered Green Beans   Tomato Sandwich

Crisp Celery Chocolate Cornstarch Pudding

Milk

Supper:

Soft Poached Egg on Toast   Cottage Cheese

Baked Apple   Cookies (2)

Milk

Tuesday

Breakfast:

Prune and Orange Juice or Prune Juice or Tomato Juice

Milk Toast   Milk

Dinner:

Scrambled Egg   Celery Sandwich

Buttered Potatoes   Scalloped Tomatoes

Rennet Custard and Peaches   Milk

Supper:

Cooked Cereal With Whole Milk

Two Graham Crackers   Crisp Bacon

Milk   Applesauce

Wednesday

Breakfast:

Sliced Orange or Canned Fruit

Buttered Whole-Wheat Toast

Cooked Cereal With Whole Milk   Milk

Dinner:

Salmon Loaf

Raw Cauliflower   Scalloped Potatoes

Buttered Peas   Whole-Wheat Sandwich

Graham Cracker   Stewed Prunes

Milk

Supper:

Coddled Egg on Toast   Crisp Lettuce

Milk   Tapioca Pudding

Thursday

Breakfast:

Stewed Apricots   Scrambled Egg

Milk   Buttered Whole-Wheat Toast

Dinner:

Broiled Liver

Parsley Potatoes   Crisp Celery

Scalloped Tomatoes Whole-Wheat Sandwich

Fruit Cup   Milk

Supper:

Cream of Pea Soup   Toast Sticks

Milk   Banana Custard

Friday

Breakfast:

Sliced Oranges or Canned Fruit

Cooked Cereal With Whole Milk

Buttered Whole-Wheat Toast   Milk

Dinner:

Creamed Codfish   Buttered Broccoli

Scalloped Tomatoes   Banana Custard

Toast   Milk

Supper:

Vegetable Soup   Toast

Crisp Lettuce   Fruit Gelatin

Milk

Saturday

Breakfast:

Stewed Peaches

Cooked Cereal With Whole Milk

Buttered Whole-Wheat Toast   Milk

Dinner:

Liver en Casserole

Onions, Peas, Carrots (cooked with the liver)

Crisp Lettuce   Toast

Fruit Cup   Animal Cookies

Milk

Supper:

Soft-cooked Egg   Baked Potato

Milk   Chocolate Bread Pudding

Sunday

Breakfast:

Orange or Tomato Juice

Cooked Cereal With Whole Milk

Buttered Whole-Wheat Toast   Milk

Dinner:

Creamed Chicken on Rice   Brown Rice

Whole-Wheat Sandwich   Buttered Carrots

Orange Betty, Orange Sauce Apple Wedges

Milk

Supper:

Vegetable Soup

Toast Sticks   Stewed Cherries

Sponge Cake   Cocoa

**One Week of Summer Menus for
Child From Two to Six**

Monday

Breakfast:

Orange or Tomato Juice

Bananas With Whole Milk

Buttered Whole-Wheat Toast   Milk

Dinner:

> Cream of Tomato Soup   Fruit Cup
>
> Buttered Green Beans   Toast
>
> Graham Cracker   Hard-cooked Egg
>
>   Milk

Supper:

>   Rice With Cheese Sauce
>
> Fresh Apple   Sandwiches
>
> Milk   Sugar Cooky

Tuesday

Breakfast:

>   Stewed Cherries
>
> Corn Flakes With Whole Milk   Milk

Dinner:

> Creamed Liver   Buttered Potatoes
>
> Carrot Sticks   Buttered Green Beans
>
> Tomato Sandwich   Milk

Supper:

> Poached Egg on Toast   Fresh Fruit
>
> Cookies (2)   Milk

Wednesday

Breakfast:

> Applesauce   Milk Toast
>
>   Milk

Dinner:

> Scrambled Egg   Buttered Cabbage
>
> Graham Cracker   Buttered Carrots
>
> Bananas, Whole Milk   Tomato Aspic
>
> Milk   Toast

Supper:

> Broiled Porterhouse Steak
>
> Whole-Wheat Lettuce Sandwich
>
> Baked Potatoes   Milk
>
>   Fruit Cup

Thursday

Breakfast:

> Sliced Orange (or other fresh fruit)
>
> Buttered Whole-Wheat Toast Grape-Nuts
>
>   Milk

Dinner:

>   Fish Timbale
>
> Buttered Potatoes   Parsley Sandwich
>
> Scalloped Tomatoes   Crisp Lettuce
>
> Fruit Gelatin   Milk

Supper:

> Cream of Spinach Soup   Baked Egg
>
> Sponge Cake   Milk

Friday

Breakfast:

> Tomato Juice   Coddled Egg
>
> Buttered Whole-Wheat Toast   Milk

Dinner:

>   Soft-baked Egg
>
> Beets With Lemon Butter Tomato Sandwich
>
> Creamed Peas   Crisp Celery
>
> Orange Ice   Milk

Supper:

> Green Beans   Cottage Cheese
>
> Fresh Fruit   Milk
>
>   Graham Crackers

Saturday

Breakfast:

    Peaches, Whole Milk Ready-to-Serve Cereal

    Buttered Whole-Wheat Toast   Milk

Dinner:

    Scrambled Egg   Buttered Potatoes

    Peanut Butter Sandwich   Tomato Wedges

    Milk   Applesauce

Supper:

    Potato Soup   Toast

    Milk   Rennet Custard With Fruit

Sunday

Breakfast:

    Orange Juice or Tomato Juice

    Milk Toast   Milk

Dinner:

    Broiled Lamb Chop

    Buttered Wax Beans   Crisp Lettuce Leaf

    Broiled Tomatoes Whole-Wheat Sandwich

    Grape Sherbet   Animal Crackers

             Milk

Supper:

    Bread and Milk   Crisp Carrot

    Cookies (2)   Cocoa

Schedule for Child Two Years Old

6:00 to 7:00 a.m. Rises, goes to toilet. Fish-liver oil or concentrate as prescribed by doctor. Juice.

Breakfast:
    Fruit
    Cooked cereal with whole milk
    Milk
    If this is eaten, toast and bacon may be added, if desired. Milk toast, banana, or prepared cereal may be substituted for the cooked cereal occasionally.
    Dresses for day.
    Brushes teeth, combs hair.
    Plays outdoors, if weather permits. In cold weather, an hour outdoors will be enough.

9:00 a.m. Brought in to toilet (continue doing this thruout the day at intervals you've found best suited to his needs).

12:00 n. Lunch:
    Vegetable soup or green vegetable
    Meat
    Potato, macaroni, rice, or tenderoni
    Simple dessert
    Milk

12:30 p.m. to 2:30 p.m. (not later than 3:00 p.m.). Nap or rest in room alone with door closed.

3:00 p.m. (on arising from nap or rest). Graham crackers. (Cup of milk also, if child is underweight.)

5:30 p.m. Supper:
    Creamed vegetable
    Poached or soft-boiled egg
    Fruit

Milk. (Omit milk at night if your child wets the bed.)
Bath, story hour.

6:00 p.m. Bed.
    or the following:

6:30 p.m. Bath, story hour.

7:00 p.m. Bed. (Depends upon the time of rising.)

Play Equipment and Material for Child Two to Four Years Old

These develop and teach control of large muscles:
    Chair swing
    Board swing
    Rocking chair
    Board to walk on
    Tricycle
    Slide
    Large wagon
    Sled
    Broom
    Snow shovel
    Garden tools
    Large floor blocks
    Balls of all sizes
    Heavy train
    Heavy truck
    Heavy automobile

These develop large muscles and senses:
    Sandbox
    Pans
    Shovel and similar toys

These develop muscles and teach co-operative play:
    Balls of all sizes

Materials that encourage self-expression and skill:
    Block nest
    Hammer and nails of different sizes
    Large dominoes
    Building blocks in brick shapes
    Crayons and paper
    Blunt scissors and cutting paper
    Blackboard and chalk
    Easel and water colors
    Beads to string
    Plasticene
    Color cubes

These stimulate imitative play and develop imagination:
    Picture books
    Telephone
    Dolls and animals to cuddle
    Outdoor tools
    Household utensils
    Doll furniture
    Laundry equipment
    Unbreakable or cloth doll to dress and undress
    Toy dishes
    Small table and chairs

CHAPTER II

Your Child From Three to Five Years

Development

Around the age of 3 years your child may:

. . . measure more than 36 inches in height.

. . . weigh more than 31 pounds.

If dressing routines have been followed, he can:

. . . unbutton and button side and front buttons, if buttons and buttonholes are big enough.

. . . put on panties and dresses, if given a little help.

. . . put on and pull up leggings, snowsuits with a bit of assistance or advice.

. . . unlace and take off his shoes.

. . . put on his shoes if someone holds the tongues down and if the shoes are marked to distinguish right from left. (A red thread on one will do this.)

. . . put on and take off galoshes, if they're large enough to slip easily over his shoes. (Tightly fitting galoshes will be beyond his powers for a long time.)

Physical Development

Once again physical development slows down. Your youngster may not gain more than three or four pounds a year for the next year or two. Mental development, however, leaps forward.

Now your child is able to reason. He can understand what you tell him, and he can learn to stay within the safe bounds you set for him. It's a good thing, too, for by 3, no fastenings you can invent will keep him in his play yard.

His active little body, plus an equally active mind, will carry him into many activities that may look to you like mischief, but to him are really explorations of his world. During the next year or two—maybe it has already happened—your lively little chap will get into your perfume and cosmetics, he'll cut his own or some other child's hair, he'll ransack your bureau drawers and cupboards, and embellish your wallpaper after his own artistic fancy. This is just a small sample of what you may expect. Your young-

"Three to five" is a little mischief. Expect that at least once he'll paint walls or woodwork according to his fancy, and keep things lively

ster will embellish it with countless improvisations of his own. The healthier, stronger, and smarter he is, the more ways he'll hit upon to upset the household.

He'll be the world's champion "why-er," for his whole environment to him is one big question mark to which he tries to find the answer. He'll run so fast and so hard in his quest that he'll always be falling and bumping himself. But that won't slow him down.

Energy boundless, trying to find the answers to all his questions, he's on the go from morning till night

He'll go thru various phases of behavior which will annoy you no end, unless you understand that it's all a sign of growth. Whatever you do or don't do about these, in a few months he'll have dropped one trick you don't like for another equally distasteful to you.

At the same time, he'll have settled down in his habits. He'll be able, at last, to look after his own toilet needs. He can wash himself and get in and out of his clothes, except for the more difficult fastenings. You realize suddenly that he isn't a baby any more.

Three, in fact, is an age of transition from infancy to childhood. One authority calls it the "adolescence of the preschool period."

Like the adolescence of the teens, it often keeps parents guessing, simply because they don't know what is normal behavior for the period and how to treat it.

Give Him Leeway

Once more we say, keep habits and routine going. It will be your job to supervise these until your hopeful's thru high school. But aside from necessary matters, allow your little fellow as much leeway as you can in his explorations. Not how to suppress his eager interest, but how to supply plenty of legitimate material on which it can grow, should be your aim.

Develop his self-reliance and independence by having him do everything for himself that he possibly can at each stage of growth.

Behavior Problems of Three to Five

As we've said, at this age your youngster will exhibit one annoying phase of behavior after another, no matter how well you've trained him or how wisely you handle him. It's a little difficult sometimes for a bewildered parent, going thru this for the first time, to know what is normal mischief and what has more serious implications.

A broad rule may be set up. If your child gets plenty of sleep and rest, eats the right food, is healthy and happy, and has plenty of interesting things to do, you can be pretty

Don't suppress his eager interest in anything and everything. Instead, give him chances to develop it

sure that he is basically all right. If his undesirable behavior is accompanied by a generally unhappy, rebellious, or unsocial attitude, then it's wise to look further into the matter, see what is wrong, and correct it.

It may mean disciplining yourself, for doing for him is such a pleasure! He'll grow sturdy, tho, only as he looks after his own needs.

Many otherwise well-behaved children become peevish or have temper tantrums late in the afternoon after a hard day of play. Or they become unmanageable when a meal is long delayed. The real problem in such cases is not how to treat peevishness or temper tantrums, but to see that the child doesn't get overtired and that his meals aren't overly late.

We're going to describe some of the commoner problems of the preschool period, and give suggestions for handling each. Many occur earlier, but they seem to come to a climax from 3 to 4.

Don't forget as you read that quite often physical condition is the cause of naughty behavior. When you're confronted with a problem that refuses to yield to the gentle but firm methods we suggest, take your child to his doctor for a thoro physical examination. Even if your child is perfect physically, medical advice will be a great help in tackling a behavior phase that has you baffled.

You must not feel that you've failed or are disgraced as a parent if your youngster displays any or all the following traits during the next year or so. Rare, not to say abnormal, would be the 3- to 5-year-old who has exhibited none of them.

There's no harm in "bumping" or "rocking" the bed, but if your 3-year-old's an addict, it's probably getting on your nerves by now. He's old enough now tho, to stop, and will if you ask him to quietly

Mannerisms and Tics

Thumb sucking. Has your child carried this habit over from baby days? If he's happy, well adjusted, and isn't nagged, he'll drop it of his own accord as soon as his developing social consciousness shows him that it brings derision from playmates. Just before giving up the practice, however, some thumb suckers seem to go at it harder than ever. You may ignore the habit, or you may ask the child to go to his own room whenever he wants to suck his thumb.

A youngster who continues thumb sucking much past the age of 5 should have some special consideration (see Chapter III of this section). But at 3, thumb sucking may be treated as a phase.

"Bumping" and "rocking." If your youngster is a tummy sleeper, he may have become a "bumper" or "rocker." Able to lift himself up on hands and knees, he develops a rocking motion, or bumps his head on the bed. Enthusiastic "rockers" propel their beds clear across the room and all but shake them to pieces. This does no harm, and is a habit that will pass if ignored. Or if it has become too hard on your nerves, simply ask your youngster in a nice way to stop it. Three-year-olds can understand a request like that, whereas it was asking a bit too much of the 2-year-old.

Nail biting, ear pulling, nose picking, face twitching. Life is so exciting for the 3-year-old

that he often develops little nervous habits. If yours does, check his routine to be sure he's getting enough rest, the right food, isn't playing too hard or getting too tired, and isn't upset emotionally.

Having made these things as right as you possibly can, you needn't worry about the mannerism. Just suggest quietly that he desist whenever you see him doing it.

Stammering. Somewhere around the age of 3, many children begin to stutter, and again the parents are worried. There is no particular need to be, for a child who has talked properly once has shown that he possesses the speech mechanism to do so again. Look to his routine and habits and be sure your child isn't overtired or emotionally strained. Should the condition continue, expert help should be sought, but much of the stammering exhibited at 3 disappears by 4.

Toilet Accidents

Involuntary urination is common thruout the whole preschool period, and should be treated casually. Any small child when excited or interested in play, may have an accident. This is particularly true when he's playing outdoors in cold weather. Don't shame or punish your little fellow if this happens. Take him to the toilet, change him without comment, and make the intervals between toilet trips shorter for a time.

However, if your child of 3 or older has been trained for a long time, and then has extended lapses of control, some emotional upset or lack of adjustment may be suspected.

Many a first-born child takes to wetting the bed after a new baby has been added to the household. A perfectly trained youngster who finds himself in a strange place may wet the bed. And some continue to do this after they're old enough for camp and boarding school.

When the London children were evacuated in 1939 to places of safety in the country, a great complaint went up that London parents hadn't trained their children to be dry. "A Niagara burst over England," is the way one writer put it. Dignified mansions had mattresses and bedding airing from every balcony.

Investigation revealed that most of the children had been trained in bladder control and that wetting the bed had been the result of removal from their homes and separation from their parents.

A youngster may wet the bed as a bid for adult attention or to "get even" for discipline.

Treat the toilet lapse casually, but try to find and correct the underlying emotional cause. If it followed discipline, carry out the discipline as tho nothing had happened. (I'm assuming now that you've employed the gentle disciplines suggested in this book—not harsh ones.)

Change him or his bed and take him to the toilet at regular intervals again for a time. You may have to get up with him in the night for a few weeks, just as you did when first training him. If he's big enough, however, it's best to let him manage this for himself. Let him have an alarm clock beside his bed, and show him how to set it so it will wake him at the right time. Put a flashlight on the table by the clock or under his pillow. Most children delight in assuming the responsibility under such thrilling circumstances. Place a chamber under your child's bed for a few weeks if there are reasons why it would be difficult for him to find his way to the bathroom.

After he has been dry day or night for a week, you can gradually lengthen the toilet intervals.

Destructiveness

We've seen that with the 2-year-old, tearing things down is quite as much a part of play as building them up. At 3, your offspring will be an even more accomplished wrecker than he was at 2, but for the most part there's no malice in his depredations. The lively little fellow who threw Grandmother's book over the garden wall and hid Grandfather's favorite magazine behind the bookcase was merely carrying out what had seemed like good ideas at the time. There will be plenty of this sort of thing when there's a 3-year-old in the house. Adults have to learn to be good retrievers. If destructiveness, however, takes the place of constructive play, the situation will bear some investigation. Maybe your youngster hasn't enough opportunity for activity, and gets bored. Perhaps his toys are so flimsy they invite being torn to pieces. Perhaps his destructiveness is a sign of rebellion and unhappiness.

If your study shows that the fault is with poorly made toys, buy better ones. If the difficulty lies in your child's environment, correct it. Then lead him into constructive ways, and make sure he succeeds with them. Have him repair the damage as much as he can. Children should have their own sturdy books, or cloth ones, for free play. Their good books, and adult books, magazines, and newspapers, should be handled only under adult supervision.

"Lying"

His rapidly developing imagination will probably lead your 3-year-old into telling tall tales. This isn't lying, and should be entered into as a game which the two of you play together with enjoyment. Let him see that you know there's no giant in the bedroom, but you can laugh together at his vivid description of the giant.

You may also expect your child to make the wonderful discovery one of these days that he can escape consequences by saying he didn't do something which in reality he did do. Harsh punishments increase a child's tendency to "lie out" of things. Our scheme of discipline, of course, doesn't call for harsh punishments. Nevertheless, your child has to be taught truthfulness as he must be taught other things.

Take care that your own attitude in questioning him doesn't frighten him into a denial. Don't ask him if he did something you're pretty sure he did, or you'll make it too easy for a small offender to resort to falsehood. Say quietly, "Johnny, where did you put the nozzle of the hose when you took it off?" rather than "Johnny, did you take the nozzle off the hose?"

Johnny's whole reaction will be to tell you where he put it—if he remembers. Then you can have him get it, and explain, as he puts it back on, why he mustn't remove the nozzle again.

If he does something he knows he shouldn't do, however, it's probably a mistake to withhold deserved consequences as a reward for truth telling. You want your child to tell the truth, not to escape punishment, but because telling the truth is the only way in which people can have confidence and trust in each other. If we tell the truth always, people will believe what we say and that's a much more satisfactory state of affairs than to be doubted.

Your youngster should learn to take the consequences of his unsocial acts. If the matter is approached in the impersonal way we've suggested, and your attitude is one of trying to get at the facts rather than of prejudging your youngster, you'll help him to admit his wrong and, at the same time, be prepared to take his punishment manfully when it's coming to him.

"Showing Off" and Bullying

Such manifestations at this age are often stages of your child's social development. Most youngsters aren't ready to be leaders in group play until they're 4 or 5 years old, because they don't as yet have the qualities which induce the other youngsters to follow them.

An ambitious little chap may want to lead before he has the ability. He may then try to win his place by showing off, or by interfering with and bullying the other youngsters.

If he carries this to an extreme, he may need some help to find a part in the group play that he'll enjoy, and that will satisfy the other children. If he interferes with them too much, try isolating him from play for a time.

Sleeping

In the period between 2 and 5 years, most children go thru three stages with regard to their afternoon nap. Up to 2½, your child will probably fall asleep almost immediately if all conditions are made right for him, and may continue to do this until he's around 3.

At any time after 2½, however, he's likely to begin staying awake at his nap time. He

has so many things to think about that he can't take time out for anything as prosaic as sleeping.

Whether your child sleeps or not, have him lie down in his bed for two hours after lunch. Close his door and keep everything

Around 4, he may stop sleeping in the afternoon. Have him rest, but he may enjoy quiet diversions such as looking at a picture book

quiet. You may insist that he stay in his bed after you've put him there, but leave it to him whether or not he sleeps. After a stage of wakefulness, most youngsters go back to sleeping again until they get to be 4½ or 5. Then they'll sleep on some days and stay awake on others. At this age, it's proper to let your youngster take a picture book or doll to bed with him so he can amuse himself quietly if he doesn't sleep.

If your child spends 12 hours in his bed every night, has the right food and plenty of outdoor play, there's no need to worry about the amount of actual sleeping he does. Until he starts to school, have him go to bed every afternoon for two hours of sleep, quiet play, or relaxation. He'll sleep or not as he needs to. Don't let him nap past 3 o'clock, as this may interfere with his night's sleep.

Eating

During the preschool period eating problems take up much more than their fair share of attention.

It's quite natural for your youngster's appetite to slacken, as his growth rate slows down. At 3, moreover, the excitement of developing mental impressions often makes children forget their hunger. We must also allow for the inevitable period of boredom,

Billy gobbles his tiny serving of squash in a big hurry, so he can have peas in potato nest and other "goodies"

or regression, after your youngster has learned to feed himself well.

Aside from these factors, which may enter into the most nearly perfect eating situation, there are 5 main reasons why your child may become a mealtime problem between the ages of 3 and 5:

1. Too much interest in what's going on around him. This is particularly true if a 3-year-old eats at the family table, or in a room where he's surrounded by toys and playthings.

2. Served with too much food. We've seen already how discouraging that can be to a little fellow with a limited stomach capacity.

3. Dislike for foods offered.

4. Trying to get adult attention.

5. Too tired.

Treat your child's problem according to its cause. If his appetite has dropped off, cut his helpings in two. He can always have another if he wants it, but don't try to urge more food upon him than he needs.

If he's bored with feeding himself, let him help set the table and serve himself. Serve his milk in a cute pitcher, and let him pour it himself into a tiny cup or glass. Or a straw for drinking may stimulate his interest. When he's thru, let him remove his dishes and help himself to dessert, according to the amount of the other food he's eaten at the meal.

If his mealtime environment is too stimulating, remove him from the family table to a little table of his own, and have him eat before the adults do. Don't leave toys or other diverting objects where he can see them when he eats.

If there's more food on his plate than he can manage, you may "divide" it. That is, take the plate away, remove part of the food, let him finish the rest, and then have as much dessert as he has had other foods.

If he dislikes a number of foods, continue the policy of insisting that he taste every dish. Then let him eat as much as he likes of favorite wholesome foods.

Attempts to get attention usually go hand-in-hand with a family table situation. Removal should help to cure it. Ignore his bids for attention, serve especially small portions. If he doesn't eat them, remove the food without comment and let him go hungry till the next meal.

If he's tired, have him come in from his strenuous play and lie down for awhile before dinner and supper, or at least engage in some quiet occupation.

That Eternal "Why?"

When he gets to be 3 years old, your child will put you thru your intellectual paces. By all means answer questions that are asked with a sincere desire for information. The little tyrant is apt to find this new game so amusing, however, that he'll ask a million senseless ones. When the child knows, or can easily figure out, the answer to his question, have him answer it himself. Otherwise he may fall into the way of having you do all his thinking for him.

Early Sex Instruction

Any time after your child is 2½—3 is a more likely age—you may expect the question "Where do babies come from?" Nearly all children ask it in just this form. Answer simply and matter-of-factly, "They grow inside their mothers." This will in most cases suffice for some time. Then some other question will be asked, usually one which elicits the information that the baby was once a tiny egg, which

grew until the baby was ready to live in the world. These first questions are as simple as can be, and can be answered without difficulty from your own knowledge. Answer each time only as much as is asked, unless an opportunity is given to expound some point you think desirable.

During this preschool period, it's natural for children to exhibit interest in the opposite sex. Don't look upon this as some degraded or perverted manifestation, but as a purely natural curiosity. Handle it tactfully and without alarm. Small children in the same family may have their baths together and it's not necessary to separate the sexes for dressing and similar operations. If yours is an only child, when a small playmate of the opposite sex comes to visit, treat the two in this respect as you would a brother and sister. A perfectly legitimate curiosity will thus be satisfied in a natural and matter-of-fact way, and will then pass.

Don't be alarmed, either, if you discover masturbation. This again is quite common to childhood, and is quickly forgotten if tactfully managed. See that the boy or girl is kept happily employed thru the day, and has his hands outside the covers at night. The healthy, normal child can be easily diverted if the matter isn't stressed in any way.

Dawdling

Parents of a 3- to 4-year-old always complain of dawdling. (The practice is usually at its height around the age of 3½.) If it begins to take your runabout an interminable length of time to perform every operation of the day, don't nag him and don't worry. Say to yourself, "Well, the dawdling phase has hit us now."

It's easier to bear when you realize that it comes about partly because your youngster's mind is working a mile a minute receiving a host of new impressions. And it's partly due to the fact that he has pretty well mastered the techniques of doing things, and hence loses interest in them.

Allow plenty of time for necessary routines, and keep his attention on what he's doing until he has finished. At mealtime, if he turns in his chair to look at things in the room instead of attending to his meal, take him by his shoulders and gently turn him around again. If he dawdles when dressing, place the next garment in his hand and remind him to put it on. He can thus be kept busy.

Vitamin Needs

OF YOUR CHILD FROM THREE TO SIX YEARS OLD

Between these ages your child needs every day:

Vitamin A —2,500 I. U. (International Units)

Thiamin (Vitamin B₁ **)**—.8 milligrams. (Remember that your child needs more whole-grain or enriched cereal foods— rich sources of thiamin—when he is very active. But remember also to keep the balance of other needed food elements.)

Vitamin C (ascorbic acid)—a minimum of 40 milligrams.

Riboflavin (Vitamin G **)**—1.2 milligrams.

Vitamin D—400 I. U.

Niacin (nicotinic acid)—a minimum of 8 milligrams.

Like most of the problem behavior of 3 to 5, dawdling, too, will pass. Around 4, your little fellow will be speeding thru his routines in order to get to engrossing activities in the playroom or out of doors. Summon your patience to endure the dawdling while it lasts. (By this time, fortunately, your patience has had an excellent workout, and likely you feel entitled to be called Griselda!)

Schedule the Same

Your child's schedule does not change, except that if you've been putting him to bed at 6 o'clock, it will be permissible to shift to 7 o'clock.

At 3 or 4 years, prepared puddings, made by adding milk and heating, may be added to your child's diet.

Play Equipment to Add at Four Years

These develop the body, teach muscular control, keep your child out of doors and encourage quick thinking:

Swing	Roller skates
Rings	Boxing gloves
Bars	Football
Trapeze	Punching bag
Steering sled	Bean bag
Coaster wagon	Pushmobile
Jumping rope	Merry-go-round
Ice skates	Seesaw

Additional materials for indoor play:

Tool chest and tools	Blocks
Real cooking material	Builder-boards
Real sewing material	Electric train
Construction sets	Art tools
Stout typewriter	Stamp books
Block printing sets	Real tools
Parlor games (flinch, tiddly-winks, parcheesi, checkers)	
Large doll for which a girl can sew	

CHAPTER III

Your Child From Five to Six Years

Development

Probably your child at 5 years will:

. . . weigh more than 41 pounds.

. . . measure more than 43 inches in height.

He should be able to:

. . . button and unbutton all buttons except the most difficult (small ones with tight buttonholes, or small buttons in the middle of his back).

. . . put on and take off all his clothing.

. . . handle his toilet needs without assistance (except for hard-to-reach buttons).

. . . wash his face and hands and comb his hair without supervision.

A Big Boy Now!

Now at last your youngster definitely puts baby days and baby ways behind him and proceeds to take a more mature role. He's ready for kindergarten, if there's one in your vicinity.

Before he starts to school, check over the list of accomplishments which head this chapter and be sure your Mary or Johnny has mastered them all. A kindergarten teacher has enough to do without buttoning and un-buttoning, and putting galoshes and rubbers on 30 or 40 children.

We also urge that, some months before it's time for him to start to school, you take your youngster to his doctor for a thoro physical checkup, including examination of his eyes, ears, and teeth. If there's anything the matter that might affect his comfort or efficiency, it's desirable to find out in plenty of time so that corrections can be made before he starts to school.

Your 5-year-old still needs 11 to 12 hours of sleep every night. Many children are better off if their afternoon nap is continued after they start to kindergarten.

If your child goes to school in the morning, have him lie down for his rest in the afternoon for a time, at least, while he's adjusting to the exciting new experiences of going to school.

Even tho your child of this age goes thru the day well without a nap, he'll benefit if you'll have him rest for 15 or 20 minutes before his dinner and supper. This relaxes him and helps his appetite. Have him get up early enough in the morning so he'll have plenty of time to eat breakfast and to have his bowel movement before going to school.

Baby Days Are Over

We've seen that 3 years was a transition age between infancy and childhood. Five quite definitely marks the end of the baby period.

Not on his fifth birthday, necessarily, but during his fifth to sixth year, your child is expected to say good-by to baby ways and to take on a more mature role.

While he was under 5, we advised you not to take lapses into infantile traits too seriously. In the preceding chapter we urged that you give lapses a chance to correct themselves, with some gentle and indirect help from you.

However, if such lapses into baby ways as thumb sucking, bed wetting, and stammering show themselves, or persist into the fifth to sixth year, we give them more attention.

The first step is always to take your youngster to his doctor for a thoro going over, and for a review of his life and habits. It can't be repeated too many times that the physical side must always be taken into account when dealing with a behavior problem. Psychology avails little with bed wetting, for instance, if the youngster has some malformation which makes control impossible.

If your doctor rules out physical causes and approves your child's regimen of sleep, eating, and play, then you must look to the emotional situation. The child who sucks his thumb much past 5, except for a little sleepy-time indulgence, is unadjusted in some way and quite often unhappy. It may be something at home or school, or an inability to get along with playmates, that causes the unhappiness. Whatever it proves to be, help him as much as you can.

Take care, moreover, not to shame or to worry the youngster about it. He's none too secure as it is or he wouldn't be sucking his thumb. Don't add to his unhappiness and feeling of insecurity.

Explain that while thumb sucking probably did little harm up to this point, if he continues now it may result in crooked teeth which would impair his appearance. Approach the matter reasonably and understandingly. Remind him with a look or an upraised eyebrow to stop when you see him doing it, and you'll help far more than by making him the butt of family attention and criticism.

The stammerer should have expert help, if possible, before he starts to school. See your doctor about this.

What was said of continuing bed wetting (eneuresis) at the 3- to 5-year stage applies even more strongly after 5. There should be a physical examination to see if there is any organic trouble. If there isn't, try to find the emotional difficulty and follow the rules in Chapter II for dealing with bed wetting.

Schedule for Child Five to Six Years Old

(Going to morning kindergarten)

6:30 a.m. to 7:00 a.m. Rises, goes to toilet. Washes face and hands. Dresses for school. Has fish-liver oil or concentrate as prescribed, followed by fruit or tomato juice.

Breakfast:
> Fruit in season
> Cooked cereal with whole milk
> Milk

If this is eaten, whole-wheat toast and bacon may be added if desired. Milk toast, banana, or prepared cereal may be substituted for the cooked cereal occasionally.

Off to school.

*12:00 n. Dinner:
> Vegetable soup or stew or green vegetable
> Meat
> Potato, macaroni, rice, or tenderoni
> Slice of whole-wheat bread with butter
> Simple dessert
> Milk

1:00 p.m. to 3:00 p.m. Rest or nap in his own room.

3:00 p.m. Arises. Fish-liver oil or concentrate as prescribed by doctor.

> Cup of milk
> Graham cracker
> Plays outdoors

5:30 p.m. Comes in from play, washes face and hands and combs hair for supper.

*Supper:

> Creamed vegetable or vegetable soup
> Poached or soft-boiled egg
> Whole-wheat toast, or whole-wheat sandwich with fruit or vegetable filling
> Milk
> (Cottage cheese may be given often)

6:30 p.m. Bathes, gets ready for bed.

> Story hour

7:00 p.m. or 7:30 p.m. Bed.

If your child goes to kindergarten in the afternoon, he'll play in the morning. Have him come in at 11 or 11:15 and lie down for 20 minutes or so. Then have him wash and get dressed for school. He should be ready to eat dinner by 12 o'clock, so that his meal need not be hurried.

----

*Note: If the main family meal is at night, the dinner and supper menu given here may be reversed.

RECIPES FOR CHILDREN UNDER TWO

Foods for the small baby must be prepared with particular care. Below are recipes for foods mentioned in Section II, "Your Baby from Birth to Two Years."

Cereals

The reputable manufacturers of cereals have gone to considerable pains to test their products from the standpoint of infant feeding. You may follow the directions on the package for preparing the various ones for babies.

In the past few years, a number of the well-known cereals have been developed in quick-cooking form, and some of these have been enriched or restored to whole nutritive values. It's desirable not to overcook these, lest valuable vitamins be lost.

Others require no cooking at all, but are ready for the baby when mixed with boiled, warm water or with some of Baby's formula, or with boiled milk.

If the package directions, however, call for

long cooking, be sure to comply. Cereals of this type may be prepared for both adults and Baby by cooking the length of time called for for the baby, and then diluting Baby's portion, with either boiled water, boiled milk or some of Baby's formula.

Any cereal may be cooked in one-half milk and one-half water.

For babies under one year, the cereal should be strained. (Unless the package directions indicate that this is not necessary.)

Vegetables

Cook quickly in a small amount of water until well done. Pressure cookers are especially good. The water in which the vegetables are cooked contains food materials of some value and should be retained so far as is convenient. Twenty to 30 minutes cooks most

If you can't obtain sieved canned foods for Baby, a food mill is an easy, convenient way to make fruits, vegetables edible for your youngest

vegetables in a saucepan. One to 2 minutes usually suffices in a pressure cooker. Season with about one-half as much salt as you would like yourself. To prepare vegetables for the baby under 1 year old, press thru a fine sieve or run thru a food mill before serving.

Creamed Vegetable Soup

Combine 2 tablespoons sieved vegetable pulp, 8 ounces milk, ½ teaspoon butter, sprinkle of salt. Bring just to boiling.

Creamed Vegetables

(Any vegetable except tomatoes.)

Use 2 tablespoons vegetable to 2 ounces milk, ½ teaspoon butter, and ½ teaspoon flour. Melt butter; add flour and blend. Add milk and cook over low heat until thick, stirring constantly. Add vegetable.

Meat Broth

Use shin bones of veal, beef, chicken, lamb. Break up to expose marrow. Cover with slightly salted water; add 1 tablespoon vinegar; simmer 2 to 3 hours; strain, cool, remove fat. In place of soup bones a small piece of lean beef or chicken, cut in small pieces, may be used. Cover with slightly salted water. Simmer 1 to 1½ hours. Cool. Remove any fat.

Vegetable Soup

Add 1 cup chopped vegetable (carrots, peas, spinach, string beans, tomatoes) to 3 cups broth. Cook 30 minutes; sieve for infant under 12 months.

Cereal-Broth

Add 4 tablespoons (¼ cup) any cereal to 1 pint (2 cups) broth. Cook in double boiler 45 minutes. If barley or rice is used cook 1½ to 2 hours.

Beef Juice

Brown small piece of beef quickly on either side; press the juice out with a meat press, potato ricer, or lemon squeezer. Do not heat. Salt slightly.

Scraped Beef

Remove all fat from small piece of steak. Hold firmly and with a silver knife scrape pulp from fiber. There should be no stringy fiber or fat in pulp when thru. Serve raw or make into small patty and brown on both sides.

Liver

Wipe small piece of liver—any kind—with damp cloth; cover with boiling water and let stand 20 minutes. Drain. Grind, then force thru sieve and serve in orange, tomato, or grape juice, in gelatin desserts, ice cream, or sandwiches. Or broil, bake, or simmer.

Poached Egg

Bring water to boiling; drop in egg; remove from heat. Let stand until white is firm.

Soft-Boiled Egg

Bring water to boiling; drop in egg; boil 3 minutes.

Baked Egg

Drop egg into ¼ cup milk in greased custard cup without breaking yolk. Bake until white is firm.

Spaghetti or Macaroni

Cook 1 cup broken spaghetti or macaroni in 2 quarts boiling, salted water until soft, about 20 minutes; drain; rinse with running cold water. When ready to serve, heat in vegetable-broth soup, white sauce, or fruit juice.

Tenderoni

Cook 1 cup tenderoni in 1½ cups boiling, salted water about 7 minutes. Serve as above.

Fruits

(Prunes, Apricots, Dried Peaches)
Wash thoroly; drain; cover with cold water. Cook slowly until tender; add sufficient sugar

You may run Baby's foods thru a sieve, such as this, for first year, or thru a sieve which fits on top of pan. Grind all meats till your child is 3

to make slightly sweet. Run thru a sieve or food mill for a child under 12 months.

Fresh Applesauce

Pare apple, cut in small pieces; add ¼ cup of water to 1 cup of apple. Cover. Cook slowly until tender; add sugar as necessary to sweeten. Run thru a sieve or food mill for a child under 12 months.

Baked Banana

Select thoroly yellow banana (brown-flecked) with skin intact; wipe with damp cloth; bake in hot oven 20 minutes. Peel. Mash and serve with 1 teaspoon butter. Add lemon juice, salt, or sugar, if desired.

II

Or peel; place in pan with small amount of butter; bake in hot oven 20 minutes.

Rennet Custard Pudding

Beat 1 egg; add 1½ tablespoons sugar, and dash of salt. Gradually stir in 1 cup milk, scalded. Cook in double boiler over hot, but not boiling, water until mixture coats spoon, stirring constantly. Cool. Dissolve ½ rennet tablet in 1 tablespoon cold water; add to 1 cup of warm milk. Then add cooled custard; pour into cups and chill.

Rennet Pudding

Dissolve 1 rennet tablet in 1 tablespoon cold water. Heat 1 pint (2 cups) fresh milk until lukewarm; add 2 tablespoons sugar, dash of salt, ½ teaspoon vanilla extract, then dissolved rennet tablet. Stir well; pour into molds; chill.

Cornstarch Pudding

Mix 1½ tablespoons cornstarch, 1½ tablespoons sugar, dash of salt; slowly add 1 cup milk, scalded. Cook slowly 20 minutes, stirring constantly. Add 1 stiff-beaten egg white, if desired. Pour into wet molds; chill.

Cornstarch Fruit Jelly

Make smooth paste of ¼ cup cornstarch and a little cold water; add 2 cups fruit juice and sugar to taste. Cook in double boiler 30 minutes, stirring constantly. Pour in wet mold; chill.

Tapioca Pudding

Mix 1½ tablespoons minute tapioca, 1½ tablespoons sugar, dash of salt. Add 1 egg yolk. Gradually add 1 cup milk, scalded. Cook in double boiler 20 minutes, stirring frequently. Beat 1 egg white stiff; fold in. Cool.

Rice Pudding

Soak 2 tablespoons rice 2 hours in small amount of water; drain. Add 1½ cups hot milk, 1 egg yolk, 1½ tablespoons sugar, dash of salt. Pour into greased baking dish. Bake 2 hours.

Boiled Custard

Combine 1 beaten egg, 1 teaspoon sugar, and dash of salt; gradually stir in 1 cup milk, scalded. Cook in double boiler over hot, but not boiling, water until mixture coats spoon, stirring constantly. Cool until ready to serve. If desired, use egg yolk only in custard; beat white stiff; add 1 tablespoon powdered sugar; place on top of custard.

FIRST AID

For ordinary home accidents and emergencies.

In case of serious ones, call the doctor at once.

Bruises and wounds in which bleeding isn't severe

Wash your hands with soap and water before touching the wound. Using sterile gauze or cotton, clean the wound carefully. Grease and oil may be removed with benzine, naphtha, oil of turpentine, or ether. For other kinds of dirt, soap and water or rubbing alcohol is the best cleanser. Begin at the edge of the wound and wash away from, never toward it.

If an antiseptic seems desirable, alcohol or one of the many antiseptic solutions on the market may be used. Spread it well over the wound and on the skin around it for a distance of from one-half to one inch. (If you use tincture of iodine, remove it with alcohol, else it may burn. This is not true of the 2 percent iodine.) Let the disinfectant dry, and then apply a sterile dressing if it's a cut or a deep bruise. Hold the dressing in place with adhesive tape. Change the dressing every day.

Serious wounds

Leave alone, except to stop excessive bleeding (see next paragraph) and to cover with a clean dressing. Take the child at once to the doctor.

Wounds with severe bleeding

Bleeding from wounds of the scalp and face can be stopped by placing a compress over the wound and bandaging tightly. Most wounds on other parts of the body can be controlled the same way. If a large artery or a vein is cut, however, apply a tourniquet until you can get the child to a doctor.

A tourniquet should be a flat band at least one inch in width, never a rope, wire, or string. A triangular bandage folded into an inch-wide strip is best, but a belt, stocking, or handkerchief will do.

For a wound in the arm, tie the tourniquet around the upper arm about a hand's breadth below the armpit. For a wound in the leg, tie

Active little fellows get many a tumble and hurt. Clean bruises and trivial wounds with alcohol, or soap and water. Begin at edge of wound, work out

it around the thigh about the same distance below the groin. A pad underneath the tourniquet places additional pressure on the artery or vein.

Wrap the material twice around the injured limb and tie a half knot. Place a short

stick or similar article on the half knot and tie a square knot over it. Turn the stick rapidly to tighten the tourniquet, but don't tighten more than is necessary to stop the flow of blood. Hold the stick in position by the ends of the bandage already applied, or by another tie looped around the ends of the stick and tied around the limb. Get the child to the doctor as soon as possible.

A tourniquet must be used with care, since it cuts off blood to the limb, so don't use it unless it's needed to stop severe bleeding. Loosen the tourniquet every 15 or 20 minutes, but don't remove. If the bleeding has stopped, let the tourniquet remain loose. If it resumes, tighten the tourniquet again.

Puncture wounds, powder burns, and gunshot wounds

These should always have the attention of a doctor because germs may be carried into the body. He may want to give anti-tetanus serum. Home care consists only in getting the wound to bleed as freely as possible in order to clean it out.

Infected wounds

Signs of infection in a wound are redness around it which soon grows into a swelling, accompanied by a feeling of heat and throbbing pain. If the wound is in a part of the body which can be immersed in a vessel, soak it in water (as hot as the child can stand) in which has been dissolved 2 teaspoons of boric acid, 3 heaping tablespoons of table salt, or 6 heaping tablespoons of Epsom Salts to each quart of water. Keep soaking for at least an hour, adding more hot solution as the water cools. Soak again at intervals. If the injured part can't be immersed, apply cloths wrung out of the hot solution, changing them often

enough to keep them hot. Cover the wet cloths with a large dry towel to keep the heat in. Apply the treatment continuously until all signs of inflammation have subsided.

Consult a doctor about an infection, for a seemingly insignificant one may prove dangerous. This is especially true of infections in or about the nose and forehead.

How to treat animal bites

Wash the wound to remove saliva, holding it under running water if possible. Dry with clean gauze. Apply an antiseptic (2 percent tincture of iodine, metaphen, or merthiolate), let it dry, then bandage like any other wound. But consult a doctor at once, as he may want to give the Pasteur treatment or anti-tetanus serum.

Insect stings (bees, wasps, hornets)

Apply a paste of wet baking soda. This can be held in place by a bandage, but should be kept moist.

Insect bites (mosquitoes)

Calamine lotion with 10 percent menthol dabbed on helps lessen the itching.

Wounds in which foreign bodies remain

Splinters are the ones most commonly acquired by children. If the foreign body is near the surface, it may be picked out. First clean the skin with alcohol. Then sterilize a needle, knife point, or tweezers by passing thru a flame. Don't touch the point after you've sterilized it. Use this to remove the splinter. Make the wound bleed if possible. After the bleeding has stopped, apply an antiseptic down into the wound. If the object is buried deeply or is quite large, simply apply disinfectant and a bandage and take the child to the doctor. Tetanus antitoxin may be needed.

Wounds in the eye

Cover the closed eye with a sterile compress and take the child to the doctor at once. Don't try to remove foreign bodies embedded in the eye.

If the child gets lime, plaster, or cement or some chemical in his eyes, wash it out immediately with great quantities of water.

Milk is also satisfactory for washing out the eyes. Then consult the doctor at once.

Nosebleed

Have the child sit with his head thrown slightly back. Apply cold, wet compresses over the nose. A pack of sterile gauze or cotton may be inserted gently back, not up, into the nostril, leaving an end outside so the cotton can be removed easily. Or you may press the nostrils together firmly with your fingers.

If these measures don't stop the nosebleed, the doctor should be called at once.

Burns and scalds

For a slight burn, put ointment on sterile gauze and cover the wound. For a more extensive one, cut clothing from around the burn and apply several layers of sterile gauze (or freshly laundered cloth) which have been soaked in a slightly warm baking soda solution. Use a clean basin and, preferably, slightly warm water that has been boiled, tho any clean water will do in a pinch. To a quart of water, add two or three heaping tablespoons of baking soda. Bandage the compress lightly in place. Cover the child with blankets to keep him warm.

If he's badly burned, call the doctor at once, undress the child quickly, and wrap him in a clean folded sheet which has been wet with the warm soda solution. Then put blankets over him. Epsom Salts may be used instead of the soda.

Never apply iodine to a burn.

Don't use absorbent cotton directly on a burn as it will stick and cause further injury when it's removed.

If wax or metal-like substances have caused the burn, don't attempt to remove any portion that sticks. Leave that to the doctor.

Large blisters should be opened only by the doctor.

Sunburn

The skin of the baby or small child is tender and burns easily. Don't expose him to the direct rays of the sun for more than a short period at a time. If the sun is hot, he should be protected by a hat and an old shirt over a sun suit or bathing suit.

If he is sunburned, cold cream, olive oil, or cocoa butter give relief. These should be applied liberally, with as little rubbing as possible. Calamine lotion is also soothing and doesn't stain clothes.

If burns are severe, take the measures described for burns by fire.

Burns and scalds from chemicals (lye, caustic soda, etc.)

Such substances as these should be kept far beyond the reach of small children. But if an accident happens, wash the burn immediately with a large quantity of water and diluted vinegar or lemon juice, until the chemical's washed away. Then apply wet packs and take the child to the doctor or call him at once. Carbolic acid burns should be washed with rubbing alcohol if it's available.

If the child has swallowed some caustic, such as lye or toilet bowl cleaners, have him swallow a tablespoon of olive, mineral, or corn oil and diluted vinegar or lemon juice. If an acid has been swallowed, give 2 teaspoons of baking soda in half a glass of water. Follow either of these medications with a glass of milk while waiting for the doctor to come.

Earache

The doctor should be notified of an earache, but in the meantime the pain may be relieved by applying either an ice bag or a hot water bag. A bag of hot salt is a time-honored remedy that still gives good results.

Poisoning from plants (poison oak, etc.)

Wash the skin with plenty of soap and water, lathering five or six times. Then wash again with rubbing alcohol, rinse in clear water and dry.

If rash develops, wash as above. Make a paste by heating soap with a little water until about the consistency of lard. Apply thickly over the part, allow to dry and leave overnight.

Or apply dressings wet with a solution of Epsom Salts, as strong as can be made with cold water. Keep the dressing wet.

Or apply calamine lotion, to which the druggist has added a 1 or 2 percent solution of carbolic acid (phenol). Shake well, apply with a cotton sponge and let dry.

Frostbite

Gently cover the frozen part with your

hand until it's thawed and circulation is restored, or cover with extra clothing. Keep the child away from heat for some time.

Sties

This is a small infection on the edge of the eye. It may be helped to come to a head more quickly and the pain may be lessened by using compresses wet with water as hot as can be borne comfortably. Application of yellow oxide of mercury in 1 or 2 percent strength—this can be purchased at the drugstore in a small tube—is often prescribed by doctors.

If your child swallows a drug or poison, doctor's directions may be to make him vomit. Stick your finger in his mouth, tickle the back of his throat

Drugs, medicines, or poisons swallowed

Call the doctor at once since he may want to have the stomach washed out immediately, or he may tell you to try to make the baby or child vomit by sticking your finger into his mouth and tickling the back of his throat. An antidote used in many types of poisons is egg white in milk. Three egg whites in a glass of milk may be given.

If the child has drunk carbolic acid, clean out his stomach by giving soapsuds, or Epsom Salts in water, followed by warm water until you get him to vomit.

Food Poisoning

Sometimes children eat poisonous mushrooms or berries, or food that has partly decayed. The symptoms of food poisoning are pain, cramps, nausea, and vomiting and purging. Treat as for drug poisons by inducing vomiting, but always get in touch with doctor immediately.

If Baby swallows a round object, hold him up by his legs, head down, and gently pat upper part of back. Don't stick your hand in his throat after an object

Swallowing objects

A round object, such as a button or small coin, usually goes into the stomach and does no harm. If the baby chokes, however, call the doctor. While waiting for him, hold the baby up by the legs, head down, and gently pat the upper part of the back to help him get rid of the object. Don't stick your hand down his throat in an attempt to recover it.

If the baby swallows a pointed object, such as an open pin or a needle, give him some food such as potato or bread to eat. This may surround the point and keep the object from doing damage until it can be removed or has passed thru the intestinal tract.

Toothache

Take the child to the dentist as soon as possible. But as dentists, like doctors, are busy these days, it may be necessary to apply home relief while waiting. If there's a cavity in the tooth, put a small bit of cotton around the end of a toothpick and clean it out. Then dip another small piece of cotton in oil of cloves and gently pack the cotton into the cavity with the end of a toothpick. If there's no cavity, apply compresses on the outside. Sometimes hot ones will give more relief, sometimes cold. You'll have to experiment.

Falls

If the baby falls from a high place, put him to bed, keep him as quiet as possible, and call the doctor for an examination to be sure he's all right. This is especially important if he vomits or seems dazed and unlike himself.

RECIPES PRESCHOOLERS LIKE

The following recipes are for the foods mentioned in the menus for the child from 2 to 6, which begin on page 160. (These menus are taken from "Your Child's Food," by Miriam Lowenberg, and are reprinted thru the courtesy of Whittlesey House, McGraw-Hill Book Company, Inc. The foods are prepared in the way which has been found most acceptable to small children, but you'll like them, too. The recipes have been endorsed by the Better Homes & Gardens' Tasting-Test Kitchen.)

Desserts

Banana Custard

3 slightly beaten eggs	1/2 teaspoon salt
1/3 cup sugar	3 cups milk, scalded

Combine eggs, sugar, and salt. Gradually stir in hot milk. Cook in double boiler over hot but not boiling, water, until mixture coats spoon, stirring constantly. Chill rapidly. In bottom of serving dish place 2 or 3 pieces of cubed banana; cover with custard. Serves 6 to 8.

Chocolate Cornstarch Pudding

1/2 cup sugar	1/2 cup cold milk
3 tablespoons corn-starch	2 1/2 cups milk, scalded
3 tablespoons cocoa	2 beaten eggs
1/8 teaspoon salt	

Mix sugar, cornstarch, cocoa, and salt; combine with cold milk. Gradually add hot milk. Cook in double boiler until thick, stirring constantly; cover and cook 15 to 20 minutes. Add small amount of hot mixture to eggs; add to remaining hot mixture. Cook 3 to 5 minutes. Serve cold with fruit sauce or top milk. Serves 6. It's a good family dessert.

Orange Betty With Orange Sauce

1 1/4 cups soft bread crumbs	2 egg yolks
3/4 cup orange juice	1 tablespoon melted butter
1/2 cup sugar	2 stiff-beaten egg whites

Combine crumbs, orange juice, sugar, egg yolks, and butter. Fold in egg whites. Pour into greased casserole. Bake in slow oven (350°) until firm, about 30 minutes. Serve with Orange Sauce. Serves 6.

Orange Sauce

1 teaspoon cornstarch	1/3 cup orange juice
1/3 cup sugar	1/2 tablespoon lemon juice
1 tablespoon cold water	
1/3 cup hot water	1 teaspoon butter

Mix cornstarch, sugar, and cold water. Stir slowly into hot water. Cook over low heat until thick and clear. Add fruit juices and butter; blend thoroly. Serves 6.

Floating Island

6 tablespoons sugar	3 slightly beaten egg yolks
3 stiff-beaten egg whites	1/4 cup sugar
2 cups milk, scalded	1/8 teaspoon salt

Gradually add 6 tablespoons sugar to egg whites; beat until mixture forms moist, lustrous peaks. Drop from tablespoon onto scalding milk. Cook meringues until firm, about 5 minutes. Do not cover. Lift meringues out carefully. Combine egg yolks, 1/4 cup sugar, and salt; gradually stir in the hot milk. Cook in double boiler over hot, but not boiling, water, until mixture coats spoon, stirring constantly. Chill. Pour cold custard into serving dishes; top with "floating islands"; if desired, meringue may be used without cooking. Serves 6. A favorite old-time recipe.

Rennet Custard

1 rennet tablet	¼ cup sugar
1 tablespoon water	Few drops red
2 cups fresh milk	coloring

Dissolve rennet tablet in 1 tablespoon water. Combine milk and sugar. Add few drops red coloring, if desired. Warm slowly to lukewarm. Add dissolved tablet; stir quickly for a few seconds. Pour at once into serving dishes. Let stand undisturbed until rennet custard is firm, about 10 minutes. Chill before serving. Serves 5.

Fruit Gelatin

Dissolve package of flavored gelatin in 2 cups hot water; chill until partially set; add desired fruits. Chill until firm. Serves 6.

Fruit Cup

3 medium-sized	3 bananas, sliced or
oranges, sectioned	diced
¾ cup grapefruit sections	

Combine fruits. Serve 6.
Note: Children enjoy honey-sweetened fruits.

Meats and Fish

Fish Timbales

2 cups flaked	3 egg yolks,
salt codfish	beaten
2 tablespoons fat	½ tablespoon
2 tablespoons en-	minced parsley
riched flour	3 stiff-beaten egg
1½ cups milk	whites

To freshen salted fish let water run over it 15 minutes; cover with cold water and heat to boiling but don't boil. Repeat 2 or 3 times. Make white sauce of fat, flour, and milk. Add egg yolks, fish, and parsley. Fold in egg whites. Bake in pan of hot water in moderate oven (350°) about 1 hour. Serves 6.

Creamed Codfish

| 4 cups flaked salt | 1 cup thin white |
| codfish | sauce |

Freshen codfish (see Timbale recipe).
Combine fish with white sauce 15 minutes before serving. Heat in double boiler. Serves 6.

Creamed Liver

| 1 pound liver | 1 cup medium |
| | white sauce |

Scald liver; drain. Remove membrane and connective tissue. Grind, using medium blade of food chopper. Fry in small amount of bacon fat over very low heat, about 7 minutes; add white sauce. Serve on toast. Serves 6.

Liver en Casserole

Scald 1 pound liver; drain. Remove membrane and connective tissue and cut into ½-inch cubes. Fry ¼ pound bacon slowly until crisp. Remove to hot platter. Brown liver in bacon fat over low heat. Add 2 carrots, sliced, 1¼ cups canned peas and liquor, 1 onion, sliced, and ½ teaspoon salt. Bake in slow oven (325°) 1 hour. Serves 6.

Soft-baked Egg

Place 1 tablespoon thin white sauce in custard cup. Break an egg into cup. Bake in moderate oven (325°) until firm, about 20 minutes. Or break egg into buttered custard cup and cover with 2 tablespoons milk, ½ teaspoon butter, and dash of salt. Bake in pan of hot water in moderate oven (350°) until egg is firm, about 20 minutes.

Meat Loaf

1¼ pounds ground	1¼ cups corn flakes
round steak	or bread crumbs
2 tablespoons	1 egg
minced onion	1 teaspoon salt
	½ cup milk

Combine ingredients. Mix thoroly. Form in 2 loaves. Place in greased baking pan. Set this in pan of hot water. Bake in moderate oven (350°) 40 minutes. Serves 6.

Salmon Loaf

1 1-pound can salmon, flaked	¼ teaspoon minced onion
1 cup soft bread crumbs	1 tablespoon minced parsley
2 beaten eggs	½ tablespoon lemon juice
½ cup milk	
¼ teaspoon salt	

Combine ingredients. Pour into greased casserole or loaf pan. Bake in pan of water in moderate oven (350°) about 1 hour. Serves 6.

Vegetables

Scalloped Tomatoes

3 cups cooked tomatoes	2 tablespoons butter
¼ cup soft bread cubes	⅛ teaspoon salt

Combine ingredients. Pour into greased individual baking dishes. Bake in moderate oven (375°) until lightly brown, 15 to 20 minutes. Serves 6.

Broiled Tomatoes

4 to 6 tomatoes	1 tablespoon melted fat
1 tablespoon lemon juice	¼ teaspoon salt
¼ cup chopped parsley	

Cut tomatoes in half crosswise; place on broiler rack 3 to 5 inches below heat. Broil 8 to 10 minutes. Combine remaining ingredients; serve over tomatoes. Serves 6.

Scalloped Potatoes

2½ cups sliced potatoes	2 tablespoons fat
1 tablespoon enriched flour	½ teaspoon salt
	¾ cup milk

Alternate layers of potatoes, flour, and fat in greased baking dish. Sprinkle with salt. Cover with milk. Bake in slow oven (325°) 1½ hours. Serves 6.

Buttered Potatoes

Dice potatoes; cook in boiling, salted water until tender, about 20 minutes; drain. Melt 1 tablespoon butter for each cup of potatoes and pour over.

Beets With Lemon Butter

2 tablespoons melted butter	2½ cups cubed, cooked beets
1 tablespoon lemon juice	1 teaspoon chopped parsley

Combine butter and lemon juice; pour over beets. Just before serving, add chopped parsley.

Cream of Tomato Soup

3 tablespoons butter	2½ cups milk
5 tablespoons enriched flour	¼ teaspoon salt
	1 No. 2 can (2½ cups) tomatoes, strained

Make white sauce of butter, flour, milk, and salt. Just before serving, slowly add hot, strained tomatoes to white sauce, stirring constantly. Do not reheat. Serves 6.

Raw Vegetables

Cauliflower

Break up the cauliflower into the flowerets. Wash and soak in cold water for ½ hour, to crisp.

Cabbage

Cut into ½-inch wedges. Crisp the cabbage in ice water.

Celery

Remove all the strings. Cut pieces about ½ inch wide and 2 inches long. Crisp the celery in ice water.

Carrot

Peel and cut in strips about 2 inches long and ½ inch square. Crisp in water.

BOOKS BEFORE SIX

The list we give below was compiled by Louise Bechtel and is reprinted from the "Horn Book Magazine" of September-October, 1941.

You will find many of the books in the bookstores, or in the book department of your local department store. Any they do not have they will be glad to order for you. Or if you have no such store in your vicinity, you may order them yourself directly from the publisher.

The ages are only suggestions. Your child may be ready for certain books sooner, or not so soon. Some continue to be enjoyed thruout pretty much the span of the preschool years.

I. For Mothers to Begin On (Books for children under 2)

Cloth Book No. 1, by "Eleska" (190 Lexington Avenue, New York 16, N. Y)

Cloth Book No. 2, by "Eleska"
This refugee artist has given us the best of the cloth books.

Cloth Book, "Our Day," by Mary Dana (W. R. Scott, 1940)

Baby's Day, M. Sutton. Illustrated by Pelagie Doane (Grosset, 1938)
A very simple verse for 2 or under. Not enough variety of rhythm. Too many pictures on some pages but a good attempt at true nursery subjects.

Pat the Bunny, Dorothy Kunhardt (Simon & Schuster, 1940)

Mother Goose, illustrated by Pelagie Doane (Random House, 1940)
These gay, simple pictures might be country babies in Austria or your own baby dressed up gaily. Very charming. A good selection for babies themselves.

The First Picture Book, Mary Steichen (Harcourt, Brace) Combined with—

The Second Picture Book, Mary Steichen (Harcourt, Brace)
No words—just the photographs. No one has done much better as to content, even in the new color books. For 16 months to 30 months old.

Where Are You? Sam See (Simon & Schuster)
A good sequel to *Pat the Bunny.*

Finger Plays and Action Rhymes, Frances Jacobs (Lothrop, Lee & Shepard Co., 1942)
Six months to 6 years.

II. For Two- to Three-Year-Olds

Here and Now Story Book, Lucy Sprague Mitchell (Dutton, 1921)

Another Here and Now Story Book, Lucy Sprague Mitchell (Dutton, 1939)
The two indispensables, for use from 2 to 6. The second seems better for homes, the first for schools, but both are full of useful instructions, suggestions, reports of real children, and very fine verses and stories. Humorous, too. Proved by many years of use with children of each age. Includes many kinds of story and verse.

Plays and Toys in Nursery Years, Beatrix Tudor-Hart (Viking, 1939)
This excellent small book briefly summarizes the best English nursery school practice, mostly parallel to our own theory. Fine photographs.

Cloth Books 1, 2, 3, and 4 (Holiday House, 1939)
Nos. 1 and 3 by Leonard Weisgard are the best, of very familiar objects.

A B C for Everyday, Helen Sewell (Macmillan 1930)
Use as book for recognition of familiar objects. Good active words.

The Gay A B C, Francois (Scribner, 1939)
Tiny stories, some few finely rhythmic. For 2 and 3.

The 1, 2, 3, Picture Book (Platt & Munk, 1939)
Colors a bit garish, but idea good.

Noisy Book, Margaret Wise Brown (Wm. R. Scott, Inc.)

The Three Bears, Dvilnsky and Kallen (Lothrop, Lee, & Shepard Co.)

Anybody at Home, H. A. Rey (Houghton Mifflin Co.)

The Story of Little Black Sambo, Helen Bannerman

Peter and the Wolf, Serge Prokofieff (Alfred A. Knopf)

The Night Before Christmas, Linenette

The Three Bears, The Three Little Pigs, The Gingerbread Man, The Little Red Hen (Merrill)

The Real Mother Goose (Rand, McNally, 1930)

Over in the Meadow, J. A. Hartell (Harper, 1936)
This lovely old nursery song is a soothing answer to an overexcited child, delightful for all children. Fairly good large pictures of baby creatures familiar to country children.

Little Black Sambo, Helen Bannerman (Stokes)

The Little Engine That Could, Watty Piper (Platt & Munk, 1930)
> The most classic of train stories.

Peter Rabbit, Beatrix Potter (Warne)

Three Little Kittens, illustrated by Kurt Wiese (Macmillan)
> Illustrated by Terry Brice (Rand, McNally)

Ask Mr. Bear! Marjorie Flack (Macmillan, 1932)
> Good story pattern for 3's, good simple pictures of familiar animals.
> **The Story of Ping** is by the same author; very good, but its text better for 5's.

The A B C Bunny, Wanda Gag (Coward McCann, 1933)
> These fine black and white pictures often liked by 3's to make up their own stories. Beautiful and interesting. Use with text and verses later on.

Panorama—Town, Clement Hurd (W. R. Scott, 1939)

Panorama—Country, Clement Hurd (W. R. Scott, 1939)
> These two gay strips of pictures can lie flat on the floor, or be tacked on the wall. Short story at the back, but better to make up your own. Splendid for home or school.

The Little Family, Lois Lenski (Doubleday, Doran, 1932)
> Style is dull, yet many children love its "just like me" quality. For many children, better at 4. One of the few good "little" books.

The Little Auto, Lois Lenski (Oxford University Press, 1937)
> There is no logic to Mr. Small's being small, but children don't mind that, they love him. The text has not a good style, but the children talk at once themselves about the auto. Other books in this series better for 5 and over—all very popular.

Sally and Her Friends, Lena Towsley (Farrar & Rinehart, 1932)

Peggy and Peter, Lena Towsley (Farrar & Rinehart, 1931)
> Photograph books proving that one publisher knew what his children liked. Text flat, but 3-year-olds will make up their own stories, noises, chants for the familiar happenings.

I Know a Surprise, Dorothy Baruch (Lothrop)

Lucky Little Lena, Marjorie Flack (Macmillan)

Wait for William, Marjorie Flack (Houghton)

The Bobbie and Donnie Books, Esther Brann (Macmillan)

William and His Kitten, Marjorie Flack (Houghton)

Everything and Anything, Dorothy Ades (Minton, Balch)
> Poetry. A "must."

III. *For Three- to Four-Year-Olds*

The City Noisy Book, Margaret Wise Brown. Illustrated by L. Weisgard (W. R. Scott, 1939)
> Perfect in every point—fun, story progress, sensory exploration, "comeback," rhythm. Starred on all lists. Every child will welcome the little dog, Muffin, some at 2 years.

The Little Fireman, Margaret Wise Brown. Illustrated by Slobodka (W. R. Scott)
> Story has good guessing quality, good response. Pictures very modern, gay, flat, and toylike. Some like it best for over 4.

Holidays and Everydays, Elinor Brown (Oxford University Press)
> Unbelievably simple and true to life.

Cinder, and the Funny Noise, Romney Gay (Grosset)

From the Ten Cent Store Books, stories to be adapted:

The Three Bears, The Three Little Pigs, The Gingerbread Man, The Little Red Hen (Merrill)

Let's Play Store, Let's Play Train, Let's Play Postman (Newton); **Buttercup Farm, Book of Airplanes, Book of Automobiles, Book of Trains, Book of Ships** (Gabriel); **A Good Little Goose, A Kind Little Kitten** (Whitman)

IV. *For Four- to Five-Year-Olds*

Pelle's New Suit, Elsie Beskow (Harper, 1934)
> A lovely simple story of sheep and wool, with beautiful childish pictures.

There Was Tammie, Dorothy and Marguerite Bryan (Dodd, Mead, 1936)
> Doggy homes will welcome this and its successor, **Tammie and That Puppy.** Story pattern good.

The Little Wooden Farmer, Alice Dalgliesh (Macmillan, 1930)
> Excellent book for play with toys. The second story not so good, about a zoo.

The Choosing Book, Alice Dalgliesh (Macmillian, 1932)
> A small book with questions that make it into a simple game.

Timothy Turtle, Alice V. Davis. Illustrated by Guy B. Wiser (Harcourt, Brace, 1940)
> A truly wonderful picture story about familiar small creatures in the country. Attention span may be a little long for younger listeners, but pictures are so good they will tide them over.

Cock-a-Doodle Doo! Berta and Elmer Hader (Macmillan, 1939)
> You can adapt text to the noisy, simple recognition for which this age likes farm pictures. These artists' **Farmer in the Dell** is good for 6 and over.

Augus and the Ducks, Marjorie Flack (Doubleday, Doran, 1931)

Angus slowly learns things about dog behavior, and continues in **Angus and the Cat. Angus Lost** and **Topsy** are equally good. Clever relation of words to pictures, fine simplicity of both.

Millions of Cats, Wanda Gag (Coward-McCann)

Deservedly famous. Some children like it better later. Must be in the home.

Mike the Monk, Dudley Morris (G. P. Putman & Sons 1942)

An up-to-date tale of a monkey's adventures with modern warfare.

The Race, Clement Hurd (Random House, 1940)

A wonderful idea, and fine big color pictures. Words don't match the text for detail, and story has poor rhythm and no comeback, but children like the idea and fix up the story themselves. Good first transportation pictures.

Babar, Jean de Brunhoff (Random House)

Better saved till 6, but if given in nursery use the pictures for your own story telling, much shorter and simpler than present text. Let the 4's and 5's make up their own stories. All the Babar pictures delight small children.

Mr. Bradley's Car, Caroline Leach. Illustrated by Angela (Stokes, 1937)

Another auto story, and a funny one, is a blessing. Pattern good.

Blue Barns, Helen Sewell (Macmillan, 1933)

Charming big pictures and simple story of a big white goose. Story to be adapted according to ages.

A Little White Teddy Bear (etc.), Dorothy Sherrill (Farrar & Rinehart, 1932)

Became very popular in days when less was available. Amusing idea. Material suitable for 3's, interest span better for 4's.

Caps for Sale, Esphyr Slobodkina (W. R. Scott, 1939)
Very funny story from a famous old tale of a cap-peddler and the monkeys. The 5's love to act it out—full of gestures and noises.

Little Black Sambo, Helen Bannerman (Stokes)

All About Copy Kitten, Helen and Alf Evers (Rand, McNally, 1940)

Junket Is Nice, Dorothy Kunhardt (Harcourt)

Snip, Snapp, Snurr, May Lindeman (Whitman)

The Little Engine That Could, Watty Piper (Platt & Munk)

Peter Rabbit, Beatrix Potter (Warne)

I Go A-Traveling; I Live in a City (Verses), James S. Tippett (Harper)
Use stories from the following informational series in adapted form:

Happy Hour Books (Macmillan)

The Postman, The Fireman, The Policeman, The Storekeeper, etc.

In City and Country Series (Silver Burdett):

Story of Corn, Story of Wheat, Milk for the City, Fun on the Farm, etc.

Scribner's Science Readers: **Policeman, Fireman, Airplane,** etc.

Co-operative Teachers' Publications: **Tabby and the Fire Boat, The Tug Boat, Fire, Fire! A Story of Milk**

Stories from many sources, some adapted, as:

Epaminondas, Sleeping Princess, Cinderella, Shoemaker and the Elves, Billy Bobtail, The Old Woman and the Crooked Sixpence.

V. Books Best Kept Till Five or Six, but Possible for the Bright Child Earlier

Johnny Crow's Garden, Leslie Brooke (Warne)

A Roundabout Turn, R. H. Charles. Illustrated by Leslie Brooke (Warne)

Animals Everywhere, Ingri and Edgar Parin D'Aulaire (Doubleday, 1940)

Favorite Poems by Eugene Field. Illustrated by Malthe Haselriis (Grosset)

Little Ones, Dorothy Kunhardt (Viking, 1935)

The Second Picture Book of Animals (Macmillan)

When We Were Very Young, Now We Are Six, Winnie the Pooh, A. A. Milne (Dutton)

Benjamin Bunny, Squirrel Nutkin, Mrs. Tiggly Winkle, The Tale of Two Bad Mice, Beatrix Potter (Warne)

Shadow and the Stockings, James S. Tippett (Harper, 1937)

The Tasha Tudor "Calico" Books (Oxford)

A Tale for Easter, Tasha Tudor (Oxford, 1941)
New, younger than the text of the little books.

The Fish With the Deep Sea Smile, Margaret Wise Brown (Dutton, 1938)

The Little Children's Bible, (Macmillan)
Brief selections from the King James version, arranged in an interesting order, by the Syndics of the Cambridge Press. Far and away the best for first home use, does all the brain work for Mother, and lures her to read on regularly. Follow up with the **Older Children's Bible,** longer and more selections. Both of these should be in every home.

The Story of a White Rocking Horse, Laura Lee Hope (Grosset and Dunlap, 1920)

MUSIC FOR SMALL CHILDREN

Music for small children may be divided into three classes: songs they can sing, rhythms to which they can march, run, skip, etc., and music to which they may listen. The first two classes should contain quite simple things for the small child; but the last class may include practically all of the world's great music. The test required of a number in the last class will be whether or not the child enjoys listening to it.

Songs for Little Children to Sing

We suggest getting at least one good collection of children's songs, of which there are a number on the market. Two particularly popular ones are: "The Most Popular Mother Goose Songs and Nursery Rhymes," published by Hines Hayden, Eldredge, Inc., New York City (these arrangements are used by many of the recording artists and so these are the tunes the child hears often on the phonograph); and "Songs Children Love to Sing," arranged by Albert E. Weir and published by D. Appleton Century Co. The latter contains nursery songs and also many old favorites such as "Billy Boy" and "Grandfather's Clock," usually liked by children.

In addition we suggest:

The Jingle Book, Mary Dana (W. R. Scott, 1940) Perfect choice of seven very first songs, on rough cloth with gay pictures. Only the tune is given.

Tinkling Tunes With Rhymes and Runes, Jean Taylor, E. W. Wilcox, 8 West 47th Street, New York City, $1.50

140 Folk Songs, Archibald Davidson and Thomas Surrette, E. C. Schirmer Music Co., 3 East 43rd Street, New York City, $2.15

Songs of Childhood, Music Education Series, Ginn & Company, Boston, Massachusetts, $ .55

First Year Music, Hollis Dann, American Book Company, Chicago, Illinois, $ .76

Children's Sing Song From Sweden, Alice Tegner, Schmidt Co., 8 West 40th Street, New York City, $ .60

English Folk Songs for Schools, Gould and Sharp, Guren, Inc., 1701 Chestnut Street, Philadelphia, Pennsylvania, $ .60

Indian Action Songs, Frances Densmore, C. C. Birchard Co., 221 Columbus Ave., Boston, Massachusetts, $ .25

Old Dutch Nursery Rhymes, R. H. Elkin and J. Jongen, McKay Co., 604 S. Washington Square, Philadelphia, Pennsylvania, $2.50

Play Songs, Alys E. Bentley, Laidlaw Bros., 118 East 25th Street, New York City, $2.50

Small Songs for Small Singers, Neidlinger, G. Schirmer, 3 East 43rd Street, New York City, $ .75

Songs for Little Children, Jessie L. Gaynor, John Church & Co., 10 E. 43rd Street, New York City, $ .75

Just So Songs, Edward German, Doubleday Doran & Co., 14 West 49th Street, New York City

Finger Play Songs, Emilie Poullson, Lothrop, Lee & Shepard, 93 Federal Street, Boston, Mass., $1.50

Christmas Carols and Hymns, Hollis Dann, American Book Company, Chicago, Illinois, $1.25

Fourteen Songs From When We Were Very Young, by H. Frazer-Simpson, published by E. P. Dutton & Company, New York City, $3

Songs and Rhythms for the Nursery School and Kindergarten, Nina M. Keragy and Francis M. Arnold (Willis)

Rhythms

Rhythms for Children, by Jean Taylor, published by Elva W. Wilcox, 8 West 47th Street, New York City

How to Choose Records

Records may be bought in the record department of your department or furniture store, and at music stores. Many selections have been recorded a number of times, by different artists for different companies. It's a good idea to listen to several recordings before selecting. This you can do in the booths at your music store or in the record section at your department or furniture store. Then buy the one you like best.

Special Children's Records

The various companies offer a wealth of records from the small child's own world. Favorite movies and story books have been ransacked to provide music and stories your tot will particularly enjoy.

Records of many of the favorite Walt Disney songs are obtainable. Victor has made the songs from "Pinocchio" and "Snow White and the Seven Dwarfs"; Bluebird a number of Silly Symphony and

Mickey Mouse ones, the latter including "The Three Little Pigs." Bluebird also has three records of songs from "Gulliver's Travels."

Victor has made several groups of "Raggedy Ann" records, from the popular stories, and two groups of "Winnie the Pooh" (A. A. Milne perennials) while Bluebird also has two groups of "Winnie the Pooh": "Popeye the Sailor Man"; and the three records of the Robert Louis Stevenson children's poems, set to music.

Bluebird offers a galaxy of favorite children's stories, told by Paul Wing—such as "Little Engine That Could," "The Five Hundred Hats of Bartholemew Chubbins," "The Elephant's Child," "The Story of Ferdinand" and the "Story of Wee Gillis," six "Little Black Sambo" records, and a group of such stand-bys as "Wynken, Blynken and Nod," told by Paul Leyssac; and "Stories in Rhythm," a miscellaneous group of Christopher Robin, Alice in Wonderland, and Mother Goose, recited by the Karolites.

Columbia has a number of albums of stories from "Vernon Crane's Story Book," told by Vernon Crane, and has an album of "Adventures of Bubble and Squeak" and of "Captain Kidd's Cats." It also presents Music Fairy Stories, sung by Yvonne Ravell (these include Little Black Sambo, The Gingerbread Boy, and others) and records of children's songs sung by Betty Martin. Both Bluebird and Columbia has a good selection of fairy tales and songs.

Your child might enjoy the sea chanteys of the Bluebird records, "Songs Under Sails," and the cowboy, sea, and Negro songs sung by John Charles Thomas, Paul Robeson, the Hall Johnson choir, and others. (Paul Robeson has made records for both Columbia and Victor, the others mentioned are found in the Victor records.) Both the Columbia and Victor lists contain a full roster of Christmas carols and songs, and Bluebird has several also. Bluebird and Victor have a number of lullaby records. Practically all the favorite Mother Goose rhymes, sung or recited, and offered in a variety of combinations, may be obtained from Bluebird, Columbia, or Victor.

Orchestra Music for Listening and Rhythm

Several recordings are available for many of these:

Bleking (Swedish); Czardas (Hungarian)

Bluff King Hal (English); Shoemaker's Dance (Danish)

Carrousal (Swedish); I See You (Swedish)

Norwegian Mountain Song (Norwegian)

Jolly Is the Miller (American)

Tap Dancing Practice (splendid practice set)

Pop Goes the Weasel

The Skaters' Waltz

Rhythms for Children (4 parts)

Gavotte in B Flat

Blue Danube Waltz

Rhythmic and Marching Pieces

Anchors Aweigh

Lights Out March

Marche Romaine

March from *Carnival*

March from *Iphigenia in Aulis*

March from *Miniatures*

March (Grotesque)

March of the Priests (from *Magic Flute*)

March of the Toys (from *Babes in Toyland*)

Parade of the Wooden Soldiers

Washington Post March

The Jolly Coppersmith

March of the Little Lead Soldiers

March Militaire

Turkish March

Orchestra Music That Tells a Story

In a Clock Store

A Hunt in the Black Forest

Tales From the Vienna Woods

Pastoral Dance No. 2, The Merrymakers' Dance, No. 3 (from *Nell Gwyn*)

The Warbler's Serenade

The Wild Horseman

Gnomes

Fairies (Scherzo)

Carnival of the Animals (Saint Saens)

On the Trail (from *Grand Caynon Suite*)

The Whistler and His Dog

The Hurdy-Gurdy (John Alden Carpenter)

Classics Children Love

As was said, music to which the child may listen can include almost all the good music available. The following, however, have been found especially appealing to children, whether as records or rendered by a home musician on piano, violin, or vocally.

Most of the following numbers have been recorded by several of the record companies, and made by different artists and orchestras, in different combinations. We suggest that you hear several recordings, where they are available. Aside from the fact that most small children like some or all of the following, you will be glad to have them in your record library.

Abendlied

Adventures in a Perambulator (3) ·

Clowns (from *Midsummer Night's Dream*)

Allerseelen (Richard Strauss)

All Thru the Night

Ave Maria (Schubert)

Bolero, Part 3 (Ravel)

The Music Box, and Russian Folk Songs (Liedov)

Elegie—Melodie

Espana Rapsodie, Part 1 (Chabrier)

Gymnopedie (Satie)

Festival March from *Tannhauser* (Wagner)

Gavotte from *Mignon* (Thomas)

Hungarian Rhapsody (Liszt)

Largo from *New World Symphony* (Dvorak) ·

Midnight Bells from *The Opera Ball* (Heuberger)

Moment Musicale

Nutcracker Suite

The Old Refrain (Mattullath)

Rheingold, Prelude (Wagner)

Scheherazade, 4th Movement—Festival at Bagdad (Rimsky-Korsakoff)

Symphony No. 5 in E Minor (Tschaikowsky)

Traumerei

Die Walkure—Ho-Yo-To-Ho, Act 2

Song of the Nightingale, Chinese March (Stravinsky)

Die Walkure—Ride of the Valkyries, Act 3

The Bumblebee Prince

The Children's Corner (Debussy)

Hansel and Gretel (Humperdinck)

Peter and the Wolf (Prokofieff)

Mother Goose ("Ma Mere L'oye") (Ravel)

Flight of the Bumble Bee (Rimsky-Korsakoff)

In a Three Horse Sleigh, Polka

In the Hall of the Mountain King, Anitra's Dance (from *Peer Gynt*)

William Tell Overture

Record Section

of Your Child's Physical and Mental Growth,
Personality, Interests, Abilities

WHY IT IS WORTH WHILE TO KEEP RECORDS

"The keeping of records is one of the most important tasks that an intelligent mother can assume," Dr. Morris Fishbein says in his foreword to this book.

Records of your child's development from birth onward have become far more than a matter of sentiment. They are proving a treasure house of valuable information as well.

Doctors are asking mothers to note down in permanent form their youngster's physical development so that physicians who may care for them in later life will be able to follow constitutional tendencies or acquired susceptibilities. Records of your child's mental progress, unfolding hobbies, interests, and talents will be guideposts toward his vocational choice at the high-school and college level.

The whole trend today, in fact, is toward more and more detailed knowledge of each individual. When you fill out the succeeding pages, you will be making a contribution to science, and to better understanding of your own youngster.

These records will serve another purpose, too. We've left some spaces for problems and difficulties when they occur. For they'll occur! And at the time, particularly with your first child, they'll floor you. But you'll find it's a wonderful help to write them down. First, just what happened and how it happened, then what you did and said, and finally, how your child responded. In the very act of writing, you'll begin to get an inkling of the causes and of the solution. Pretty soon you'll acquire a technique not only for meeting problems serenely and competently, but for keeping them from coming up.

The nicest thing is the pleasure you'll take from these records. It will surprise you to find out how unreliable even a mother's memory can be. It will be a never-ceasing thrill to look back over these pages, and recall what a cute little rascal Johnny really was at 3. And how Mary had you all going around in circles for awhile when she was 10, only to acquire an entirely different personality at 11!

In order, therefore, that you may reap full benefit from the records, we have left ample space for noting down anything in your child's unfolding which may (1) interest his future doctor or medical examiner; (2) be a guide to his vocational counselor in high school or college days; (3) help you to a better understanding of your own youngster and (4) be a source of personal pleasure to you in years to come. To have the records complete, we have carried them thru to the age of 18.

For the convenience of doctors, vocational guidance experts and others who may refer to the records in later years, we have arranged them so physical development may be followed thru without a break, and mental, personality and character development likewise; yet they're so planned that physical and mental development can be compared easily at any given age.

We urge that you keep them, not for your sake alone but to help those who will be interested in your youngster later on.

And think of the possibilities!

Some day John and Mary will be grown to fine manhood and womanhood. They'll have children of their own, and will be tussling with the very same problems which now furrow your brow, for child nature doesn't change. Then out comes the book, and you can show John and Mary what little demons THEY were at the same age, and just how you coped with them. You'll be able to settle any family argument by the book.

These records, in fact, will have many uses, if you fill them out fully and faithfully. And not the least will be that after the little mite for whom you are starting them now is grown up and gone, they will be your favorite reading matter.

Personal Record of

....
(Baby's name in full)

Born..
(Year, month, day, hour, and minute)

Mr. and Mrs..
(Parents' names in full)

Address..
(At time of Baby's birth)

Subsequent addresses:

....

....

....

....

Birth Certificate

Identification

Hand- or footprints

Any distinguishing marks—list them and describe them and their location on

Baby's person. . . . .

. . . .

. . . .

. . . .

. . . .

Mark Location of Distinguishing Marks

Baby's first
snapshots

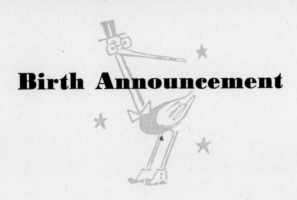

Birth Announcement

Gifts Received: From:

. . . .

. . . .

. . . .

. . . .

. . . .

. . . .

. . . .

. . . .

. . . .

. . . .

World Happenings on Baby's Birthday

Paste here headlines and clippings from
newspapers of day Baby was born.

From Birth to Six Weeks

Physical Development

Birth

Pains began at. . . . .

Mother went to hospital at. . . . .

Delivered at. . . . .

Baby's weight. .Pounds. . . . . .Ounces. . . . .

Baby's height. . . . .

Circumference of head. . . . .

Circumference of chest. . . . .

Condition at birth. . . . .

Describe fully any circumstances of birth or of Baby's condition which departed in any way from the normal. . . . .

. . . .

. . . .

First Physical Examination

   To be filled out by attending physician. (Baby should have a thoro physical examination a few days after birth by a pediatrician or by the attending physician. This record may be of interest to medical attendants in later years and the findings should be given in detail. See preceding pages)

Head

Circumference...............

Symmetrical.................

Size of fontanels.............

Eyes

Crossed....................

Discharge...................

Nose

Free breathing..............

Discharge...................

Mouth and Throat

Tonsils.....................

Adenoids...................

Neck

Lymphatic glands............

Thyroid gland...............

Skin

Texture....................

Color......................

Chest

Circumference..............

Shape......................

Thymus....................

Heart......Size............

   Rate......Murmurs.......

Lungs......................

Abdomen

Size.......................

Shape......................

Liver......................

Spleen.....................

Hernia.....................

Back

Posture....................

Arms

....

Fingers

....

Genitalia

....

Legs and Feet

Knees......................

Nails......................

Reflexes

....

Nutrition

....

Height

....

Weight

....

Hemoglobin

....

Add any recommendations as to feeding, care, etc.:

....

....

....

First Few Days

First put to breast at

. . . .

(Give time of day and interval after birth.)

Any difficulties in nursing?

Describe . . . .

How dealt with . . . .

Was 3-hour or 4-hour schedule employed at first?

. . . .

Bottle feedings given:

When begun? After breast feeding, or in place of it? . . . .

. . . .

First formula . . . .

. . . .

. . . .

Weight lost . . . .

Regained birth weight at . . . . days . . . . .

Note any problems or difficulties encountered in getting Baby started, together with methods found effective in solving them: . . . .

. . . .

. . . .

Home From the Hospital

Your doctor has already placed Baby upon either a 3-hour or 4-hour feeding schedule. Feed Baby at the times your doctor indicates. Then note down for a few days the times at which Baby sleeps, wakes, cries, and seems to be hungry. This will help you to determine Baby's own personal rhythm.

First Night at Home

Slept thru. . . . .

Cried from. . . . . .to. . . . .

Had nursing or bottle at. . . . .

Further comments:. . . . .

. . . .

. . . .

. . . .

(If Baby is on a 3-hour schedule, feedings at this time will probably come at 6 a.m., 9 a.m., 12 n., 3 p.m., 6 p.m., 10 p.m., 2 a.m. If on a 4-hour schedule feedings will probably be at 6 a.m., 10 a.m., 2 p.m., 6 p.m., 10 p.m., with a feeding at 2 a.m. if Baby wakens and cries.)

First Day at Home

Wakened at. . . . .

Had nursing or bottle at. . . . .
(If bottle feeding, how much taken.)

Slept from. . . . . .to. . . . .

Cried from. . . . . .to. . . . .

Weight. . . . .

Bath at. . . . .
(Nursing or bottle follows bath. If bottle feeding, note how much taken.)

Slept from. . . . . .to. . . . .

Cried from. . . . . .to. . . . .

Nursing or bottle feeding at. . . . .

Slept from. . . . . .to. . . . .

Cried from. . . . . .to. . . . .

Nursing or bottle feeding at. . . . .

Slept from. . . . . .to. . . . .

Cried from. . . . . .to. . . . .

Nursing or bottle feeding at. . . . .

Rest of night:

　　Slept from. . . . . .to. . . . .

　　Cried from. . . . . .to. . . . .

　　Had nursing or bottle feeding at. . . . .

Further comments:. . . . .

. . . .

Second Day at Home

Wakened at..

Had nursing or bottle at...

(If bottle feeding, how much taken.)

Slept from................................to..............................

Cried from................................to..............................

Weight...

Bath at..

(Nursing or bottle follows bath. If bottle feeding, note how much taken.)

Slept from................................to..............................

Cried from................................to..............................

Nursing or bottle feeding at..

Slept from................................to..............................

Cried from................................to..............................

Nursing or bottle feeding at..

Slept from................................to..............................

Cried from................................to..............................

Nursing or bottle feeding at..

Rest of night:

    Slept from................................to..............................

    Cried from................................to..............................

    Had nursing or bottle feeding at.......................................

Further comments:...

....

Third Day at Home

Wakened at...

Had nursing or bottle at..
(If bottle feeding, how much taken.)

Slept from................................to...........................

Cried from................................to...........................

Weight...

Bath at..
(Nursing or bottle follows bath. If bottle feeding, note how much taken.)

Slept from................................to...........................

Cried from................................to...........................

Nursing or bottle feeding at..

Slept from................................to...........................

Cried from................................to...........................

Nursing or bottle feeding at..

Slept from................................to...........................

Cried from................................to...........................

Nursing or bottle feeding at..

Rest of night:

    Slept from..........................to...........................

    Cried from..........................to...........................

    Had nursing or bottle feeding at..............................

Further comments:..

....

....

Fourth Day at Home

Wakened at...

Had nursing or bottle at...
(If bottle feeding, how much taken.)

Slept from.....................................to.....................

Cried from.....................................to.....................

Weight..

Bath at...
(Nursing or bottle follows bath. If bottle feeding, note how much taken.)

Slept from.....................................to.....................

Cried from.....................................to.....................

Nursing or bottle feeding at..

Slept from.....................................to.....................

Cried from.....................................to.....................

Nursing or bottle feeding at..

Slept from.....................................to.....................

Cried from.....................................to.....................

Nursing or bottle feeding at..

Rest of night:

    Slept from.................................to.................

    Cried from.................................to.................

    Had nursing or bottle feeding at...........................

Further comments:..

....

....

Baby's Schedule at ...... Weeks

The notations made on the foregoing pages have given you an idea of Baby's own natural rhythm.

Consult it in making out Baby's daily schedule. Then follow this schedule until Baby's rhythm of sleeping, crying, and waking times begins to change.

....

....

....

....

....

....

....

....

....

....

....

....

....

....

Vitamin Record

Vitamins A and D begun at . . . . .weeks

Kind and dosage prescribed by doctor. . . . .
(Cod-liver oil—other fish-liver oil—concentrate)

First given. . . . .
(date)

Amount Baby took. . . . .

Describe method used, Baby's reaction:

. . . .

. . . .

. . . .

Further comments:. . . . .

. . . .

. . . .

. . . .

. . . .

. . . .

. . . .

. . . .

. . . .

(Vitamin C) begun at. . . . . weeks

(Orange, grapefruit, sweetened lemon or tomato juice.)

Kind and dosage prescribed by doctor. . . . .

First given. . . . .
(date)

Amount Baby took. . . . .

Describe method used and Baby's reaction:

. . . .

. . . .

. . . .

(Vitamins A, D, and C are now added to your baby's schedule. Amounts are increased until you reach the dosage prescribed by your doctor.)

Thiamin (Vitamin B₁)

(If your doctor prescribed additional amounts.)

Kind. . . . .

Dosage. . . . .

When begun. . . . .

Further comments:. . . . .

. . . .

. . . .

. . . .

. . . .

. . . .

. . . .

Growth Record

Age	Pounds	Weight	Ounces
At birth			
On leaving hospital			
At two weeks			
At three weeks			
At four weeks			
At five weeks			
At six weeks			

Six-Weeks Examination

By Doctor . . . .

City . . . .

When Baby is six weeks old, there should be another thoro physical examination by a competent physician. Note down his findings and also suggestions made by the doctor for Baby's feeding and care.

Illnesses

Describe symptoms, severity and duration of attack, and treatment.

....

....

....

....

....

....

....

....

....

....

....

....

....

....

....

....

Special Problems

Write down circumstances in detail. What had happened before, how did Baby act, what did you do? Had schedule been followed or had there been lapses?

Describe method of handling which seemed to be successful.

. . . .

. . . .

. . . .

. . . .

. . . .

. . . .

. . . .

. . . .

. . . .

. . . .

. . . .

. . . .

. . . .

. . . .

. . . .

From Six Weeks to Four Months

Growth Record

Age	Pounds	Weight	Ounces
Seven weeks...			
Eight weeks...			
Nine weeks...			
Ten weeks...			
Eleven weeks...			
Twelve weeks...			
Thirteen weeks...			
Fourteen weeks...			
Fifteen weeks...			
Sixteen weeks...			
Further comments:...			
....			

[*Mental Development*]

Weeks

Noticed light at. . . . .

Followed bright object with eyes at. . . . .

Held head up when placed on abdomen at. . . . .

Turned head in the direction of a sound at. . . . .

Reached for an object at. . . . .

Recognized parents at. . . . .

Smiled at. . . . .

Further comments:. . . . .

. . . .

. . . .

Snapshot   Snapshot

Illnesses

Describe symptoms, severity and duration of attack, and treatment.

. . . .

. . . .

. . . .

. . . .

. . . .

. . . .

. . . .

. . . .

. . . .

. . . .

. . . .

. . . .

. . . .

. . . .

. . . .

. . . .

Special Problems

Write down circumstances in detail. What had happened before, how did Baby act, what did you do? Had schedule been followed or had there been lapses?

Describe method of handling which seemed to be successful.

. . . .

. . . .

. . . .

. . . .

. . . .

. . . .

. . . .

. . . .

. . . .

. . . .

. . . .

. . . .

. . . .

. . . .

. . . .

From Four to Six Months

Growth Record

Age	Pounds	Weight	Ounces
Seventeen weeks...			
Eighteen weeks..			
Nineteen weeks..			
Twenty weeks..			
Twenty-one weeks..			
Twenty-two weeks..			
Twenty-three weeks......................................			
Twenty-four weeks.......................................			
Further comments:.......................................			

....

Mental Development

	Weeks
Laughed out loud at....................................	....
Held toy at..	....
Held head up well at..................................	....
Rolled over at..	....
Giggled at..	....
Coughed artificially (a polite little cough to get attention) at.	....
Pulled self forward in an attempt to sit up at.............	....
Further comments:.....................................	

....

....

Snapshot

Snapshot

[*Physical Development*]

Solid Foods

First solid food given.............Begun at...............weeks.

Describe method used and Baby's reactions:

....

....

....

....

Second solid food given.............Begun at..............weeks.

Describe method used and Baby's reactions:

....

....

....

....

....

Third solid food given.............Begun at..............weeks.

Describe method used and Baby's reactions:

....

....

....

....

....

List subsequent solid foods. Note age at which first given, and Baby's reaction:

Food	*Age*	*Reaction*
....	....	....
....	....	....
....	....	....
....	....	....
....	....	....
....	....	....
....	....	....
....	....	....
....	....	....
....	....	....
....	....	....
....	....	....
....	....	....
....	....	....
....	....	....
....	....	....
....	....	....
....	....	....
....	....	....
....	....	....
....	....	....

Illnesses

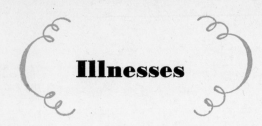

Describe symptoms, severity and duration of attack, and treatment.

. . . .

. . . .

. . . .

. . . .

. . . .

. . . .

. . . .

. . . .

. . . .

. . . .

. . . .

. . . .

. . . .

. . . .

. . . .

. . . .

Special Problems and Difficulties

Write down circumstances in detail. What had happened before, how did child act, what did you do?

Describe method of handling which seemed to be successful.

....

....

....

....

....

....

....

....

....

....

....

....

....

....

....

....

Physical Development

Six to Twelve Months

Growth Record

Age	Pounds	Weight	Ounces
Seven months...			
Eight months...			
Nine months...			
Ten months...			
Eleven months...			
Twelve months...			

	Weeks
First tooth appeared at......................	....
Second tooth appeared at....................	....
Third tooth appeared at.....................	....
Fourth tooth appeared at....................	....
Fifth tooth appeared at......................	....
Sixth tooth appeared at......................	....
Sat up alone at..............................	....
Weaning begun at............................	....
Completed at................................	....
Began creeping at...........................	....
Pulled himself up at.........................	....

Mental Development and Habit Training

Bowel training begun at.......................................weeks.

Reasonably complete at.......................................weeks.

(You may have begun bowel training earlier. If so, enter it at the age when begun.)

Cup feedings begun at.......................................weeks.

Accepted reasonably well at.......................................weeks.

Baby's comprehension is now increasing rapidly. Give examples by conduct:

....at...........weeks.

....at...........weeks.

....at...........weeks.

....at...........weeks.

First words spoken at.......................................weeks.

They were.......................................

Snapshot

Snapshot

Illnesses

Describe symptoms, severity and duration of attack, and treatment.

....

....

....

....

....

....

....

....

....

....

....

....

....

....

....

....

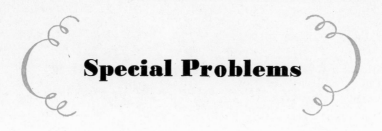

Special Problems

Write down circumstances in detail. What had happened before, how did Baby act, what did you do? Had schedule been followed or had there been lapses?

Describe method of handling which seemed to be successful.

. . . .

. . . .

. . . .

. . . .

. . . .

. . . .

. . . .

. . . .

. . . .

. . . .

. . . .

. . . .

. . . .

. . . .

Immunization Record

1. Whooping Cough (recommended age —8 to 9 months):

   1st dose.........................

   2nd dose.........................

   3rd dose.........................

2. Combined Diphtheria-Tetanus Alum Precipitated Toxoid (recommended age—9 months):

   1st dose.........................
   2nd dose...(3 months after first dose) Stimulating dose of tetanus toxid.

   Date............Age.............

   ### Lifetime Protection
   Smallpox vaccination should be repeated when child first enters school and again when junior high is entered.

   Diphtheria immunization is repeated depending upon the reaction to the Schick test at 18 months, 5 years, and 10 to 15 years.

3. Smallpox Vaccination (recommended age—6 to 12 months):

   Date of successful primary "take"....

   Subsequent vaccinations:

   Date of...Type of reaction...Age..

   Date of...Type of reaction...Age..

   Date of...Type of reaction...Age..

4. Tetanus Alum Precipitated Toxoid (any age):

   1st dose.........................

   2nd dose...(2 months after first dose)

   Stimulating dose: Date.....Age...

   Date.....Age...

   Tetanus (Lockjaw) Prevention:
   If your child has completed the tetanus toxoid injections, either in combination with the diphtheria tox-oid or by itself, advise your physician of the fact in case of any injury which would ordinarily require tetanus (lockjaw) prophylaxis.

   Present evidence indicates that, under such circumstances, a stimulating dose of tetanus toxoid may be employed more advantageously than tetanus antitoxin.

   In case no injury is received within one year of the time of the last tetanus toxoid injection, it is desirable to give a stimulating dose of tetanus toxoid.

5. Scarlet Fever Toxin:

   1st dose.........................

   2nd dose.........................

   3rd dose.........................

   4th dose.........................

   5th dose.........................

6. Typhoid Inoculations:

   1st dose.........................

   2nd dose.........................

   3rd dose.........................

7. Schick Test (recommended ages—18 mos., 4 yrs., 10 to 15 yrs.):

   Type of reaction....Age...Date....

   Type of reaction....Age...Date....

   Type of reaction....Age...Date....

8. Dick Test:

   Type of reaction....Age...Date....

   Type of reaction....Age...Date....

9. Tuberculin Test (recommended at 3-year intervals):

   Type of reaction....Age...Date....

   Type of reaction....Age...Date....

   Type of reaction....Age...Date....

Illnesses

Describe symptoms, severity and duration of attack, and treatment.

....

....

....

....

....

....

....

Special Problems

Write down circumstances in detail? What had happened before, how did Baby act, what did you do? Had schedule been followed or had there been lapses?

Describe method of handling which seemed to be successful.

....

....

....

....

....

....

....

One to Two Years

Growth Record

Age	Weight	Height
One year...		
Fifteen months..		
Eighteen months......................................		
Further comments.....................................		

Teething

Indicate on the chart below the order of their appearance and the age in weeks and months at which each tooth appears. The order of the appearance and the age at which they come thru is expected to vary with each child. A dentist should be consulted when there is unusual delay.

1. Central incisors: usually appear during the sixth to ninth months
2. Lateral incisors: usually appear around the eighth to tenth months
3. First molars: usually appear between the twelfth and fourteenth months
4. Cuspids: usually appear from the eighteenth to twentieth months
5. Second molars: often appear by the twenty-fourth month
6. Molars: these are the first of the permanent teeth

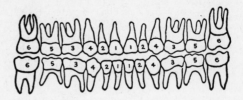

Age Teeth Appeared

Upper Teeth		Lower Teeth	
Right	Left	Right	Left
1.............	....	1.............	....
2.............	....	2.............	....
3.............	....	3.............	....
4.............	....	4.............	....
5.............	....	5.............	....
6.............	....	6.............	....

Mental Development and Habit Training

Showed preference for....right or....left hand in reaching at....months.

Held cup to drink at.... months.

Daytime bladder training begun at....months.

Reasonably completed at.....months.

Night bladder training begun at....months.

Reasonably completed at.....months.

Used spoon with good control at....months.

Pointed to eyes, nose, or hair at....months.

First tantrum at....months.   First said "I won't!" at....months.

Began to feed self at....months.   (Beginning of negativism)

Used sentences at....months.   Snipped with scissors at....months.

Story hour begun at....months.   Identified pictures at......months.

Snapshot   Snapshot

Physical Development

Walked with help at....months.

Lowered self from standing to sitting position at....months.

Stood up without help at....months.

Walked alone at....months.

Threw a ball at....months.

Climbed stairs with help at....months.

Climbed stairs unaided at....months.

Climbed into chair unaided at....months.

Ran with confidence at....months.

Jumped down at....months.

Further comments:..

....

....

....

....

....

....

....

....

Mental Development and Habit Training

Regressions in Habit Training

List age at which each occurred. Note measures used. What new form of learning was beginning at the same time?

....

....

....

....

....

....

....

....

....

....

....

....

....

....

....

....

Illnesses

Describe symptoms, severity and duration of attack, and treatment.

....

....

....

....

....

....

....

....

....

....

....

....

....

....

....

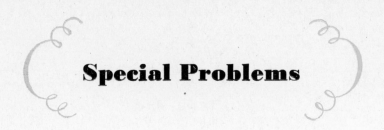

Special Problems

Write down circumstances in detail. What had happened before, how did youngster act, what did you do?

Describe method of handling which seemed to be successful.

. . . .

. . . .

. . . .

. . . .

. . . .

. . . .

. . . .

. . . .

. . . .

. . . .

. . . .

. . . .

. . . .

Two to Three Years

Growth Record

Age	Weight	Height

Two years..

Two and one-half years....................................

List favorite outdoor play apparatus:

List new physical skills and ages (in months) at which acquired:

Further comments:...

....

Mental Development and Habit Training

Vocabulary at two years......words.

List several typical sentences or sayings:

Fed self whole meal unaided at....months.

Began to dress self at....months.

   Able to do reasonably good job at....months.

Began to wash self at....months.

Put toys away after play at....months.

Snapshot

List favorite songs and stories: . . .

. . . .

. . . .

. . . .

. . . .

. . . .

. . . .

. . . .

. . . .

. . . .

. . . .

List favorite indoor toys and amuse-

ments:. . . . .

. . . .

. . . .

. . . .

. . . .

. . . .

. . . .

. . . .

. . . .

. . . .

First memorized song or poem at....months.

Carried tune at....months.

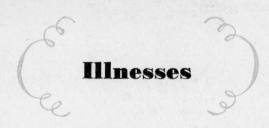

Illnesses

Describe symptoms, severity and duration of attack, and treatment.

....

....

....

....

....

....

....

....

....

....

....

....

....

....

....

....

Special Problems

Write down circumstances in detail. What had happened before, how did child act, what did you do? Had schedule been followed or had there been lapses?

Describe method of handling which seemed to be successful.

. . . .

. . . .

. . . .

. . . .

. . . .

. . . .

. . . .

. . . .

. . . .

. . . .

. . . .

. . . .

. . . .

. . . .

Three to Five Years

Growth Record

Age	Weight	Height
Three years..		
Four years..		

List favorite outdoor play apparatus and special physical abilities at:

Three years..

Four years..

Mental and Social Development

Vocabulary at three years contained......words.

List typical comments:...

....

....

....

Attitudes toward other children:

Friendly toward all............   Painfully shy...............

Friendly with a few............   Takes lead in social relationship...

Shy at first..................   Over-aggressive...............

Describe special traits and skills, favorite indoor play materials, stories, and songs:...

Three years...

Four years..

....

....

Snapshot

Snapshot

Physical Development

Five to Seven Years

Growth Record

Age	Weight	Height
Five years..		
Six years...		

List favorite outdoor activities, any special physical skills:

Five years..

Six years...

Illnesses

Describe symptoms, severity and duration of attack, and treatment prescribed.

....

....

....

....

....

....

Mental, Personality, and Character Development

Describe reactions at entering kindergarten, any adjustments required, how worked out. . . . .

. . . .

Describe reactions at entering first grade, any adjustments required, how worked out . . . .

. . . .

List favorite indoor games and play materials; special skills; favorite books songs, and stories:. . . . .

. . . .

Five years. . . . .   Six years. . . . .

. . . .

. . . .

. . . .

. . . .

Special Problems and Difficulties

Write down circumstances in detail. What had happened before, how did child act, what did you do? Had there been late bedtimes or over-stimulation?

Describe method of handling which seemed to be successful.

. . . .

. . . .

. . . .

. . . .

[Physical Development]

Seven to Eleven Years

Growth Record

Age	Weight	Height
Seven years		
Eight years		
Nine years		
Ten years		
Eleven years		

Describe physical characteristics. List favorite outdoor games and sports, special physical skills and accomplishments.

Seven years...

Eight years...

Nine years...

Ten years...

Eleven years...

Illnesses

Describe symptoms, severity and duration of attack, and treatment.

....

....

....

....

....

....

....

....

....

....

....

....

....

....

....

....

INTERESTS

GRADE	Best-liked School Subjects	Least-liked School Subjects	Books Read Outside School	Home Duties and Responsibilities Carried
Second Grade				
Third Grade				
Fourth Grade				
Fifth Grade				
Sixth Grade				

ABILITIES

Special Talents Training in	Hobbies and Special Skills	Leading Character and Personality Traits	Clubs and Organizations

Physical Development

Twelve to Fourteen Years

Growth Record

Age	Weight	Height
Twelve years		
Thirteen years		
Fourteen years		

List favorite sports and outdoor pursuits:

Twelve years..

Thirteen years..

Fourteen years..

List team games played:

Twelve years..

Thirteen years..

Fourteen years..

List special physical abilities, skills, and accomplishments:

Twelve years..

Thirteen years..

Fourteen years..

Special Problems and Difficulties

Write down circumstances in detail. What had happened before, how did youngster act, what did you do?

Describe method of handling which seemed to be successful.

. . . .

. . . .

. . . .

. . . .

. . . .

. . . .

. . . .

. . . .

. . . .

. . . .

. . . .

. . . .

. . . .

. . . .

. . . .

INTERESTS

GRADE	Best-liked School Subjects	Least-liked School Subjects	Books Read Outside School	Home Duties and Responsibilities Carried
Seventh Grade				
Eighth Grade				
Ninth Grade				

ABILITIES

Special Talents Training in (Kind, Amount)	Hobbies and Special Skills	Outstanding Character and Personality Traits	Social Attitudes, Clubs and Organizations

[Physical Development]

Fifteen to Eighteen Years

(Senior-High Period)

Growth Record

Age	*Weight*	*Height*
Fifteen years..		
Sixteen years..		
Seventeen years..		

List favorite sports and outdoor pursuits:

Fifteen years..

Sixteen years..

Seventeen years..

List team games played:

Fifteen years..

Sixteen years..

Seventeen years..

List special physical abilities, skills, and accomplishments:

Fifteen years..

Sixteen years..

Seventeen years..

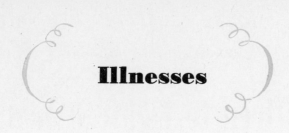

Illnesses

Describe symptoms, severity and duration of attack, and treatment.

. . . .

. . . .

. . . .

. . . .

. . . .

. . . .

. . . .

Special Problems and Difficulties

Write down circumstances in detail. What had happened before, how did youngster act, what did you do? Had there been late bedtimes or over-stimulation?

Describe method of handling which seemed to be successful.

. . . .

. . . .

. . . .

. . . .

. . . .

INTERESTS

GRADE	Best-liked School Subjects	Least-liked School Subjects	Books Read Outside School	Home Duties and Responsibilities Carried
Tenth Grade				
Eleventh Grade				
Twelfth Grade				

ABILITIES

Special Talents Training in (Kind, Amount)	Hobbies and Special Skills	Work Outside Home	Outstanding Personality and Character Traits	Clubs and Organizations	Social Attitudes Toward Own Sex Toward Opposite Sex

Mother's Notes

....

....

....

....

....

....

....

....

....

....

....

....

....

....

....

....

The Family Tree

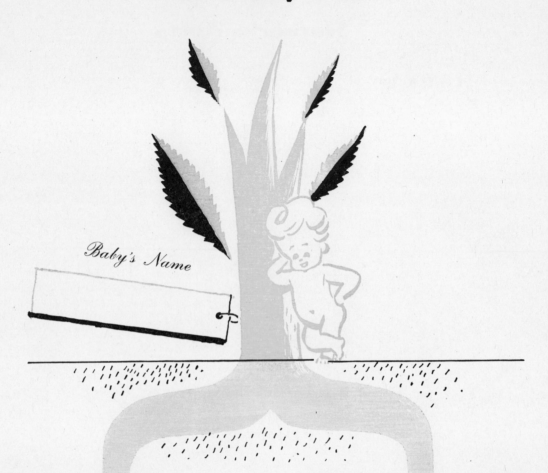

Baby's Name

Father

Mother

Grandfather   Grandmother   Grandfather   Grandmother

Great-grandfather   Great-grandmother   Great-grandfather   Great-grandmother   Great-grandfather   Great-grandmother   Great-grandfather   Great-grandmother

INDEX